ENCYCLOPAEDIA
OF FUNGI

GERRIT J. KEIZER

ENCYCLOPAEDIA
OF FUNGI

REBO
PRODUCTIONS

For Nelly and Morag

Explanation of symbols and abbreviations:

∅	Diameter	R	Rare
C	Cap	VR	Very rare
G	Gills	RDL	Red Data list (endangered)
Tu	Tubes		
Po	Pores	ⓦ	Edible
Spi	Spines		
St.	Stem	ⓦ	Suspect
Spo	Spore-print colour		
Fl	Flesh	†	Poisonous
Sm	Smell		
Ta	Taste	ⓦ	Lethally poisonous
M	Mycorrhizal		
Sa	Saprophyte (saprothophic)	♀	< 1 cm : magnifying glass
Pa	Parasitic		

CIP-DATA ROYAL LIBRARY, THE HAGUE,
THE NETHERLANDS

Mushroom encyclopaedia
G.J. Keizer
With index, bibliography, 789 photographs
Keywords: Mushrooms; fungi; moulds

© 1996 Rebo Productions, Lisse, the Netherlands
© 1997 Published by Rebo Productions Ltd.
text and 770 photographs: Gerrit Keizer,
    Poortugaal/Maartensdijk, the Netherlands
cover design: Ton Wienbelt, The Hague,
    the Netherlands
production: TextCase, Groningen, the Netherlands
    editor: Elke Doelman
    typesetting: Hof&Land Typografie,
    the Netherlands

ISBN 1 901094 219

Cover photographs from left to right, from top to bottom:
Ramaria formosa, Amanita muscaria, Tremiscus helvelloides
Aleuria aurantiam (albino), *Cantharellus cibarius*
Schizophyllum commune, Coprinus picaceus, Fomitopsis pinicola
Back cover from left to right:
Gomphidius roseus, Geastrum schmidelii, Verpa conica

Contents

Foreword

This book is the result of 20 years of photographing mushrooms. The species were photographed in their natural habitats and on natural substrates during field trips in the Netherlands, Belgium, Luxembourg, Germany, France, the UK and Sweden, using a tripod and with minimum of artifice.

This encyclopedia has 790 photographs of macrofungi, microfungi and slime moulds, showing the rich variety of colours, shapes and special characteristics of mushrooms. From the thousands of species found in Central and Northern Europe, we have selected the species that occur in the Netherlands, Belgium or Luxembourg. In addition to common, frequently shown species, we have also included rare, threatened or unusual species and species rarely shown, with small fruiting bodies. For the English and Latin names we have used X. In the case of Latin names that have recently been changed, the former genus and species names are given in parentheses. It was not possible to retain the alphabetical order of the former Latin genus names. For detailed descriptions, microscopic features and identification tables we refer to the books and journals listed in the bibliography.

The author endorses the view of the Dutch Mycological Society that fungi require protection. They should not be damaged, picked or removed unnecessarily or in large numbers. Collecting a limited number of specimens for scientific research or educational purposes is permissible.

Gerrit Keizer

Left: *Ganoderma lipsiense*

Geotropism in *Fomes fomentarius*, see p. 20

Introduction

People have always been intrigued by fungi and mushrooms. Their mysterious way of life, their wide variety of shapes and colours, their smell, taste and other characteristics have held our fascination since times immemorial.

Explanations for the origin and appearance of mushrooms were often sought in the realm of magic or devils. The fruiting bodies, which mostly grew above ground and occasionally underground (truffles) were associated with toads, snakes and dragons, with elves, nymphs (oreads, dryads) and gnomes, with thunder, lightning and the moon, with trolls, wizards, witches, poisoners, druids, brahmans and shamans and with devils, satyrs and death. There are a great number of mushroom names that refer to these associations, names such as toadstool, Death Cap, Dead Man's Fingers, Dryad's Saddle, Witches' Butter, Devil's Boletus, Destroying Angel, Devil's Urn, Scarlet Elf Cup (*Sarcoscypha coccinea*), Inonotus dryadeus, Fairy Ring Mushroom (*Marasmius oreades*), Fairies' Bonnets (*Coprinus disseminatus*), and Jew's Ear. In stories about the 'children of darkness' and in superstition, fairy tales, sagas and legends from all over the world, you find similar names for mushrooms. Other names refer to mythical and biblical characters and to emperors, kings and nobles, such as Adonis Mycena (*Mycena adonis*), Caesar's Mushroom (*Amanita caesarea*), King Alfred's Cramp Balls, King Alfred's Cakes, St George's Mushroom, and The Prince. The edible and tasty *Tricholoma equestre* was reserved for the nobility, whereas *Suillus bovinus* was a lesser species, fit for cowherds.

Mushrooms were thought to be, like corals, a conglomerate of the shells of small animals, which were supposed to multiply by means of eggs, the spores. Truffles were thought to be produced when a thunderbolt fused soil and roots or where a rutting deer lost its sperm. The subterranean bulb of *Polyporus tuberaster* was thought to grow at the spot where the lynx marked its territory with urine.

Species known for their hallucinogenic or medicinal properties in particular have played a role in religious rituals (shamanism) and have been associated with the origin of old local beliefs and world religions. Fly agaric is known both from Germanic mythology (the Edda), which holds that the fruiting bodies are produced when froth from the mouth of Woden's snorting horse falls on the ground, and from Greek mythology (ambrosia or the food of the gods). Fly agaric is also believed to have played a role in the development of Hinduism (Rig-Veda, Soma) and the religion of the early Christians. In Taoist medicine, tonics incorporating plants and mushrooms, among which *Ganoderma lucidum* (Reishi or Ling Chi), canonized by a Chinese emperor, play an important part. In ancient American Indian cultures, *Psilocybe* and *Panaeolus* (teonanacatl or teyuinti) were used as intoxicants and hallucinogens to meet the gods. Images of these mushrooms exist which date back to long before the Christian era. Mushroom motives associated with shamanism were used in the paleolithic rock drawings in French and Spanish caves. In Scandinavia and Siberia, petroglyphs and objects with similar images and motives dating back to the Bronze Age have been found. In the Yugoslavia, neolithic mushroom-shaped, green rock crystal statuettes have been found. In Mexico and Guatemala, stone and ceramic figurines and frescoes of the 'flesh of the gods' or 'the little flowers of the gods' from the Aztec, Maya and Inca cultures can be seen. In an Egyptian royal grave dating back to 1450 B.C., wall paintings with images of musrooms have been found. On the bronze doors of the cathedral of Hildesheim in Germany, which was completed in 1015, there is a relief showing *Adam and Eve after the Fall*, which shows the tree of the forbidden fruit as two mushrooms resembling Liberty Cap (*Psilocybe semilanceata*). Instead of a fig leaf, Adam and Eve each hold a cap of the mushroom to cover their genitals. Images of Fly Agaric (*Amanita muscaria*) as the tree of wisdom in paradise can be found on a faded Roman fresco in a chapel near the castle of Plaincourault (13th century) in France and on an old painting of the Fall of Eve in the Marienkirche in Lübeck. Stylized Reishi or Ling Chi motives, representing *Ganoderma lucidum*, are seen in reliefs on buildings in the Forbidden City in Beijing. Such motives are still being used in Chinese and Japanese statuettes, paintings, silk garments and tapestries. *Ganoderma lucidum* was depicted on stamps of the Chinese empire in the 19th century. This makes mycophilately, collecting stamps with images of mushrooms, one of the

oldest subjects for stamp collectors special-
izing in certain motives.

Their inexplicable and sudden appearance and
their intriguing shapes and characteristics
have turned the fruiting bodies of certain
species of *Phallales* into phallic symbols. The
notorious Stinkhorn *(Phallus impudicus)* (=
shameless penis) regularly turns up in folklore
and superstition. Witches are believed to use
the fully grown fruiting bodies, which carry
the sperm of the devil on their caps, to produce shared offspring. The largely subterranean
'devil's eggs' or 'witches' eggs' were boiled and
eaten as aphrodisiacs or dried, ground and
added to cattle fodder to induce the animals to
mate, as were *Elaphomyces*. The fruiting
bodies, which rupture the wall of the 'witches'
eggs' with a sort of egg tooth or disc, were
used in wedding ceremonies and mating
rituals. The most popular species for this
purpose were Stinkhorn *(Phallus impudicus)*,
Phallus duplicatus or *Dictyophora duplicata*,
or Dog Stinkhorn *(Mutinus caninus)*. Eating
'witches' eggs' of *Phallus duplicatus, Clathrus*
archeri or *Anthurus archeri* and *Clathrus*
ruber is popular, especially in Asia, in spite of,
or perhaps because of their bizarre and smelly
appearance. Images of *Phallus duplicatus*
with its hanging, white veil and the red
Clathrus ruber can be seen at centre left and
at bottom right in the middle in the photograph below (mycophilately).

Mycofilately

1 Characteristics, features and functions of fungi

Macrofungi and microfungi

Mushrooms are the fruiting bodies of the mycelia of higher fungi or macrofungi present in the soil or substrate. The macrofungi include the species that are visible to the naked eye, with fruiting bodies larger than approximately 1 mm. All of them are at least capable of sexual reproduction. Together with the lower fungi or microfungi, they form the two fungal kingdoms. The plants, animals, and fungi together form the so-called Eukaryotes, organisms with a distinct nucleus. Of all these organisms, the fungi, which spread by means of spores, constitute the largest group, with over 100,000 species.

Most microfungi are smaller than 1 mm. They usually reproduce during an asexual phase of their life cycle in a so-called imperfect form (anamorph) by tying off asexual spores or conidia on specialized parts of the mycelium, or on and in simple reproductive organs. The Yeasts, Rusts and Blights are also included in the fungi.

In contrast to plants, fungi are not capable of photosynthesis: they cannot make carbohydrates from sunlight and carbonic acid. Fungi lack the nececessary chlorophyll or leaf green. They therefore have to obtain the substances necessary for their growth and existence from living or dead organic matter, vegetable or animal.

Lower fungi or microfungi

We will now give a few examples of lower fungi or microfungi that can be easily seen by the naked eye or at least with a magnifying glass.

Pilobolus

Species of the genus *Pilobolus* can be found on cow, horse, sheep and deer dung and on hare and rabbit droppings. By means of a light-sensitive lens, they turn a sporangium, a capsule containing spores and enclosed in a black membrane, which is placed on top of a bottle-shaped organ, towards the light. A tiny jet of liquid under a pressure of 7 atmospheres ejects the sporangium at a speed of 150 to 600 km per hour. The sporangium will travel a distance of up to 2 m, and stick to stems and leaves. When these are subsequently eaten, the sporangium will end up in the gastointestinal tract of the animal, and eventually in its faeces. *Pilobolus crystallinus* is found on for example damp horse manure. The bottle-shaped reproductive organs, measuring a few mm, are watery white translucent with a black, oval, flattened sporangium on a ring zone at the apex. Depending on the distance of the mycelium to the light, they have either short or long stems.

Pilobolus crystallinus

Paecilomyces farinosus

The species of the genus *Paecilomyces* belong to the *Fungi imperfecti*, fungi of which only an imperfect or asexual form occurs independently. Like the bright orange Scarlet Caterpillar Fungus *(Cordyceps militaris)*, *Paecilomyces farinosus* grows on buried pupae of butterflies and moths infected with spores when they were caterpillars. The tough, yellowish conidiophores are a few centimetres long and a few millimetres in diameter. The occasionally slightly swollen upper part is covered with a white, powdery mass of conidia.

Often several specimens grow from a single pupae among leaves or moss.

Paecilomyces farinosus

Rhizopus stolonifer

Rhizopus stolonifer grows on damp vegetable debris, in this case on rotting apple peels in a compost container in a cool, dark place. On a white web of mycelium filaments, erect filaments appear, up to half a centimetre in length. On the tip, translucent pallid buds filled with conidia appear, measuring 1 to 2 mm and with pitted undersides. When ripe, the buds turn black.

Rhizopus stolonifer

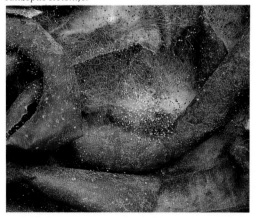

Spinellus fusiger

The mycelium of *Spinellus fusiger* grows in the fruiting bodies of smaller species of agarics such as *Mycena zephirus*.

The spores are produced in white buds measuring 1 mm, large numbers of which emerge through the skin of the cap of the wilting mushroom on filaments a few millimetres in length. On ripening, the buds turn black.

Spinellus fusiger

Lichens

Within the fungal kingdom, the over 18,000 species of crusty, leafy, scaly, thread-like and club-shaped lichens *(Lecanorales)* constitute a special group. A lichen is a symbiotic organism consisting of a dominant fungus or mycobiont and an alga or phycobiont. The fungus appears to draw more benefit from the relationship than its partner. Together they form highly stable structures, called thalli, which can live for millenia and can survive harsh conditions. They can reproduce asexually or vegetatively by means of parts or outgrowths of the thallus which break off easily, or sexually by means of spores produced by the fungal constituent. In addition, the mycobiont extracts water and minerals from the substrate. The alga is capable of photosynthesis thanks to the chlorophyll it possesses. In this way, the phycobiont supplies the lichen with carbohydrates such as sugars, which are necessary for its development. Most mycobionts are lichenized Ascomycetes. Their partners are algae, mostly green or blue-green algae. In addition, a few lichens occur with a lichenized Basidiomycete as the mycobiont, namely *Corticiaceae* of the genus *Athelia,* funnel-shaped *Phytoconis* species or club-shaped *Multiclavula* species. *Cladonia floerkeana* is common on peaty or sandy soil and on rotting wood. On pale green crusts, up to 2 cm high, concolorous, warty, often branched rods develop. At their tips, red globose or cushion-shaped structures (apothecia) grow, in which spores are produced in sacs or asci.

Ascomycetes

Depending on microscopic features such as the construction of the sexual reproductive organs, fungi are classified as Ascomycetes or Basidiomycetes.

In the Ascomycetes, the spores are produced, in a club-, worm-, or balloon-shaped cell, the sac or ascus, usually containing 8 spores, in a hymenium. The spores ripen in the ascus. When they are ripe, they are projected from the cell with great force, like water from a water pistol. The pressure inside the ascus can rise to 30 atmospheres.

To project the spores, the top of the ascus is ruptured at the centre, or a lid is opened or torn off. A cloud of thousands of ripe spores is projected towards the light, and is spread by the wind. The stemmed cups of the tropical genus *Cookeiana* (see photograph of mycophilately: at centre, with red frogs) produce over a million and a half spores per square centimetre of hymenophore.

A number of *Aspergillus, Penicillium* and *Erysiphaceae* species, which mostly occur in an imperfect or asexual stage (anamorph), and some yeasts *(Saccharomycetes)*, also occur as a rarer, perfect stage or teleomorph. The *Sphaeriales*, which produce their spores in

Cladonia floerkeana

globose or crust-like fruiting bodies in asci, also often have an imperfect stage, which produces conidia.

Species of the genus *Penicillium* occur particularly on and in foods such as fruit, bread and dairy products and are used to inoculate cheese (Camembert, Roquefort).

Penicillium digitatum occurs as a green, powdery crust on the skin of oranges infected by the fungus.

Penicillium digitatum

Sepodonium chrysospermum, the asexual form or anamorph of the extremely rare *Hypomyces chrysospermus* or *Apiocrea chrysosperma* is often found as a yellow, powdery mass on rotting boletus and *Paxillaceae*.

Sepedonium chrysospermum

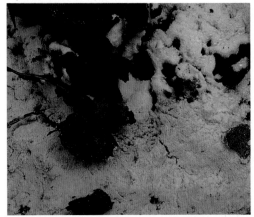

On apples that are turning brown and decaying due to fungal infection, zones with yellowish cushions can be found in autumn, containing the conidiophores of *Monilinia*

fructigena or *Sclerotinia fructigena*. The perfect form or teleomorph, an elongated, bowl-shaped, grey-brown or yellow-brown Discomycete, is rare.

Sclerotinia fructigena

In damp conditions, on poplar branches a mass of conidia *(Cytospora)* resembling a red filament occasionally emerges from a central opening surrounded by a dingy white collar. They grow from the black fruiting bodies of *Leucostoma niveum*, belonging to the genus *Sphaeriales*. The fruiting bodies measure only a few millimetres and are sunk into the bark.

Conidia of Cytospora *(Leucostoma niveum)*

Uncinula aduncta is usually found only as grey blotches, powdery due to conidia, on the affected leaves. On willow leaves, the rarer perfect form of *Uncinula aduncta* forms solitary fruiting bodies measuring a few millimetres, with a black centre surrounded by a ring of pale white appendices, curving away from the centre and rolled in at the tips.

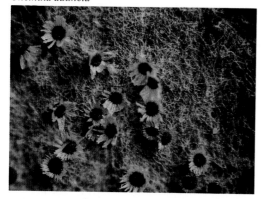

Uncinula aduncta

Ascospores exist in many shapes, sizes and colours. The spores often contain visible drops of oil.

The elliptical spores of *Ascobolus furfuraceus*, which measure approximately 25 microns (= twenty-five thousandths of a millimetre), resemble almonds at large magnifications. Unripe spores are covered with a slimy mass. When ripe, the spore walls are longitudinally wrinkled and grooved and the spores take on a violet-brown colour.

Ascobolus furfuraceus

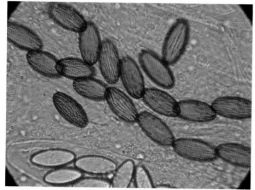

The spores of *Chaetosphaerella phaestroma*, 30 to 40 microns long, which turn partly blue in methylene blue, have three partitions (septa), dividing the spore into four cells. The inner cells are brown, the outer ones watery translucent.

In some Ascomycetes, such as *Peziza sepiatra*, the ascus tips turn blue in a red-brown iodine-containing liquid. Surrounded by sterile, elongate cells, the asci are arranged

Ascus tips of *Peziza sepiatra* (in Melzer's reagent)

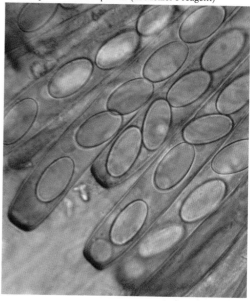

in the hymenium like palisades. These sterile cells or paraphyses contain the colouring matter that gives the hymenium of *Melastiza chateri* its orange-red colour. On the spore walls, fragments of a net of interconnected ridges are visible.

Most Ascomycetes have simple disc-, saucer-, bowl-, or cup-shaped fruiting bodies with or without stem.

The hymenium with the asci is on the inside of the cup. Reversed, strongly pleated caps or

Spores of *Chaetosphaerella phaeostroma* (in methyl blue)

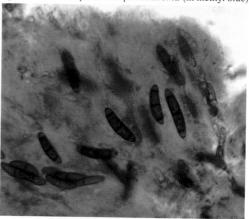

15

Spores, asci and paraphyses of *Melastiza chateri*

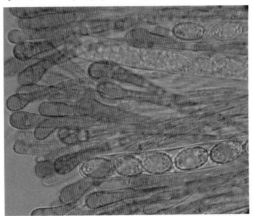

Morchella esculenta

caps consisting of several 'cups' with fused rims, occur in *Verpa conica, Helvella* species and morels.

In *Sphaeriales*, the asci are in a cavity in closed urn- or bottle-shaped fruiting bodies, the perithecia, which occur singly or in groups sunk into a crust or stroma.

The asci ripen one after the other, the ripe spores being projected through a central opening. In *Hypocrea aureoviridis*, the topmost ripe spores can be seen as green dots in the yellow stroma.

Hypocrea aureoviridis

Spores of *Hypocrea aureoviridis*

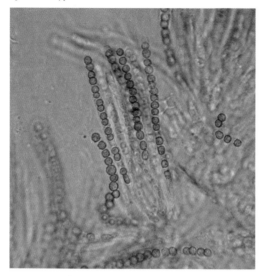

Spores on *Entoloma clypeatum* (in Congo red)

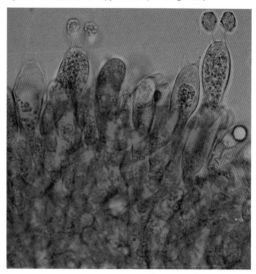

In the asci, 16 green spores are produced, which sometimes split up.

When you cut off the red-brown surface of the stroma of *Hypoxylon rubiginosum,* the shiny black bottoms of the perithecia become visible.

Perithecia in stroma of *Hypoxylon rubiginosum*

Basidiomycetes

In Basidiomycetes, the spores are produced on two or four short stalks or sterigmas at the tip of club-shaped or tuning-fork-like cells, the basidia. In most Basidiomycetes, the spores ripen exposed to the air.

In the Gasteromycetes, they grow and ripen in cavities in the fruiting bodies.

To be able to determine the genera of the Basidiomycetes, the colour of the spore mass in a spore print made on glass, plastic foil or on black or white paper is important. Spore prints can be nearly colourless to white, pink, cream to pale yellow, green-tinged or blue-tinged, yellow-brown, cinnamon and rusty brown to purple-brown or chocolate-brown and black.

In identifying a species, microscopic features such as size and shape of the spores also play a big part.

On the spore walls of *Russula* and *Lactarius,* warts or ridges occur.

Spores of *Lactarius acris* (in Melzer's reagent)

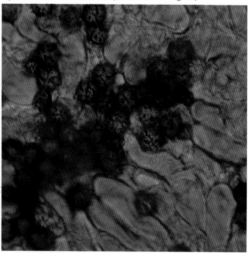

Spores of *Coprinus semitalis*

In some species of agarics, perispores occur, which are spores covered with a slimy mass. Basidiomycetes are also capable of producing huge numbers of spores.

If you put all the spores (measuring 12 microns) produced by a fully grown Dryad's Saddle *(Polyporus squamosus)* produced during an eight-day period end to end, they would cover a distance of nearly 6000 km. The spores are usually spread by the wind. In *Geastraceae* and puffballs, the pressure of falling raindrops causes the spores, which are in a ball or cavity, to be expelled as clouds through a central opening. Ruptured bovistas form a type of cup, from which clouds of spores are expelled upwards by raindrops. In *Nidulariales,* the 'eggs', spore capsules enveloped in a membrane, are projected from their cups by raindrops, on which the covering ruptures. *Nectriaceae* spread their spores or conidia by means of raindrops splashing from the substrate.

With a saucer that reverses as a result of changing internal pressure, *Sphaerobolus stellatus* projects a viscid, black spore ball up to a height of 4 m and up to a distance of 5 m. In *Phallales,* the spores, which are located on the cap in a slimy, stinking mass, are transported sticking to the legs of and in the stomachs of flies attracted by the fetid smell. Insects such as bees and beetles also play an important part in spreading the spores of rusts and blights and of *Ophiostoma ulmi,* which causes Dutch elm disease.

Subterranean fungi such as truffles and *Hymenogastrales* secrete substances that attract wild boar and deer. They dig up the ripe truffles and eat them. The spores germinate from the droppings on the ground.

Fungal spores can travel long distances in the higher layers of the atmosphere. They are nearly always ubiquitous: the substrate and the weather and environmental conditions determine whether they germinate. After a winter with plenty of black ice, *Agaricus bernardii,* which is normallly found on the coast, was found in large numbers growing on the soft shoulder along a motorway which had become saline as a result of scattered salt.

Often the shapes and structures of hyphae in and on different parts of the cap and stem and the presence or absence of club-shaped, lancet-shaped or more irregularly shaped cells like cystides, which can only be seen through a microscope, are essential in identifying a species.

The hymenium with the basidia can be located on surfaces varying widely in shape: on simple, smooth, wrinkled, or spiny crusts, as thin membranes, balls or fans, or on the wall

Cystides of *Macrocystidia cucumis* (in phloxine)

of the tubes of annual or perennial *Polyporus* species that end in pores on the underside. The rusts and blights are classified in a group separate from the Basidiomycetes.

The 'classic' mushroom shape is characteristic of the agarics, boletes and *Hydnum* species: a cap spread open, with spore formation on the underside on gills, tubes or spines, and with a stem with or without a ring, with or without a volva at the base. The main features for identification are whether the gills are free from the stem, adnate or adnate with a tooth, slightly or strongly decurrent on the stem or ending in a ring on the stem. Russulas have thick-fleshed gills ending on the stem, regularly spaced.

The tubes of *Boletus subtomentosus* are of irregular length, the pores are relatively large and angular. Pores and tubes are bright yellow. In some boletes, the colour of the pores differs from the colour of the tube layer.

Gills of *Russula*

The spines under the cap of *Hydnellum aurantiacum*, which are up to 5 mm long, are dull white at first. They become brownish to orange-brown.

Tubes of *Boletus subtomentosus*

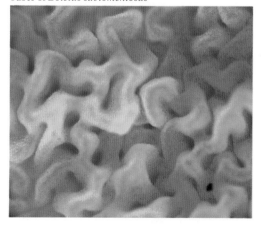

The pinprick-like pores in the pale white to yellow white hymenium on the underside of *Ganoderma lipsiense* can only be seen clearly through a magnifying glass.

Spines of *Hydnellum aurantiacum*

The pores of *Polyporus brumalis* are round, elongate of slightly angular. They are 1 mm in diameter and slightly decurrent.

Pores of *Ganoderma lipsiense*

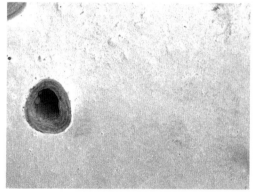

In Maze-Gill *(Daedalea quercina)*, the tube layer has a labyrinthine structure.
Some agarics and boletes have a membrane, the partial veil, that connects the cap margin with the stem when it is closed. When the cap opens, this veil remains as a ring on the stem

Pores of *Polyporus brumalis*

or as remnants on or hanging from the cap margin. In *Cortinarius* species, the partial veil consists of a pallid, translucent or coloured,

Labyrinth of *Daedalea quercina*

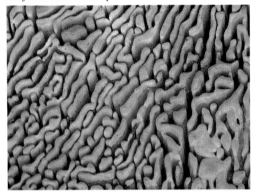

cobweb-like curtain or cortina, usually leaving a ring-shaped zone on the stem. Velar remnants in the form of warts or scales on the cap, like the evanescent white dots on Fly Agaric (*Amanita muscaria:* see cover photograph top centre) and/or in the form of a volva at the base of the stem are the remnants of the universal veil. The universal veil is a membrane that encloses the entire closed fruiting body like a soft or leathery egg-shell.

In *Lepiota aspera* even the dull white partial veil is covered with scattered brown spines.

To allow the spores projected from the basidia to make a free fall from the pores or from between the gills, the gills or tubes should be directed perpendicularly at the soil.

Geotropisu of *Fomes fomentarius*

Veil of *Lepiota aspera*

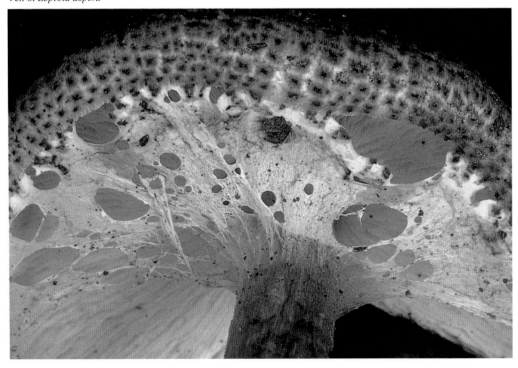

When their position changes, for instance when the infected tree falls down, certain perennial *Polyporus* species are capable of producing a new fruiting body at right angles to the old fruiting body. This phenomenon is called geotropism.

A number of *Aphyllophorales* and *Tremella* species is able to produce asexual spores or conidia. *Abortiporus biennis* and Sulphur Polypore *(Laetiporus sulphureus)* occasionally produce bulbous fruiting bodies producing conidia *(Ceriomyces)*. In *Oligosporus ptychogaster*, the perfect and imperfect forms, which produce spores or conidia, respectively, occur together. Conidia can also be produced in and on the caps of agarics such as *Asterophora* species. Agarics that have remained sterile, with gills not discoloured due to ripe spores (black-brown in *Psathyrella* species) are rare.

Albino Ascomycetes, in which the (orange) colouring in the paraphyses is lacking, such as Orange Peel Fungus *(Aleuria aurantia)*, are rare (see cover photograph: centre left).

When spores germinate, they develop into tube-like structures with septa, the hyphae, which together form the mycelium, in the soil or in or on the substrate. Under favourable conditions the mycelium produces buds from which, like apples on a tree, grow the fruiting bodies, which spread the spores.

One connected mycelium of *Armillaria lutea* was found to spread over an area of 15

Sterile *Psathyrella*

hectares; it weighs over 100,000 kg and is 1500 years old. If the mycelium filaments grow radially from the centre, like the spokes of a wheel, at equal speeds, the fruiting bodies on the surface will form a fairy ring which

increases in diameter every year. The oldest one known is 1 km in diameter and is approximately 700 years old. The fused fairy rings of the Fairy Ring Mushroom *(Marasmius oreades)* on the hills around Stonehenge, which are 100 m in diameter and 300 years old, are renowned. The growing mycelium of Fairy Ring Mushroom produces prussic acid,

Mycelium *Marasmius*

killing the grass on the outside of the growth circle.

In some cases the mycelium develops in the form of a compact bulb, the *sclerotium*, which may or may not be covered with a membrane. *Sclerotia* occur in the soil *(Polyporus tuberaster)* and, in the case of *Sclerotinia*, a number of small Collybias and Ergot *(Claviceps)*, in or fused with the substrate. When conditions are favourable, the fruiting bodies will appear on and from the *sclerotia*, which do not dry out as easily as a regular mycelium.

Most mushrooms are found in autumn. Whether the fruiting bodies appear can vary widely from year to year, however, depending

Fairy rings of *Clitocybe nebularis*

on the species, as a result of variations in habitat, weather and environment. Perennial *Polyporus* species grow a new tube layer on the underside every year. They can go on doing this for dozens of years. By contrast, some *Coprinus* species growing on manure live for a few hours only. The fruiting bodies of Scarlet Elf Cup (*Sarcoscypha coccinea*), *Ciboria amentacea* as well as *Encoelia furfuracea* appear from February to April, after the frosts. Morels, *Verpa conica*, *Disciotis venosa*, *Stromatinia rapulum*, *Monilinia johnsonii*, *Mitrula paludosa*, as well as a number of *Helvella* species, appear exclusively in spring. A large number of species have a strong preference for wet summers. Velvet Shank (*Flamullina velutipes*) and Oyster Mushroom (*Pleurotus ostreatus*) can be found from late autumn until far into the winter, occasionally even with a snow-covered cap.

Mycorrhiza

Approximately one quarter of the species of macrofungi in Britain live in symbiosis with the roots of broad-leaved trees such as oak, beech, hornbeam, birch, alder, poplar, willow, lime, chestnut, and hazel of coniferous trees such as fir, spruce and larch. They form a so-called *ectomycorrhiza*, a mycelium that envelops the roots and protects them from drying out, and from heavy metals and parasites. From there it grows as a finely branched net of hyphae among the tree roots, thus improving the stability of the roots. This extensive net provides the supply of water and nutrient salts dissolved in water from the soil to the tree. The fungus uses the mycorrhiza to supply its energy needs, by absorbing carbohydrates in the form of sugars and starch produced by the tree. Trees would not survive without a root system greatly extended by fungal hyphae and protected by a fungal covering; mycorrhizal fungi in their turn cannot do without trees. When the equilibrium in this relationship of mutual dependance is disturbed, the symbiosis can turn into one-sided parasitism. Over 90 percent of all higher plants enter into a form of symbiosis with a mycorrhizal fungus. A small number of these macrofungi, the specialists, can only enter into symbiosis with one particular species of tree, whereas the generalists form mycorrhiza with several species of broad-leaved and/or coniferous trees. Larch Boletus (*Suillus grevillei*) and *Boletinus cavipes*, for instance, occur exclusively as symbionts of larch. Brown Roll-rim (*Paxillus involutus*), which forms ectomycorrhiza with broad-leaved and coniferous trees, can even grow saprotrophically on dead wood. Most ectomycorrhiza-forming fungi belong to the Basidiomycetes. Ectomycorrhiza-formers often occur in succession. In young fir woods, for instance, you find large numbers of *Cortinarius semisanguineus* and *Suillus bovinus*. In old woods, their role is taken over by the Bay Boletus (*Boletus badius*) and by *Russula* species. Near broad-leaved trees, *Laccaria* and *Hebeloma* species and Brown Roll-rim (*Paxillus involutus*) are often the pioneers. Occasionally you find a root ring of their fruiting bodies, resembling a fairy ring, around a tree.

Mycorrhiza with fluffy mycelium strands are especially important to the water supply of plants and trees. The ectomycorrhiza of *Lactarius* species consist of compact masses of mycelium, smooth at the surface, enveloping roots and often concolorous with the fruiting bodies at the surface. They play an important part in the assimilation of organic nitrogen and phosphorous compounds by broad-leaved and coniferous trees.

Maple, ash, plane, elm and horse chestnut have fungal coverings on their roots, the so-called endomycorrhiza or (vesicular) arbuscular mycorrhiza (VAM or AMF fungi), which are not capable of forming fruiting bodies above ground. In addition, there are mycorrhiza of heather, orchids, the so-called Arbutus mycorrhiza in *Arbutus* species and evergreens and even symbioses between fungi and insects such as lice, beetles, ants and termites. The symbioses of fungi and trees are

Ectomycorrhiza of *Lactarius*

fragile. As a result of environmental pollution and drying out, particularly the specialists among the macrofungi which form ectomycorrhiza with trees have shown a marked decline in recent years.

In spite of forming its own mycorrhiza with fir, *Gomphidius roseus* also obtains part of its nutrients from the mycorrhiza of Suillus bovinus. The same probably goes for Chroogomphus rutilus, which parasitizes on the mycorrhiza of Boleti *(Suillus)* and *Rhizopogon* species. *Monotropa hypopithys*, a plant lacking chlorophyll, parasitizes on a conifer to obtain carbohydrates, which it assimilates through the fungi-covered roots. It extracts its nutrients from mycorrhiza of *Xeroconius* and *Tricholoma* species growing around the roots.

Parasites and saprophytes

Fungi which are not able to enter into symbiosis with plants or trees, live as saprophytes or parasites. Wood and litter saprophytes or saprotrophs recycle dead organic matter. In the carbon and nutrient cycle they are among the few organisms capable of enzymatically breaking down lignin and cellulose and converting them into substances that are useful to themselves and to other forms of life. Over 90 percent of the breakdown of organic residues is done by fungi. Without them, a wood would be killed by its own refuse. *Bjerkandera adusta*, *Psilocybe* and *Mycena* species break down the substrate with chlorinated carbohydrates they themselves produce. Obligate parasites live at the expense of a host which continues to live, whereas opportunistic parasites kill a diseased or weakened host plant, and subsequently sometimes continue their life as saprophytes. Wood and litter parasites occur on all parts of plants and trees; saprotrophs even live on burnt and mummified parts and on partially digested parts in manure. Some of them are highly specialized and for instance occur exclusively on male alder catkins or on fir needles, whereas others always occur in a fixed succession. *Trametes gibbosa*, for instance, grows as a saprotroph on beech, and at the same time parasitizes on the mycelium of *Bjerkandera adusta* already present in the wood. Coprinus species growing on manure secrete substances which kill the hyphae of competing Ascomycetes. There are bark pioneers and *Polyporus* species living off the exposed heartwood. On a trunk of an old beech felled by lightning over a hundred

Monotropa hypopithys

successive species of macrofungi and slime moulds were observed over an 8-year period. When competing fungi meet, 'trenches' or demarcation lines are formed, delimiting the domains of the mycelia. When wood is broken or sawn, these demarcations show up as black lines.

Species such as Honey Fungus (*Armillaria mellea*), Pine Fire Fungus (*Rhizina undulata*) and Dry-rot Fungus (*Serpula lacrymans*) can spread not only by means of spores carried by the wind, but also by means of root-like mycelium strands or rhizomorphs in the soil or in the substrate, and thus colonize tree roots or wood. Just like the gills of *Omphalotus illudens* or *Omphalotus olearius*, which occurs mainly in Southern Europe, the black rhizomorphs of Honey Fungus (*Armillaria mellea*) glow in the dark. In aquatic and amphibious fungi, the life cycle takes place entirely or partially under water. *Fungi imperfecti* and Ascomycetes of the genera *Paecilomyces*, *Laboulbenia* and *Cordyceps* live parasitically on insects and butterfly pupae. *Onygena corvina* and other *Onygenales* have feather shafts, beaks, pellets, hooves, horns, hair (wool) and human and animal skin (mycosis) as their substrate. *Boletus parasiticus*, *Volvarius surrecta*, *Squamanita odorata*, and species of the genera *Cordyceps*, *Hypocrea*, *Hypomyces*, *Asterophora* and *Collybia* live on and off other fungi. Hyphae of *Hohenbuehlia* species catch and digest nematodes. On the mycelium of the Oyster Mushroom (*Pleurotus ostreatus*) buds are formed which kill the nematodes with poison and grow hyphae in them. Anamorphs of *Orbilia* species catch springtails and nematodes. Fungi and yeasts also occur in humans. *Candida albicans*, for instance, causes thrush and Leukorrhea, *Histoplasma capsulatum* causes histoplasmosis and psittacosis, *Epidermophyton floccosum* and *Trichophyton rubrum* are known as athlete's foot and as fungal nail infection and *Trichophyton tonsurans (Tinea tonsurans)* appears as ringworm on the skin, especially on the scalp.

In addition, mycelia and fruiting bodies are of importance as incubator and source of nutrients for numerous creatures living in and on the soil, such as slugs and worms, and insects and their larvae (flies, wood lice, beetles, millipedes, mites, springtails) and in autumn the fruiting bodies, which are rich in protein, are on the daily menu of mammals such as mice, squirrels, rabbits, deer, and wild boar. *Agathomyia wankowiczi* lays its eggs in the hymenium of *Ganoderma lipsiense*. The larvae emerge through the central opening of the nipple-shaped gall, pupate and fly off. Three species of *Coprinus* occasionally produce an orange-brown sterile ozonium on wood.

Many fungi are capable of breaking down cellulose or hemicellulose, but only a few groups of mushrooms are able to break down lignine at the same time. Simultaneous breakdown of hemicelllulose or cellulose and lignin results in white rot. The breakdown of lignin turns the wood pale. The breakdown of lignin and hemicellulose or cellulose results in a damp, fibrous longitudinal structure of the wood, which remains fairly flexible. Hoof or Tinder Fungus (*Fomes*

Nipple-shaped galls (*Agathomyia wankowiczi*)

fomentarius) is increasingly to blame for causing white rot in standing and lying beech and birch trunks.
The photograph of Many-zoned Polypore

Rhizomorphs of *Armillaria mellea*

Ozonium of *Coprinus*

White rot *(Fomes fomentarius)*

(Trametes versicolor) shows white rot in the heartwood below.

The breakdown of cellulose and hemicellulose alone results in brown rot. The wood becomes rusty brown or dark brown and its structure becomes dry and crumbly, disintegrating into cube-shaped granules. As a result, heavy branches and trunks become susceptible to breaking and to being blown down by the wind. Eventually the heartwood pulverizes into brown dust. Brown rot is more frequent in the wood of coniferous trees than in the wood of broad-leaved trees. On damaged old oak you can find Beefsteak Fungus *(Fistulina* hepatica), which uses acetic acid as an energy source and causes brown rot, and Sulphur Polypore *(Laetiporus* sulphureus), which pulverizes the heartwood of other broad-leaved trees as well. The mycelium of Birch Polypore *(Piptoporus betulinus)* causes brown rot in standing and lying birch trunks. The photograph of *Coniophora arida* shows brown rot under damp conditions.

In a less frequent type of wood rot, soft rot, hemicellulose and cellulose are broken down and the lignin is slightly modified. It is caused by *Fungi imperfecti* and *Sphaeriales* such as *Ustulina deusta* and occurs in permanently very damp wood lying on the ground, or often below ground, in the base of the trunks and in the main roots of trees.

In the case of *Ustulina deusta*, which occurs mainly on beech and lime, you will find characteristic black dividing lines and zones in wet-rotting wood, which is predominantly white and locally discolouring brown.

Some *Polyporus* species colour the surface of the wood red, whereas the mycelium of *Chlorociboria* colours the wood green.

Fungi and lichens as bio-indicators

Fungi form an indispensible link in the chain of natural processes of water and nutrient uptake and nutrient transport, and of the conversion and breakdown of organic residues. They can also assimilate and store heavy metals. They are sensitive to disturbances and shifts in the ecosystems of green plants.

Fungi and lichens are useful bio-indicators, as a number of them react strongly to environmental pollution, acidification, overfertilization, dividing land up into plots and draining or drying out. The presence or

Brown rot *(Piptoporus betulinus)*

absence of certain indicator species provides guidelines for management.

In recent years, there has been an increasing decline in and threat to especially the specialists among the ectomycorrhiza-forming fungi and the macrofungi of biotopes poor in nutrients, such as poor grasslands and woods on poor sandy soils. By contrast, opportunistic parasites and nitrogen-loving species that break down wood, humus, and litter, increase in number and frequency of occurrence.

Fungi as food

On the one hand, fungi such as Dry-rot Fungus *(Serpula lacrymans)* are responsible for damage to buildings, and others damage crops and harvests and cause spoilage of foods. For this reason, quarantine measures, the prevention of rusts to complete their life-cycle on the alternative host, fungicides and preservation methods are used to fight their occurrence and spread. On the other hand, the edible fruiting bodies of macrofungi, rich in protein, make an important contribution to our diet.
Especially the fresh, dried or preserved fruiting bodies of morels, truffles, boleti, chanterelles, field mushrooms, *Hydnaceae* species *(Hydnum repandum)*, *Lactarius* species *(Lactarius deliciosus)*, Fairy Ring Mushroom *(Marasmius oreades)*, Shaggy Ink Cap *(Coprinus comatus)*, Giant Puffball *(Langermannia gigantea)*, Caesar's Mushroom *(Amanita caesarea)* and of *Tricholoma* species such as *Tricholoma matsutake* and *Termitomyces* species occurring on termitaria, which are gathered in the wild, are of considerable economic importance. Other popular species include The Blusher *(Amanita rubescens)*, Parasol Mushroom *(Macrolepiota procera)*, *Agrocybe cylindracea*, Wood Blewit *(Lepista nuda)*, *Rozites caperatus*, Cauliflower or Brain Fungus *(Sparassis crispa)*, Ramariaceae species such as *Ramaria botrytis* and *Ustilago maydis*.

On wood, wood pulp and sawdust, straw, dung, compost and other organic waste the following are grown: tropical *Volvariella* species or rice-straw volvariellas *(Volvariella volvacea (esculenta))*, *Flammulina* species, Oyster Mushrooms *(Pleurotus* species*)*, Champignons *(Agaricus bisporus)*, Shiitake *(Lentinula edodes)*, *Psilocybe rugosoannulata* or *Stropharia rugosoannulata*, *Tremella* species *(Tremella fuciformis)*, *Auricularia* species *(Auricularia polytricha)*, Hericiaceae

and 'witches' eggs' of *Phallus duplicatus*. Wild rice inoculated with the blight *Ustilago esculenta* yields a crop of edible fungi.

Without microfungi and yeasts, the production of foods and stimulants such as soy sauce, miso, tempeh (Indonesian fermented soy bean cake), Quorn, cheese and bread and of alcoholic drinks such as wine, sake, rum, whisky and beer would not be possible. In agriculture, horticulture and fruit growing, fungi are increasingly used to control insect plagues.

Moulds and mushrooms as medicine or tonic

The healing properties of penicillin, discovered by accident by Fleming in 1928, and produced from *Penicillium notatum*, and of other antibiotics have been known for centuries. Fungi growing on spoilt food and dung used to be part of the medieval 'dung pharmacopeia'. In the past, peasants from the Dutch provinces of Groningen and Drenthe used the green mould growing on rye bread to spread on festering wounds. The spore powder of puffballs and bovistas, which used to be known as *Fungus chirurgorum*, was used as a remedy for nose bleeds and varicose veins and as baby powder.
For centuries, *Ganoderma lucidum* has been used in elixirs of life is now receiving renewed attention because of its cancer-inhibiting properties. *Laricifomes officinalis*, which grows on larch, is known for its haemostatic and abortive properties. Caterpillars and butterfly pupae parasitized by *Cordyceps sinensis* used to be sold in Chinese markets as a delicacy or as medicine (dong chong xia cao). Wrestlers in Shanghai used to eat the pupae, covered with fruiting bodies, in preparation for a fight. In some *Auricularia* species, popular in China and Japan, a substance has been identified which inhibits blood coagulation. Eating 'witches' eggs' of *Phallus duplicatus* is said to lower blood cholesterol and help to bring down high blood pressure. From the fruiting bodies of the Orange Peel Fungus *(Aleuria aurantia)*, gathered in the wild, nowadays the tumour-inhibiting substance lectin is produced.

The sclerotia of Ergot *(Claviceps purpurea)* were used to induce contractions, despite the serious consequences of prolonged use, and were used for migraine even as late as the 1940s. *Psilocybe* species and the popular Wood Blewit *(Lepista nuda)*, Shiitake

(Lentinula edodes) and *Tremella fuciformis* are also said to have medicinal properties.

Poisonous and hallucinogenic mushrooms

Death Cap *(Amanita phalloides)* poisonings, which end in gruesome agony when discovered late, are notorious, and so are those by the much rarer Destroying Angel *(Amanita virosa)* and Spring Amanita *(Amanita verna)*.
Poisonings by the amatoxines present in their fruiting bodies occur frequently as a result of these Amanitas being mistaken for field mushrooms gathered in the wild. Death Cap was also used for murders and suicides, and was the mushrooms used in the attempt to poison Claudius, which failed when Claudius vomited. The same poison occurs in *Galerina*, *Lepiota* and *Conocybe* species. Poisonings by orellanine, found in *Cortinarius* species, which was not identified until later, caused 19 deaths in Poland in the 1950s. In spite of repeated warnings against the potentially serious consequences of the so-called *Gyromitra* syndrome, people die every year after eating False Morel *(Gyromitra esculenta)* or *Sarcosphaera crassa*, which is found in the Alps. The Paxillus syndrome, which may first occur after eating Brown Roll-rim *(Paxillus involutus)* for years, occasionally has fatal consequences.
In addition, non-fatal poisoning occurs as a result of ingesting muscarine, which is found in certain *Inocybe* and *Clitocybe* species. The Pantherina syndrome, which occurs after ingesting the fruiting bodies of the Panther Cap *(Amanita pantherina)* or *Amanita gemmata*, is not fatal either.

In some countries, there are mushroom counsellors, who will check the mushrooms gathered in the woods by mycophagous laymen for poisonous species. Historic figures such as Siddharta Buddha, pope Clemens VII and the emperors Diocletian and Charles VII are thought to have died as a result of mushroom poisoning nevertheless.
Furthermore, poisoning occurs as a result of ingesting raw or insufficiently heated mushrooms or of ptomaine, produced in spoilt mushrooms. Boleti, *Coprinus* species and Giant Puffballs can store heavy metals and radioactive compounds in their fruiting bodies, and concentrations of these compounds can exceed concentrations allowed in foods. Inhaling a cloud of Oyster Mushroom spores causes a violent asthmatic reaction.

Mycotoxins such as aflatoxin, produced by the mould *Aspergillus flavus*, which occurs on peanuts, nuts, grains and fruit, cause liver cancer and disorders of the gall bladder in humans and animals. During the Vietnam war, the Americans used a chemical weapon, 'yellow rain', based on mycotoxins produced by *Fusarium* species.
As a result, the Vietnamese suffered severe gastrointestinal disorders and internal bleeding which as a rule were fatal.
Before the introduction of fungicides, baking bread and hardtack from flour polluted with Ergot, due to faulty gleaning of the grain, led to frequent poisonings. The sclerotia ground up together with the flour contained alkaloids which caused ergotism, also called Saint Anthony's fire, which produces fits of madness and epilepsy or necrosis and blackening of the limbs (gangrene).
Many poisonings, often of an epidemic character, have been recorded; in 9th-century Germany for instance large numbers of people died of ergotism after a period of a few days or weeks. The last recorded incidence was the bread poisoning in the French town of Pont-Saint-Esprit in 1951.
Occasionally hallucinations occurred, due to a compound related to LSD also present in the sclerotia. The bizarre behaviour of a few women in Salem (Massachusetts), which was probably due to such hallucinations, led to a witch-trial, which ended with the 'witches' being burnt at the stake.
The Common Ink Cap *(Coprinus atramentarius)* is not tolerated in combination with alcohol. It contains coprine, a compound which has an effect similar to the drugs Refusal or Antabus, used to treat alcoholism. This compound has also been found in Club Foot *(Clitocybe clavipes)*, *Boletus luridus* and *Tricholoma flavovirens*.
Fly Agaric *(Amanita muscaria)* derives its name from the popular practice of soaking its red veil in sugared water or milk to kill flies. In spite of the presence of toxins lethal to flies, the caps of Fly Agaric used to be eaten or drunk as an extract to induce hallucinations or a high. Under the influence of Fly Agaric, oracles talked gibberish, which was interpreted by high priests according to their own judgement. The purpose of tonsuring monks' heads is thought to have been to place the red veil on the shaven patch, so the scalp could absorb the hallucigenic substance. As a preparation for battle, the footmen used to drink the urine of the warriors on horseback, which contained residues of digested Fly Agaric. The use of Fly Agaric declined with the

introduction of drinks with a high alcohol content, such as vodka.

At the beginning of the present century, the active substance in a few *Panaeolus* and *Psilocybe* species, already used in Aztec rituals, was discovered. Some time after eating these mushrooms, you become euphoric and experience visual hallucinations with a rich variety of shapes and colours. At the end of the sixties, the use of psilocybine (present in *Psilocybe* species) and LSD was encouraged by the gurus of the youth culture. Nowadays there are specialist shops where you can buy these 'ecodrugs', which are grown in greenhouses.

The effect of hallucinogenic mushrooms on the user's experience and behaviour depends in part on his or her personality, which varies widely from person to person.

As psychiatric symptoms, even requiring hospitalization, can sometimes occur after one-off use, at least unstable people and certainly people with a tendency to depression or psychosis should be discouraged from using hallucinogenic mushrooms.

Mushrooms and their practical use

Before the invention of the match, the core of Tinder or Hoof Fungus *(Fomes fomentarius)* was beaten to a soft, fluffy substance, the tinder. The tinder was carried in a tinderbox, together with flints. The flints were beaten together to produce sparks, which were used to light a plug of tinder, and the smouldering tinder could be used to light a wood fire. Discs cut from the core were processed into a kind of Russia leather, which was used to make kid gloves and wound dressings; it is still used to make hats. Birch Polypore *(Piptoporus betulinus)* was dried for use as a blotter for documents written with quill and ink, and it was also used smouldering in a bee-keeper's pipe to stupefy bees. A few years ago they were found tied to a rope around the waist of Ötzi, the iceman found buried in a glacier, and who lived about 3000 B.C. The caps of *Inonotus hispidus* contain a yellow dye which was used to dye silk and leather chestnut-brown. The mycelium of *Chlorociboria* species colours affected wood green. Wood that is slightly affected and has become green is used in marquetry to decorate furniture and statuettes (Tunbridge ware). Litmus used to be produced from lichens.

Conclusion

This encyclopaedia is a book of photographs first of all, a book of reference intended to show the diversity of species. It is a visual guide, which should be consulted frequently to be able to recognize mushrooms in the field on the basis of external features. The encyclopaedia does not contain identification tables or keys. One third to one half of the X species found in Britain can only be identified with certainty by using a microscope and specialist literature. For the genera included and the species shown of the slime moulds or Myxomycetes, the Ascomycetes and the Basidiomycetes, respectively, the following chapters will give those features that can be observed with the naked eye, with a magnifying glass and with the hands, mouth or nose. The abbreviations and symbols used in the descriptions are explained on the colophon page and the mycological terms used have been explained in this chapter.

Enteridium lycoperdon (Reticularia lycoperdon), see p. 33

2 Slime moulds or Myxomycetes

Although the slime moulds or Myxomycetes do not form part of the fungal kingdom, they are usually the object of study of fungal biologists or mycologists. The nearly 500 species of Myxomycetes or *Dictyostelida* form a group of organisms distinct from all other forms of life.

Microscopically small, creeping or swimming initial stages grow from spores, and resemble amoebas (myxamoebas) or flagellates (myxomonads); these develop into a horizontally or vertically mobile stage, the *plasmodium*, and finally become a fixed stage with fruiting bodies in which the spores develop with which they reproduce and spread.

The creeping mass of plasma, which feeds on micro-organisms such as bacteria and on fungal spores and hyphae, the so-called plasmodium, usually leaves a shiny, mother-of-pearl-like trail with food remains on or in the substrate.

Several Slime moulds have a somewhat more voluminous and compact, often brightly coloured plasmodium. The plasmodium of *Lycogala epidendrum*, which is found world-wide, is orange to vermillion or carmine-red to carmine-pink in colour.

Plasmodium of *Lycogala epidendrum*

Lycogala epidendrum

Stemless **fruiting bodies** or *aethalia* in small groups, occasionally touching each other, globose or cushion-shaped, ∅ 3-15 mm, pink

to buff or dark grey, with scales. On rotting wood, bark and fallen branches or on the ground next to stumps.

Most Myxomycetes have a strongly veined plasmodium, spreading fan-like and growing

Lycogala epidendrum

like a net, which moves in 'streams' over or in the substrate.

Under unfavourable conditions, a plasmodium can contract, the internal parts will then be provided with a firm wall and sclerotia will

Plasmodium

develop. After sufficient food intake and occasionally under the influence of light, a plasmodium will proceed to form one or more large or small fruiting bodies. If the plasmodium contracts into a number of separate lumps, separate, stemmed fruiting bodies or *sporangia* will be produced. The sporangia which continue to develop are often concolorous with the plasmodium.

♀

Occasionally a stem is formed first, after which the plasmodium creeps upwards in or

Formation of Sporangia

along a hollow stem and assumes its final sporangium shape. When ripening, the fruiting bodies often change colour. The spores

develop on the stem and within the wall of the peridium of the fruiting body. The surrounding membrane ruptures, after which the (nearly) round spores, measuring 5-20 micron in diameter, are spread by wind and raindrops in red-brown or purple-brown to brown-black clouds.

Badhamia utricularis

Sporangia in large groups, often with several sporangia on fused stems like 'bunches of grapes' hanging from or under the substrate, pear-shaped or conical, ∅ 0.5-0.8 mm, including stem 5-18 mm long, blue-grey with green, purple or red flushes. **Stem** strawcoloured or ochre to red-brown. **Plasmodium** egg-yellow. Frequent on dead wood and bark also covering the fungi or lichens growing on it.

♀

Arcyria denudata

Sporangia erect, in crowded groups, stemmed, ovoid to shortly cylindrical, ∅ 0.5 mm, 1-3 mm high, scarlet, vinaceous red or carmine to redbrown. **Stem** red-brown. **Plasmodium** white.

Badhamia utricularis

Common on dead (mossy) wood, stumps and branches.

♀

Fuligo septica

Aethalia irregularly cushion-shaped, often with trail, ∅ 2-13 cm, 0.5-3 cm high, spongy, brittle, rough and fragile, lemon-yellow, green-yellow to ochre. **Plasmodium** yellow. Frequent on dead wood and other substrates. In the past often on the tannin-containing bark used in tanneries.

Fuligo septica

Enteridium lycoperdon (Reticularia lycoperdon)

Aethalium usually solitary, cushion-shaped, ∅ 2-10 cm, at first soft and white, then with a silvery shine, becoming brown due to spore

dust. **Plasmodium** white. Common on standing or lying dead wood, often as early as spring.

Enteridium lycoperdon

Didymium serpula

Fruiting bodies solitary or in small groups, sessile, very thin, ∅ up to a few centimetres, 0.1-0.2 mm high, grey-white. **Plasmodium** yellow. Fairly common on dead foliage in woods and on piles of leaves.

♀

Didymium serpula

Tubifera ferruginosa

Sporangia crowded, sessile, in groups from 1 to 5 cm wide, stemless, cylindrical or club-shaped, ∅ 0.3 mm, up to 5 mm high, pale brown to dark brown or red-brown to purple-brown.
Plasmodium orange, pink or vermillion, often in pink, strawberry-like lumps. Frequent on dead wood of broad-leaved and coniferous trees.

♀

Tubifera ferruginosa

Dictydiaethalium plumbeum

Aethalium fairly strongly flattened, ∅ 4-5 cm, 0.5-1 mm high, buff, brown, ochre or grey,

with a protruding white, with a silvery-shiny membrane (hypothallus) under the aethalium.
Plasmodium pink. Fairly common, especially on recently felled trunks and on loppings.

Leocarpus fragilis

Sporangia all or some of them crowded, forming a cluster of small groups, short-stemmed or sessile, 2-4 mm high, ∅ 0.5-1.5 mm, globose or ovoid to shortly cylindrical, rounded at the top, shiny yellow, brown-yellow, chestnut or red-brown. **Plasmodium** yellow. Common on dead foliage, fallen branches, occasionally a few centimetres above the surface on living herbaceous plants and small tree trunks.

♀

Leocarpus fragilis

Dictydiaethalium plumbeum

3 Ascomycetes

Onygenales

A small group of fungi growing on keratin. Species of the genus *Onygena* on the shafts of feathers, hooves, horns and hair (wool), species of the genera *Trichophyton* and *Epidermophyton* on skin (mycosis).

Onygena corvina

Fr 5-20 mm, a pale ochre to light brown, pruinose, clayey ball, ∅ 1-2 mm, with stem. **St** smooth, white, 4-18 x 1-2 mm. Solitary or in groups.
Not uncommon on pellets and feathers (shafts), VR on hair (socks made of goat's wool), bird skulls and beaks.

This species can only be distinguished with certainty from *O. equina*, which occurs on hooves and horns, by microscopic features.

Sa

Onygena corvina

Taphrinales

A small group of fungi parasitizing inflorescences, fruits, leaves and branches of trees, causing discoloration, deformation and abnormal growth of the substrate.

In Britain, 21 species occur, including *Taphrina amentorum* on alder cones, and *Taphrina deformans*, which causes leaf-curl in peach foliage.

Taphrina betulina

WITCHES'-BROOM

Causes abnormal growth and deformation of branches and leaves, resulting in Witches' Broom.
Common on the crown of living birch.

Pa

Taphrina betulina

Taphrina johansonii

Forms a golden yellow layer covering the separate inflorescences and fruits of the

Taphrina johansonii

female catkins of the trembling poplar hanging on the tree and swells to a thickness of 10 mm. Spring.

Pa VR

Pezizales

A group of fungi which includes *Morchella*, *Helvella*, *Peziza* and truffles, which show a rich variety of shapes and species. They grow on or in the soil, on sites of fires and on mosses, rotting wood, paper, straw, fibres, compost, manure, cement and damp walls. They have opercular asci, sacs with a small cover on top that opens on ripening and that usually turns blue in Melzer's reagent (see photograph of ascus tops of *Peziza sepiatra*, Chapter 1).

Morchella esculenta

MOREL

Fr 6-25 cm. **C** 5-15 x 4-10 cm, irregular egg- or pear-shaped to spherical, consisting of deep irregular pits (alveoles), connected by angular ridges. Pits honey-yellow to ochrous brown or grey-brown; ridges occasionally coloured lighter or darker. Margin attached to the stem.

St hollow, pleated or grooved at the swollen base, granular or scurfy, white to pale ochrous yellow, 3-11 x 1-5 cm. **Fl** pallid, elastic. **Sm** pleasant. **Ta** mild. On roots of trees (elm, ash, beech) and shrubberies, on humus-rich sand, clay and loam in broad-leaved woods, shrubberies and parks, fairly common on coastal sand dunes. Solitary or in groups. April to May (for young specimens, see Chapter 1). Also *M. elata* (R), with an acutely conical cap.

Sa 🍴

Morchella semilibera
(Mitrophora semilibera)

Fr 10-20 cm. **C** usually small in proportion to the stem, 2-6 cm, conical or campanulate, ridges strongly vertically oriented, with few transverse ribs, with shallow pits. Pits honey-brown to olive brown; ridges dark brown to black. Margin free from the stem.
Lower surface free until halfway down the stem, white to ochre.
St hollow, fragile, thickening at the base, smooth or grooved, with granular scales, dingy white to pale ochrous yellow, 4-15 x 1-4 cm. **Fl** white. **Ta** mild.
Not uncommon on humus-rich (dug) soil

Morchella esculenta

under broad-leaved trees in parks and kitchen gardens. Solitary or in groups. April to May.

Sa 🍴

Morchella semilibera

Verpa conica

Fr 5-15 cm. **C** 2-4 cm, campanulate to thimble-shaped. Upper surface wrinkled or smooth, honey-yellow-brown to red-brown. Cap centrally ached to stem apex, lower surface felty, dingy white. **St** becoming hollow, fragile, finely felty, white to dingy cream, with horizontal zones of yellow-brown scales, 3-12

Verpa conica

x 1-2 cm. Not uncommon on rich, humous soil under broad-leaved trees and shrubberies (hawthorn) in broad-leaved woods, shrubberies, parks and kitchen gardens (strawberries). March to May.

Sa

Disciotis venosa

Fr deeply cup-shaped to flattened saucer-shaped, 5-18 cm, on short, rooting stem. Inner surface strongly radially veined and wrinkled

Disciotis venosa

at the centre, yellow-brown to dark date-brown. Margin more pallid, strongly undulated and curved. Lower surface felty, grey-white to yellow-brown. **Fl** pallid. **Sm** of bleach. Locally occasionally in large numbers on bare or moss-covered, rich loam or clay in broad-leaved woods and poor roadsides. March to May. Also *D. maturescens* (VR RDL).

R Sa

Gyromitra esculenta

FALSE MOREL

Fr 5-16 cm. **C** 4-12 cm, irregularly round, brain-like convoluted, with 3 broad, deeply convoluted lobes, yellow-brown to red-brown, later grey-white pruinose. **St** hollow or chambered, finely mealy, strongly pleated and furrowed, white or dingy white to flesh-brown, 3-10 x 2-6 cm. On manured, bare soil or on litter under coniferous trees (pine), occasionally under broad-leaved trees. March to May. Also *G. gigas* (VR RDL) and *G. infula* (VR RDL).

R RDL Sa †

Gyromitra esculenta

Helvella crispa

COMMON WHITE HELVELLA

Fr 5-15 cm. **C** 3-6 cm, undulated, saddle-shaped, 2- to 3-lobed. Upper surface dingy white to creamy ochre. Margin free from the stem, lower surface coarsely hairy, cream to yellow-brown. **St** hollow, chambered, longitudinally deeply grooved and ribbed, white or dingy white to pale grey-brown, 4-13 x 1-5 cm. Common on humous sand, clay and loam in

woods and on the edge of woods. Summer to autumn. Also *H. lactea* (VR).

Sa †

Helvella crispa

Helvella lacunosa

BLACK HELVELLA

Fr 8-15 cm. **C** 4-7 cm, irregularly undulated, saddle-shaped, 3- to 4-lobed. Upper surface grey to grey-brown or deep grey. Margin occasionally attached to the stem; lower surface light grey. **St** hollow, longitudinally deeply grooved and ribbed, light grey to grey-brown, often whitish at the base, 4-10 x 1-3 cm. Common in woods on humus-rich sand, loam and clay. Summer to autumn. Also *H. atra*.

Sa †

Helvella lacunosa

Helvella elastica

Fr 5-10 cm. **C** 2-4 cm, irregularly lobed, saddle-shaped, 2-lobed. Upper surface ochre, grey-yellow to pale grey-brown. Margin free from the stem, lower surface smooth, whitish. **St** hollow, twisted or curved, with hollows in places, hairy, white to pale cream, 6-12 x 1-2 cm. Not uncommon on humus-rich sand and loam in woods and dune scrub. Summer to autumn.

Also *H. ephippium* (R RDL) and *H. latispora* (R RDL).

Sa

Helvella elastica

Helvella fusca

Fr 3-9 cm. **C** 3-5 cm, saddle-shaped, 2- to 3-lobed. Upper surface brown-black with light margins when young, later yellow-brown to date-brown. Margin usually attached to the stem in places; lower surface with striking

Helvella fusca

branched veins, dingy white to pale brown. **St** hollow, markedly ribbed, finely hairy, white to yellow-brown, 3-5 x 1-2 cm. On humus, calcareous sand and in poor grassland on clay under broad-leaved trees (poplar). Autumn.

VR RDL Sa

Helvella spadicea (H. leucopus)

Fr 5-10 cm. **C** 3-6 cm, saddle-shaped, 3-lobed. Upper surface black-brown. Margins attached to the stem in places; lower surface smooth, white. **St** hollow, with deep hollows at the base, whitish to creamy yellow, 3-5 x 1-2 cm. On calcareous sand and sand dunes, under poplar and trembling poplar.
April to May.

R RDL Sa

Helvella spadicea

Helvella acetabulum

Fr 4-8 cm. **C** ⌀ 2-8 cm, deeply bowl-shaped. Inner surface olive yellow-brown to dark brown. Lower surface ribbed, the ribs ex-

Helvella acetabulum

tending from the stem about halfway up the cup, downy, yellowish to olive brown, whitish towards the apex. **St** hollow, chambered, strongly ribbed, granular or smooth, white to yellowish brown, 2-4 x 1-3 cm. Not uncommon on humus-rich sand, in broad-leaved woods (oak). April to June.
Also *H. costifera* (R RDL), *H. leucomeleana* (R RDL) and H. unicolor (VR).

Sa

Helvella villosa

Fr 2-5 cm. **C** ⌀1-3 cm, bowl- to saucer-shaped. Inner surface matt dark grey to grey-brown. Lower surface felty-clayey, ashen-grey with yellowish to whitish tinge, occasionally with ciliate margin. **St** stuffed, straight or curved, floccose-clayey, with hollows at the thickened base, ashen-grey to light grey-brown, 1-3 x 0.5-1 cm. Not uncommon on humus-rich sand, loam, or clay in woods. Often in groups. Spring to autumn.
Also *H. corium* (R), *H. cupuliformis* (R RDL), *H. macropus* and *H. queletti*.

Sa

Helvella villosa

Rhizina undulata

PINE FIRE FUNGUS

Fr irregularly saucer- or cushion-shaped, ⌀ 4-12 cm. Upper surface chestnut to black-brown, with white, downwards incurved margin, stem absent.

Lower surface yellow or ochraceous yellow, attached to the buried mycelium by mycelium strands; the mycelium can penetrate the roots of coniferous trees with rhizomorphs.

Rhizina undulata

40

On sites of fires, burnt wood and felled areas near coniferous trees. Solitary or (fused) in groups.
Spring to autumn.

To prevent spreading of this root parasite via bonfire sites, in the past forestry workers were not allowed to make bonfires.

R Pa

Peziza ammophila

Fr cup-shaped, ∅ 2-4 cm, developing partly below ground. Stellate, opening with 4 to 6 lobes.
Emerging only slightly from the sand. Inner surface dark yellow-brown to date-brown. Outer surface pale grey-brown, covered with sand, rooting with a fragile mycelium strand.

On (rotting) roots of marram grass (*Ammophila arenaria*) in outer coastal sand dunes.

R Sa

Peziza badia

Fr cup- to saucer-shaped, ∅ 3-10 cm. Inner surface red-brown to dark olivaceous brown. Outer surface red-brown to dark chestnut, clayey. **Fl** brownish, yielding a watery milk. Common among leaf and needle litter or on bare, sandy or loamy soil. Often in close groups.
June to autumn.

Sa

Peziza badia

Peziza ammophila

Peziza bovina

Fr shallowly cup- to saucer-shaped, Ø 8-12 mm. Inner surface amber to dingy ochrous yellow. Outer surface floccose-scurfy, pallid at the margin, dingy ochrous yellow.
On manure (cowpats) in grassland.

VR SA ♀

Peziza bovina

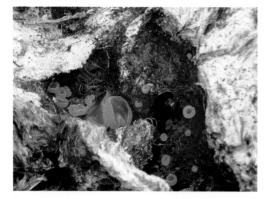

Peziza cerea

Fr shallowly cup-shaped to flattened saucer-shaped, Ø 5-15 cm. Inner surface bright ochrous yellow to reddish yellow-brown. Outer surface felty-scurfy, white to yellowish brown. **Fl** dingy white to faintly brownish.

Common on rotting wood, cardboard, paper, straw, sisal or coconut mats and on cement and mortar on damp walls.

Sa

Peziza cerea

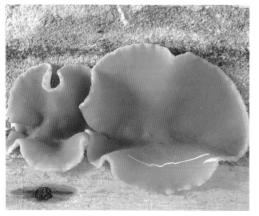

Peziza depressa

Fr flattened saucer-shaped, Ø 2-4 cm. Inner surface purple-brown to chestnut. Outer surface scurfy, light purple-brown, purple-tinged at the margin. **Fl** yielding a watery white milk. On clay rich or deficient in humus in broad-leaved woods and shrubberies.

R Sa

Peziza depressa

Peziza emileia

Fr cup-shaped, Ø 2-7 cm. Inner surface ochrous yellow-brown to purple-brown. Outer surface smooth or finely felty, whitish to watery grey-blue. On rich clay rich or deficient in humus, in broad-leaved woods and parks, also on fire sites.

R RDL Sa

Peziza emileia

Peziza michelii

Fr cup-shaped, occasionally torn at one side (like *Otidea onotica*), ∅ 2-7 cm. Inner surface yellow-brown with violet tinge to olive brown or purple-brown. Outer surface felty-scurfy, ochraceous yellow-brown to olive green-yellow or purple-brown, white-felty at the base. **Fl** yielding a watery milk, which becomes yellow after a while. Not uncommon on clay, loam, (or sand) under broad-leaved and coniferous trees.

Sa

Peziza michelii

Peziza subviolacea
(Peziza praetervisa)

Fr cup-shaped, ∅ 2-4 cm. Inner surface purple to dingy violet-brown or brown-lilac. Outer surface with yellow-brown scales at the margin, pale grey-violet to yellow-brown, white-felty at the base. **Fl** yielding a watery

Peziza subviolacea

white milk. On sites of fires ground in broad-leaved and coniferous woods, occasionally on sand rich in minerals and deficient in humus.

R Sa

Peziza proteana f. sparassoides

Fr convoluted and curly, sponge-like, ∅ 3-15 cm. Cavities whitish to ochre. Outer surfaces floccose, whitish with pink tinges, becoming pink-brown to dark brown.
On fire sites.

VR Sa

Peziza proteana f. sparassoides

Peziza repanda

Fr cup-shaped, ∅ 2-5 cm. Inner surface pale ochraceous yellow-brown to reddish brown. Outer surface scurfy-felty, brown-yellow, drying white, with serrate margin.
Common on humus-rich soil and rotting wood,

Peziza repanda

occasionally on paper or cardboard and on sites of fires.

Sa

Peziza sepiatra

Fr flattened saucer-shaped, ⌀ 0.5-1 cm. Inner surface greyish brown to black-brown. Outer surface clayey, sepia, with slightly protruding, serrated margin.
On fire sites and bare, humous soil in broad-leaved woods (see also microphotograph in Chapter 1).

R Sa ♀

Peziza succosa

Fr cup-shaped, ⌀ 2-5 cm. Inner surface light buff-brown to yellow-brown. Outer surface thinly felty or smooth, light yellowish grey to light yellowish brown. **Fl** white, becoming sulphur-yellow. Not uncommon on humus soil in broad-leaved woods.

Sa

Peziza vesiculosa

Fr cup-shaped, remaining vesicular for a long time, ⌀ 3-10 cm. Inner surface pale ochraous yellow to ochrous brown-yellow. Outer

Peziza succosa

Peziza vesiculosa

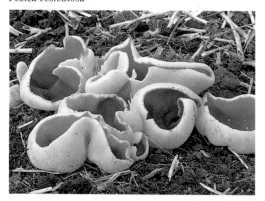

Peziza sepiatra

surface floccose-scurfy, whitish or pale dingy ochraceous yellow to pale yellow-brown, with irregularly torn margin. **Fl** thick, fragile, pale ochrous yellow.

Common on litter, wood chips, straw, compost, manure and cardboard. Often fused in groups. Spring to autumn.

In Britain, 40 species of the genus *Peziza* occur.

Sa

Otidea onotica

HARE'S EARFUNGUS

Fr irregularly ear-shaped, 6-10 cm high. Inner surface ochraceous yellow to orange-yellow, with pink tinges when young. Outer surface scurfy-felty, slightly wrinkled, salmon to ochraceous yellow. **Fl** white.

Not uncommon among litter and on soil that is deficient in humus, under broad-leaved trees, favouring oak.

RDL M

Otidea bufonia

Fr irregularly bowl- to ear-shaped, split at one side, ∅ 2-8 cm. Inner surface ochrous to

cinnamon yellow-brown. Outer surface smooth to wrinkled, coarsely warty, ochrous brown to sepia grey-brown, white-woolly at the base.

Fl brown.

Not uncommon among litter on humus-rich soil in avenues and (mixed) woods.

RDL M

Otidea bufonia

Otidea alutacea

Fr irregularly undulate, bowl-shaped, split at one side, ∅ 3-5 cm. Inner surface dark loam-coloured to grey-brown or yellow-brown. Outer

Otidea onotica

surface clayey-floccose, dingy ochrous yellow to pale yellow-brown. **Fl** yellowish. Among litter on sand, loam or clay that is deficient in humus to humous-rich, in broad-leaved woods.

R RDL M

Otidea alutacea

Otidea cochleata

Fr bowl-shaped, split at one side down to the base, ∅ 4-6 cm. Inner surface brown to dark olivaceous brown. Outer surface felty, lighter olivaceous brown, whitish hairy at the base. Occasionally in trooping groups. On clay or loam that is deficient in humus, under broad-leaved trees.
Also *O. leporina* (R RDL) and *O. platyspora* (VR).

R RDL M

Otidea cochleata

Tarzetta catinus (Pustularia catinus)

Fr cup- to saucer-shaped, ∅ 1-4 cm. Inner surface cream to pale yellow-brown. Outer surface scurfy-floccose, cream to pale ochrous yellow, with serrated, whitish to brown-blotched margin, with stem. **St** 0.5-2 x 0.5 cm, grooved, scurfy, pale ochraceous yellow. Common on loam or clay that is deficient in humus to humus-rich, occasionally on sand, under broad-leaved trees. June to autumn.

Sa

Tarzetta catinus

Tarzetta cupularis (Pustularia cupularis)

Fr cup-shaped, ∅ 1-2 cm. Inner surface pale grey-yellow to dingy white-yellow. Outer surface covered with fine, brownish warts, dingy ochrous yellow to pale grey-yellow, with

Tarzetta cupularis

serrated, torn margin with 'cobweb', stem absent or sunk into the soil.
Fairly common on sand, loam or clay that is humus-rich or deficient in humus, in broad-leaved woods, occasionally also in coniferous and mixed woods.
April to autumn.
T. cupularis cannot always be distinguished with certainty from *T. catinus*.
Also *T. gaillardiana* (VR) and *T. rosea* (VR RDL).

Sa

Sowerbyella imperialis (S. unicolor)

Fr flattened cup- to saucer-shaped, ∅ 2-4 cm. Inner surface bright orange-yellow. Outer surface clayey, creamy yellow, deep-rooting with felty stem. **Fl** whitish.On humus-rich soils in broad-leaved woods and (dune) scrub. Also *S. radiculata* (R RDL).

VR RDL Sa

Sowerbyella imperialis

Geopora arenicola (Sepultaria arenicola)

Fr cup- to saucer-shaped, often remaining deeply sunk into the soil, ∅ 1-2 cm. Inner surface bluish grey to pale yellow-brown. Outer surface with matted hairs, covered with grains of sand, with appendiculate or torn margin, yellow-brown to brown. **Fl** whitish. Not uncommon on sand deficient in humus. Spring to autumn.

Sa

Geopora sumneriana (Sepultaria sumneriana)

Fr cup-shaped, at first globose, hollow and entirely subterranean, splitting to form irregular star shape and breaking the soil, ∅ 2-7 cm. Inner surface buff to light grey-ochre. Outer surface with mattted dark brown hairs, red-brown. **Fl** thick, white. On partly decayed needles on soil deficient in humus under cedar (and yew).
April to May.

VR Sa

Geopora sumneriana

Geopora tenuis (Sepultaria tenuis)

Fr shallowly cup- to saucer-shaped, somewhat sunk into the soil, ∅ 1-2 cm. Inner surface watery grey to dingy yellow-white. Outer surface sparsely hairy, with irregularly

Geopora arenicola

splitting margin, yellow-brown to reddish brown. On rich loam or clay in broad-leaved woods.
Also *G. foliacea* (VR).

R Sa

Geopora tenuis

Neottiella rutilans
(Leucoscypha rutilans)

Fr shallowly saucer-shaped, ∅ 1-2 cm. Inner surface orange to orange-red. Outer surface covered with white hairs, orange-yellow background showing through, with stem. **St** sunk into the substrate. Not uncommon, parasitizing on living mosses on sand that is deficient in humus.

Pa

Neottiella rutilans

Tricharina gilva

Fr cup- to saucer-shaped, ∅ up to 0.5 cm. Inner surface yellow-orange to yellowish grey-brown. Outer surface clayey, covered with

brownish hairs, light grey to grey-brown. On fire sites and sand that is rich in minerals and deficient in humus. Often in groups.
Spring to autumn.

R Sa ♀

Tricharina gilva

Humaria hemisphaerica
(Mycolachnea hemisphaerica)

Fr cup- to saucer-shaped, ∅ 1-3 cm. Inner surface watery grey-blue to creamy white. Outer surface covered with with dark brown hairs, yellow-brown.
Common on bare soil or among leaf litter on sand, loam or clay under broad-leaved and coniferous trees.

M

Humaria hemisphaerica

Trichophaea woolhopeia

Fr hemispherical to flattened saucer-shaped, ∅ up to 0.5 cm. Inner surface white-grey to dingy yellow. Outer surface covered with matted yellow-brown hairs, dingy yellow to faded light brown. On rich soil in broad-leaved woods. Often in groups. Summer to autumn.

R Sa ♀

Trichophaeopsis bicuspis *(Trichophaea bicuspis)*

Fr flattened cup- to saucer-shaped, ⌀ up to 0.5 cm.
Inner surface dingy white. Outer surface with sparse brown hairs protruding far over the dark margin, pale dingy yellow. On humus,

leaves, branches and rotting wood on rich soil in broad-leaved woods and parks.

R Sa ♀

Trichophaeopsis bicuspis

Scutellinia scutellata

EYELASH FUNGUS

Fr flattened saucer-shaped to disc-shaped, ⌀ 0.5-1 cm. Inner surface orange-red to

Scutellinia scutellata

scarlet. Outer surface with brown-black hairs up to 2 mm long, protruding far over the dark margin, pale brown to dingy red-brown. Common on damp, rotting wood, leaves, herbs and surrounding soil in damp (alder and willow) woods and grasslands.
Spring to autumn.

In Britain, 15 species of the genus *Scutellinia* occur.

Sa ♀

Cheilymenia fimicola

Fr disc- to saucer-shaped, ∅ 2-6 mm. Inner surface orange-yellow to yellow. Outer surface with translucent, pale brown hairs, pale orange-yellow. On cow dung in grasslands. Spring to autumn.

R Sa ♀

Cheilymenia granulata (Coprobia granulata)

Fr flattened saucer-shaped, ∅ 1-5 mm. Inner surface granular, rough, bright yellow-orange to orange-red. Outer surface clayey-granular,

orange-yellow. Common on cowpats in rich grasslands. Spring to autumn.

Sa ♀

Cheilymenia granulata

Cheilymenia pulcherrima

Fr flattened saucer-shaped, ∅ 1-2 mm. Inner surface egg-yellow to orange-yellow. Outer surface covered with sparse, pale brown hairs,

Cheilymenia fimicola

with floccose margin, egg-yellow. On cow and sheep dung.

R Sa ♀

Cheilymenia pulcherrima

Cheilymenia theleboloides

Fr cup- to saucer-shaped, ∅ 5-10 mm. Inner surface egg-yellow to orange-yellow. Outer surface and margin with sparse, pallid hairs, pale yellow to orange-yellow. On compost and (horse) dung containing straw. In close groups. Spring to autumn.

In Britain, 15 species of the genus *Cheilymenia* occur, on manure, compost and rich clay deficient in humus or humus-rich sand.

R Sa ♀

Cheilymenia theleboloides

Melastiza chateri

Fr bowl- to flattened saucer-shaped, ∅ 0.5-2 cm. Inner surface orange to orange-red. Outer surface densely covered with brown,

hairy-looking spots at the margin, dingy orange-yellow to brownish orange. Common on humus-rich soil in broad-leaved woods, grasslands, fields and kitchen gardens (see also microphotograph in Chapter 1).

Sa

Melastiza chateri

Anthracobia melaloma

Fr flattened cup- to disc-shaped, ∅ 2-6 mm. Inner surface dingy orange. Outer surface with patches of tufted and dark brown hairs. Common on sites of fires. In groups. Spring to autumn.

Sa ♀

Anthracobia melaloma

Aleuria aurantia

ORANGE PEEL FUNGUS

Fr irregularly cup-shaped to flattened saucer-shaped, ∅ 2-10 cm. Inner surface vividly orange or red-orange. Outer surface white-felty, creamy yellow to orange-yellow. Common on virtually bare soil or rich, clay, loam or sand in broad-leaved and mixed woods, parks, avenues and lawns, often along pathsides. Occasionally in groups (see also cover photo: an albino specimen).

Sa

Smardaea amethystina (Jafneadelphus amethystinus)

Fr flattened cup-shaped, ∅ 1-2 cm. Inner surface dark blue to dark purple-violet. Outer

Smardaea amethystina

surface smooth, dark blue to purple. On rich, bare soil under hazel.

VR Sa

Geopyxis carbonaria

Fr bowl- to chalice-shaped, ∅ 1-2 cm. Inner surface yellowish red-brown to dingy orange-yellow. Outer surface finely scurfy, with whitish, dentate margin and deep-rooting,

Geopyxis carbonaria

Aleuria aurantia

slender stem, light red-brown to orange-yellow. On bonfire sites near coniferous trees. Spring to autumn.

VR M

Octospora humosa

Fr saucer- to disc-shaped, ∅ 0.5-1 cm. Inner surface pale orange to orange. Outer surface floccose-scurfy, slightly appendiculate, orange-yellow to pale salmon.
Not uncommon on hair mosses on sand deficient in humus.
Spring to autumn.

Pa ⚲

Octospora humosa

Octospora melina

Fr flattened cup- to disc-shaped, ∅ 1-2 mm. Inner surface orange-yellow to orange. Outer surface floccose-scaly, orange.
On mosses.

Octospora melina

In Britain, 24 species of the genera *Octospora* and *Lamprospora* occur.

VR Pa ⚲

Ascobolus furfuraceus

Fr saucer- to disc-shaped or shallowly cup-shaped, ∅ 2-5 mm. Inner surface light sulphur-yellow to green-yellow with purple-black dots of ripening spores. Outer surface scurfy, with somewhat dentate, more pallid margin, pale green-yellow.
Common on (cow) dung.
Spring to autumn (see also microphotograph in Chapter 1).

Sa ⚲

Ascobolus furfuraceus

Ascobolus furfuraceus

Ascobolus carbonarius

Fr cup-shaped to flattened saucer-shaped, ∅ 2-7 mm. Inner surface yellowish olive green to dark olivaceous brown with black dots. Outer surface scurfy, olive brown to dark brown.

On bonfire sites and burnt wood. Spring to autumn.

R Sa ♀

Ascobolus carbonarius

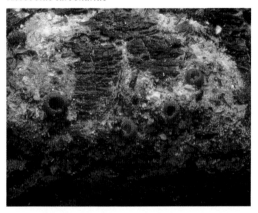

Ascobolus albidus

Fr cup-shaped to flattened saucer-shaped, ⌀ 0.5-1 mm. Inner surface dingy white to buff, with a few violet-black dots. Outer surface dingy white to buff. On cowpats and rabbit droppings.
In Britain, more than 25 species of the genus *Ascobolus* occur.

VR Sa ♀

Ascobolus albidus

Lasiobolus papillatus (L. ciliatus)

Fr bowl- to flattened disc-shaped, ⌀ 0.5-0.8 mm. Inner surface dingy yellow to dingy orange-yellow. Outer surface with sparse, pale

yellow hairs protruding far over the margin, dingy orange-yellow. On dung of cows, horses, sheep and deer.

R Sa ♀

Lasiobolus papillatus

Iodophanus carneus

Fr capitate to flattened cushion-shaped, ⌀ 1-2 mm. Inner surface rough, flesh-pink to watery orange. Outer surface flesh to watery orange. Common on manure, also on rotting fibres (sisal, cotton).
Spring to autumn.

Sa ♀

Iodophanus carneus

Pyronema domesticum

Fr capitate to cushion-shaped, ⌀ 0.5-1 mm. Inner and outer surface whitish to salmon or orange-red.

On fire sites and on steamed soil used in greenhouses.
In clustering groups on a white hyphal mat. Spring to autumn.

Also *P. omphalodes* (R)

R Sa ♀

Pyronema domesticum

Sarcoscypha coccinea

SCARLET ELF CUP

Fr bowl- to cup-shaped, ∅ 1-5 cm. Inner surface vermillion to bright red. Outer surface whitish floccose-clayey, occasionally with a deep-rooting stem, dingy flesh to red. **St** felty, white. **Fl** tough.
On buried branches (alder, willow) and decayed wood of broad-leaved trees in broad-

Sarcoscypha coccinea

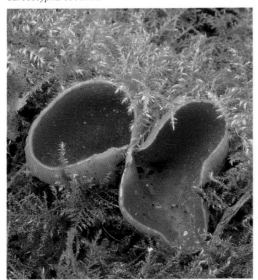

leaved woods on damp, rich soil. February to April.Only by microscopic features can this species be distinguished from *S. austriaca* (R RDL), occurring on the same substrate, and from *S. jurana* (VR RDL), occurring on branches of lime trees.

VR RDL Sa

Tuber rufum

Fr regularly globose to somewhat lobed, ∅ 2-4 cm. Outer surface felty to smooth, with felty patches at the base, straw-colour to rusty brown. **Fl** firm, white to cream, marbled with white veins, purplish grey to chocolate-brown when ripe. **Sm** faintly nutty to disagreeably sourish. **Ta** sharp, nutty.
Often partially sunk into humus, in moderately damp, rich, often calcareous clay and sandy soil, especially near broad-leaved trees (oak, beech, hazel).
In Britain, 15 species of truffle of the genus *Tuber* occur.

R M ⊕

Tuber rufum

Elaphomyces muricatus

Fr regularly globose to irregularly bulbous, ∅ 2-5 cm. Outer surface with fairly large, rather pointed warts, with a gluey crust of sand, humus and root-hair, light yellow-brown to dark rusty brown. **Fl** hard and tough, grey-pink to purplish black-brown, marbled with yellowish white veins.
Fairly close to the surface in a thin layer of litter of broad-leaved trees (oak, beech, hornbeam, birch), occasionally coniferous

trees (spruce), on poor, acid to calcareous sandy soil. Often attacked by *Cordyceps*.

Also *E. granulatus* (R RDL) and *E. maculatus* (VR RDL).

In addition, In Britain, 15 truffle species belonging to the genera *Genea*, *Hydnobolites*, *Hydnotria*, *Stephensia*, *Pachyphloes* and *Balsamia* occur.

R RDL M

Elaphomyces muricatus

Ascocorticium anomalum

Leotiales (Helotiales)

A group of earth tongues and smooth or externally hairy cup-shaped and disc-shaped fungi (discomycetes), both with and without stem, showing a rich variety of shapes and species.

They have inoperculate asci (sacs without a lid), the top usually rupturing at the centre.

Ascocorticium anomalum

Fr a very thin layer often forming fused blotches, ⌀ 0.5-1 cm. Upper surface mealy pruinose, dull white to dark blue-grey.
Common on the inner surface of loose or fallen bark of coniferous trees.

Sa ♀

Trichoglossum hirsutum

Fr spatula- to club-shaped, 3-8 cm high. Upper part broad spatula-shaped to tongue-shaped, bilaterally compressed, with two or more longitudinal grooves, clearly separate from the stem, matt black-brown to black. **St** densely

covered with fine hairs, matt black, 2-6 x 2-4 mm.

Not uncommon on the ground in (dune) grasslands on sand deficient in lime, sand valleys and peat moors, occasionally on damp, rich clay in broad-leaved woods.

RDL Sa

Trichoglossum hirsutum

Geoglossum glutinosum

Fr club-shaped, 3-6 cm high. Upper part widening to 5 mm, greasy-glutinous, shiny black. **St** greasy, shiny black, 2-4 cm x 2-3 mm.

Geoglossum glutinosum

Not uncommon on dry sand in unmanured or sparsely manured grasslands and roadsides, in damp sand valleys and on rich clay in broad-leaved woods.

RL SA

Geoglossum umbratile
(G. nigritum)

Fr tongue- or cup-shaped, 4-10 cm high. Upper part widening to 8 mm, finely clayey, matt grey-black to black, distinct from the

Geoglossum umbratile

stem. **St** clayey or finely scaly, matt brown-black to black, 2-6 cm x 2-7 mm.

Not uncommon on dry sand deficient in lime in unmanured or hardly manured (dune) grasslands and roadsides, in peat bogs and marshland and in woods on dry or damp, poor sandy soil.

In Britain, 11 species of earth tongues of the genus *Geoglossum (Thuemenidium)* occur.

RDL Sa

Leotia lubrica

JELLY BABIES

Fr with cap and stem, 3-6 cm high. **C** 1-2 cm wide, convex with inrolled, irregularly lobed margin, gelatinous. Upper surface greasy, green-yellow to greenish olive brown.
St finely clayey, ochre with fine, greenish granules, 2-4 cm x 3-8 mm. Fairly common on poor, loamy or loam-free sandy soil or rich clay or sand in broad-leaved and mixed woods and avenues.

RDL Sa M

Leotia lubrica

Microglossum viride

Fr tongue- to club-shaped, 3-6 cm high. Upper part widening to 7 mm, flattened with longitudinal grooves, distinct from the stem, matt to shiny olivaceous green.
St flattened with longitudinal grooves, finely clayey, blue-green to yellow-green, 2-3 cm x 2-4 mm.

On dry and damp, loamy sandy soil in mixed woods and along brooks.

VR RDL Sa

Microglossum viride

Mitrula paludosa

Fr with stem, capitate to club-shaped, 2-5 cm high. **C** round to club-shaped, egg-yellow to orange-red. **St** smooth with white hairs at the base, white to faintly pink, 1-2 cm x 1-3 mm.

On leaves and needles submerged in water in

Mitrula paludosa

(poor) mud flats and source areas, peat bogs, marshland and marshy woodlands. Spring to autumn.

VR RDL Sa

Sclerotinia trifoliorum

Fr a small disc up to 3 cm high, with stem, ∅ 4-8 mm. Inner surface pale yellow-brown. Outer surface yellow-brown.
St yellow-brown.
On, and usually with a black **sclerotium** in stems and roots of *Papilionaceae* (clover).

R Pa ♀

Stromatinia rapulum

Fr chalice- to cup-shaped, ∅ 1-3 cm. Inner surface hazel to dark brown. Outer surface dark brown, deep-rooting. **St** brown.

On rhizomes of Polygonatum odoratum on calcareous sand on the edge of woods and in shrubberies and grasslands in sand dunes. April to May.

Sclerotinia trifoliorum

Also *Dumontinia tuberosa* or *Sclerotinia tuberosa* on the rhizomes of wood anemone.

R Pa

Stromatinia rapulum

Monilinia johnsonii

Fr cup- to saucer-shaped, ⌀ 4-9 mm. Inner surface pale brown. Outer surface pale brown to reddish brown, deep-rooting. **St** brown. On mummified (buried) haws on calcareous soil in dune scrub and along the edge of woods. Imperfect stage on hawthorn foliage. March to April.

R Pa ⚲

Monilinia johnsonii

Ciboria batschiana

Fr saucer-shaped to flattened, ⌀ 0.5-1.5 cm. Inner surface cinnamon to brown. Outer surface finely downy, cinnamon to brown, with stem. **St** dark brown with black-brown base.
Common on fallen, blackened acorns in woods and avenues on dry, sandy soils.

Sa

Ciboria batschiana

Ciboria amentacea

Fr cup- to saucer-shaped, ⌀ 3-10 mm. Inner surface creamy ochre to ochraceous brown. Outer surface faintly pruinose, with white-ciliate, appendiculate margin, ochrous brown, with (long) stem. **St** light brown. Common on mummified (buried) male alder catkins in damp woods and shrubberies. February to April.

Sa ⚲

Ciboria amentacea

Rutstroemia echinophila

Fr cup-shaped to flattened saucer-shaped, ⌀ 2-10 mm. Inner surface matt, yellow-brown to chestnut. Outer surface with somewhat dentate margin, ochrous brown, with stem. **St** ochrous brown with dark base. On (the inside of) shells of sweet chestnut on poor, sandy or loamy soils in broad-leaved woods and parks. Often in groups.

VR Sa ⚲

Rutstroemia echinophila

Poculum firmum (Rutstroemia firma)

Fr cup- to saucer-shaped, ∅ 0.5-1 cm. Inner surface olive brown to red-brown. Outer surface olive brown to red-brown, with stem. Common on fallen, lightly decayed branches of oak and alder in broad-leaved and mixed woods, parks and avenues.
Spring to autumn.

In Britain, 26 species of the genera *Ciboria*, *Poculum* and *Rutstroemia* occur.

Sa ♀

Poculum firmum

Neobulgaria pura f. pura

Fr top- to disc-shaped, gelatinous, ∅ 1-3 cm. Inner surface white to pinkish ochre with lilac tinge. Outer surface scaly, flesh-pink.

On dead trunks and branches of beech (occasionally birch and elm) on all kinds of

Neobulgaria pura f. pura

soil in broad-leaved and mixed woods. Often in crowded groups.

Sa

Ascotremella faginea

Fr brain-like convoluted globose, ∅ 2-5 cm. Outer surface matt when dry, shiny when damp, pink to violet-brown.
Fl gelatinous, tough, pink. Not uncommon on thick branches and fallen trunks of beech (occasionally ash, alder) on damp, rich soil in broad-leaved woods. Summer to autumn.

Sa

Ascotremella faginea

Ascocoryne sarcoides

Fr top- to disc-shaped, ∅ 0.5-2 cm. Inner surface flesh-pink to violet-pink. Outer surface finely white-clayey when dry, violet-

Ascocoryne sarcoides

pink. Mostly found in the shiny, purple to purple-brown, capitate to cushion-shaped, imperfect stage *(Pirobasidium sarcoides)*. Common on dead wood of broad-leaved and coniferous trees.

Also *A. cyclichnium*, which can only distinguished from this species by microscopic features.

Sa

Ascocoryne sarcoides

Bulgaria inquinans

BLACK BULGAR

Fr top- to disc-shaped, ∅ 1-4 cm. Inner surface matt when dry, shiny brown-black to black when damp. Outer surface clayey-floccose, with somewhat protruding margin, dark brown to black. **Fl** ochrous brown. Fairly common on bark. Rupturing the bark of recently cut trunks and fallen branches of oak and beech in broad-leaved and mixed woods. Often in groups.

Sa

Bisporella citrina

Fr flattened cup- to disc-shaped, ∅ 1-3 mm. Inner surface lemon-yellow to golden yellow. Outer surface somewhat darker at the margin, golden yellow.

Common on dead branches and trunks of broad-leaved trees (beech, ash). In close groups. Summer to autumn.

Sa ♀

Bulgaria inquinans

Bisporella citrina

Bisporella sulfurina

Fr flattened cup- to saucer-shaped, ∅ 0.5-1.5 mm. Inner surface sulphur-yellow. Outer surface finely felty, pale sulphur-yellow. Common on or near crust-like Sphaeriales on dead wood of broad-leaved trees. Scattered or in groups.

Sa ♀

Bisporella sulfurina

Cudoniella acicularis

Fr top-shaped with stem, 5-10 mm high. **C** disc- to cushion-shaped, ∅ 1-4 mm. Upper surface white. Lower surface with incurved margin, white to dull white. **St** dull white with grey-brown base. Fairly common on decayed trunks and stumps of broad-leaved trees, favouring oak.

Sa ♀

Cudoniella clavus var. *clavus*

Fr top-shaped with (long) stem, 1-2 cm high. **C** disc- to cushion-shaped, ∅ 4-10 mm. Upper surface dull white to ochraceous white, occasionally with violet tinge. Lower surface dull ochraceous white. **St** dull ochraceous white to white-grey, with brown-black base, up to 2 cm long. Not uncommon, often on the underside of wet stumps, fallen, (mossy) trunks and branches of broad-leaved trees, occasionally on leaves and herbaceous stems. May to June.

Sa ♀

Cudoniella clavus var. *clavus*

*Hymenoscyphus calyculus*EN

Fr cup-shaped to flattened saucer-shaped with stem, up to 1 cm high, ∅ 2-3 mm. Inner surface lemon-yellow to ochrous yellow. Outer surface finely floccose, whitish to white-yellow. **St** white-yellow with tapering base.

Cudoniella acicularis

Common on fallen branches of broad-leaved trees, favouring alder. In groups

Sa ♀

Hymenoscyphus calyculus

Hymenoscyphus salicinus (*H.conscriptus*)

Fr flattened cup- to saucer-shaped, ⌀ 4-7 mm. Inner surface ochraceous yellow to egg-yellow. Outer surface smooth, whitish yellow. **St** whitish, hairy at the base. Common on branches, twigs and wounds on the trunks of broad-leaved trees, favouring willow (also alder, poplar).

Also young *Xylaria hypoxylon*.

Sa ♀

Hymenoscyphus salicinus

Hymenoscyphus fructigenus

Fr cup-shaped to flattened saucer-shaped, ⌀ 1-4 mm. Inner surface white-yellow to whitish ochrous yellow.

Outer surface whitish yellow, with stem. **St** whitish yellow.
Common on acorns, beech and hornbeam mast and shells, hazelnuts and alder cones.

Sa ♀

Hymenoscyphus fructigenus

Calycina herbarum (*Hymenoscyphus herbarum*)

Fr cup- to saucer-shaped, ⌀ 2-4 mm. Inner surface creamy yellow to ochrous yellow. Outer surface finely felty, light yellow, with short stem. Common on herbaceous stems, especially of stinging nettles, occasionally on branches or on fallen leaves.

In Britain, 50 species of the genera *Hymenoscyphus*, *Calycina* and *Cyathicula* occur.

Sa

Calycina herbarum

Calycina herbarum

Pezizella alniella

Fr top- to disc-shaped, ∅ 0.3-0.7 mm. Inner surface cream to pale yellow. Outer surface mealy pruinose, cream. Common on (parts of) fallen, lignified alder cones in woods on rich soils. Winter to spring.

In Britain, 32 species of the genus *Pezizella* occur, on catkins, ferns, grass, plants, needles and branches.

Sa ♀

Pezizella alniella

Chlorociboria aeruginacens (chlorosplenium aeruginacens)

GREEN WOOD-CUP

Fr cup-shaped to irregularly saucer-shaped, ∅ 2-5 mm. Inner surface blue-green, with yellow blotches. Outer surface finely clayey,

whitish to blue-green, with stem. On dead branches of oak and other broad-leaved trees in broad-leaved and mixed woods.

Also *C. aeruginosa* (VR), distinguished from this species only by microscopic features

R Sa ♀

Chlorociboria aeruginascens

Encoelia furfuracea

Fr closed, like a bladder when young, opening star-like and becoming irregularly cup- to saucer-shaped, ∅ 0.5-1.5 cm. Inner surface cinnamon to dark brown. Outer surface clayey-floccose, pale brown.
On dead, attached and fallen branches of hazel (and alder). In dense clusters, December to March.

Also *E. fascicularis* (R).

R Sa ♀

Encoelia furfuracea

Polydesmia pruinosa

Fr top-shaped to flattened cushion-shaped, ⌀ 0.3-0.5 mm. Inner surface mealy pruinose, white. Outer surface finely felty, white.

Common on and near Sphaeriales on branches of broad-leaved trees. Autumn to winter.

Sa ♀

Polydesmia pruinosa

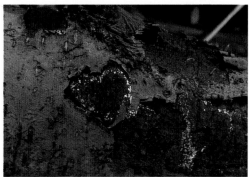

Albotricha acutipila
(Dasyscyphus acutipilus)

Fr cup-shaped, ⌀ 0.5-1 mm. Inner surface whitish to white-yellow. Outer surface and margin covered with white hairs, often with

colourless droplets, with short stem. Fairly common on reed stems and grasses, especially in reed-land (flood-marks).
Summer to autumn. In groups.

Sa ♀

Trichopeziza mollissima
(Dasyscyphus mollissimus)

Fr cup- to saucer-shaped, ⌀ 0.5-2 mm. Inner surface grey-white. Outer surface and margin closely covered with pale yellow to golden yellow hairs. On dead stems of *Umbelliferae*

Trichopeziza mollissima

Albotricha acutipila

(cow parsley, hogweed) in nutrient-rich biotopes.

R Sa ♀

Trichopeziza sericea
(Dasyscyphus sericeus)

Fr flattened saucer-shaped, ∅ 1-3 mm. Inner surface whitish, with dark green or blue-green blotches. Outer surface and margin with white hairs, dark green or blue-green, with short stem. On stumps of oak.

VR Sa ♀

Trichopeziza sericea

Dasyscyphella nivea
(Dasyscyphus niveus)

Fr cup- to saucer-shaped, ∅ 0.5-2 mm. Inner surface white to cream. Outer surface and margin closely covered with white hairs,

Dasyscyphella nivea

white, with long stem. Common on dead wood and bark of broad-leaved trees, favouring oak (also hornbeam, hazel, willow). Throughout the year.

This species can only be distinguished from *Lachnum virgineum* by microscopic features.

Sa ♀

Lachnum virgineum
(Dasyscyphus virgineus)

Fr cup- to saucer-shaped, ∅ 0.5-1 mm. Inner surface (translucent) white to cream. Outer surface and margin closely covered with white hairs, white, with stem. Margin often with colourless droplets.
Common on dead wood, herbaceous stems, pine cones and leaves. In groups. Spring to autumn.

In Britain, 20 species of the genera *Albotrica, Cistella, Dasyscyphella, Lachnum, Lasiobelonium* and *Trichopeziza* occur.

Sa ♀

Lachnum virgineum

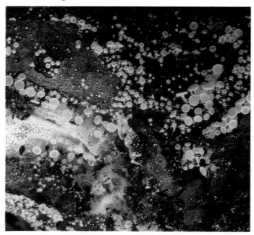

Lachnellula occidentalis
(L. hahniana)

Fr cup- to saucer-shaped, ∅ 1-5 mm. Inner surface egg-yellow to orange. Outer surface and margin closely covered with white hairs, with short stem. On branches and twigs of larch.

R Sa ♀

Lachnellula occidentalis

Lachnellula willkommii

Fr cup- to saucer-shaped, ∅ 1-5 mm. Inner surface egg-yellow to orange. Outer surface and margin closely covered with white hairs, with short stem. On branches of larch and on or near tumours on larch *(Larix decidua)*.

This species can only be distinguished from *Lachnellula occidentalis* by microscopic features. Also *L. calyciformis* and *L. subtilissima* on larch.

R Pa ♀

Lachnellula willkommii

Arachnopeziza aranea
(Arachnoscypha aranea)

Fr cup- to saucer-shaped, ∅ 0.2-0.3 mm. Inner surface white-yellow. Outer surface with pointed, colourless hairs at the margin, white. Grows scattered on a colourless, cobweb-like hyphal mat. On the inside of sweet chestnut shells.
In Britain, 6 white, white-yellow or yellow species of the genus *Arachnopeziza* occur.

VR Sa ♀

Arachnopeziza aranea

Orbilia alnea (O. xanthostigma)

Fr flattened saucer-shaped, ⌀ 0.5-1 mm. Inner surface golden yellow to orange-yellow. Outer surface orange-yellow to orange-red, waxily translucent when damp. Common on decaying, damp wood of broad-leaved trees. In groups. Summer to autumn.

Mollisia cinerea also occurs.

Sa ♀

Orbilia alnea

Catinella olivacea

Fr flattened saucer-shaped, ⌀ 0.5-1.5 cm. Inner surface olivaceous black to olivaceous brown. Outer surface mealy-clayey, dark brown to black-brown, with finely furrowed, dingy ochraceous yellow to olive green margin. On wet, rotting trunks and stumps of willow and poplar in shrubberies and copses. Summer to autumn.

R Sa

Catinella olivacea

Orbilia sarraziniana

Fr top-shaped to flattened saucer-shaped, ⌀ 0.3-0.8 mm. Inner surface dull pink. Outer surface dull pink, glassily translucent. On dead wood or broad-leaved trees. In groups. Summer to autumn.
In Britain, 20 species of the genus *Orbilia* occur.

R Sa ♀

Orbilia sarraziniana

Mollisia cinerea

Fr cup-shaped to irregularly saucer-shaped, ⌀ 0.5-2 mm. Inner surface grey to grey-blue. Outer surface finely floccose, grey-brownish, with whitish margin. Common on dead, decayed wood of broad-leaved trees. In groups. Spring to autumn (see also photograph of *Orbilia alnea*).

Sa ♀

Mollisia cinerea

Mollisia ventosa

Fr cup-shaped to flattened cushion-shaped, ∅ 0.5-1.5 mm. Inner surface yellowish to dull ochrous yellow. Outer surface yellowish brown. On dead trunks, stumps and branches of broad-leaved trees (alder, beech).
R Sa ♀

Mollisia ventosa

Mollisia rosae

Fr cup- to saucer-shaped, ∅ 0.5-1.5 mm. Inner surface dark grey to nearly black. Outer surface downy-floccose, brown-black. Grows on a web of black-brown filaments.
On woody parts of roses and sloe. In dense clusters.

In Britain, 62 species of the genera *Mollisia (Tapesia)* and *Mollisiopsis* occur.

R Sa ♀

Mollisia rosae

Calloria neglecta
(Callorina fusarioides)

Fr disc- to lens-shaped, ∅ 0.5-1 mm. Inner and outer surface rough, orange. Flesh soft. On dead stems of stinging nettles. In groups. Spring.

Sa ♀

Calloria neglecta

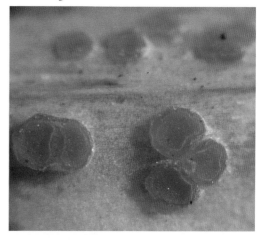

Rhytismatales

A small group including among others the species of the genus *Rhytisma,* which cause 'tar-spot' disease on leaves.

Rhytisma acerinum

Fr stroma irregularly, flattened cushion-shaped, ∅ 1-2 cm. Outer surface veined and

Mollisia rosae

black. **Fl** ochraceous grey. Common on maple leaves.

Sa

Rhytisma acerinum

Rhytisma salicinum

Fr stroma elongate, flattened cushion-shaped, thin, 1-2 x 0.5 cm. Outer surface veined, black. On willow leaves.

VR Sa

Rhytisma salicinum

Hypoderma rubi

Fr breaking partly through the stem surface, spindle-shaped, with tapering ends, 1-2 x 0.5-1 mm. Outer surface shiny black, splitting longitudinally to show brown contents. On dead bramble stems.

R Sa ♀

Lophodermium arundinaceum

Fr elongate, acutely spindle-shaped, breaking through a longitudinal split in the stem surface, 0.4-0.8 x 0.2-0.4 mm. Outer surface black, splitting longitudinally. Common on dead reed stems. Summer.

Sa ♀

Lophodermium arundinaceum

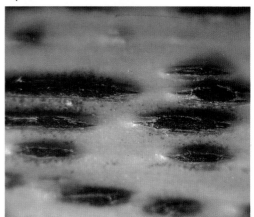

Clavicipetales

A group of highly specialized, parasytic Ascomycetes. Perithecia in a stroma on a globose or club-shaped part with a separate stem.

Sclerotia Claviceps microcephala

Sclerotia protruding beak-like from the inflorescences, longitudinally grooved, brown-black to black, 0.5-1.5 cm x 2-3 mm. Common

Hypoderma rubi

on the seeds of grasses such as purple moor-grass and reed.

Pa ♀

Sclerotia Claviceps microcephala

Claviceps purpurea

ERGOT

Fr develops from a slereotium fallen on the ground. **C** globose, Ø 1.5-3 mm, ochrous yellow to orange-yellow, dotted with dark ostioles. **St** reddish brown, 5-15 x 1-1.5 mm. Often several specimens on a **sclerotium.** On grasses (rye-grass) and grains (rye). May to July.

R Pa ♀

Claviceps purpurea

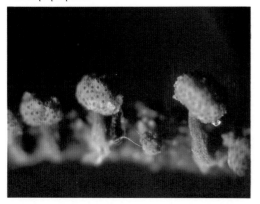

Cordyceps militaris

SCARLET CATERPILLAR FUNGUS

Fr tongue- to club-shaped, 2-6 x 0.5-1 cm. **C** widened, finely warty, orange to orange-yellow. **St** pale orange to ochrous yellow. Fairly common on butterfly pupae in moderately manured or unmanured grasslands, broad-leaved or mixed woods and avenues on poor, dry sandy or loamy soil, often among Rhytidiadelphus spp.
Pa

Cordyceps militaris

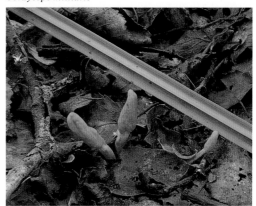

Cordyceps longisegmentis (C. canadensis)

Fr club-shaped with oval to round head, 3-10 cm high. **C** globose, warty, chestnut to black. **St** tough, yellow to light olive green, 2-8 x 0.5-1 cm.
On *Elaphomyces* in broad-leaved and mixed woods.

R RDL Pa

Cordyceps longisegmentis

Cordyceps ophioglossoides

Fr tongue- to club-shaped, 4-8 cm high. **C** widened, warty, olive brown to red-brown to black. **St** matt, brownish, yellowish towards the base, 3-6 cm x 4-8 mm, with yellow mycelium strands.

On *Elaphomyces* in broad-leaved and coniferous woods and parks.

R RDL Pa

Cordyceps ophioglossoides

Hypocreales

Species with strikingly coloured perithecia, solitary, clustering or embedded in a stroma.

Hypocrea aureoviridis

Fr cushion-shaped, ⌀ 0.5-1 cm. Upper surface yellow to pale yellow, dotted green when ripe. Lower surface matt, whitish to white-yellow. **Fl** firm, white.

On trunks and branches of broad-leaved trees.

Sa ♀

Hypocrea citrina

Fr crust-like, ⌀ from a few square centimetres to several square decimetres. Upper surface creamy yellow to lemon-yellow, evenly dotted

Hypocrea aureoviridis

Hypocrea citrina

dark yellow (like semolina pudding) and with irregular, white margin.

Often growing on pieces of rotting wood and stumps, often covering and enclosing leaves and mosses.

R Sa

Hypocrea nigricans f. nigricans

Fr cushion-shaped, ⌀ 0.5-1 cm. Upper surface black-brown to black. Lower surface black.

Fl whitish to light grey. On rotting specimens of *Polyporus badius*.

VR Sa ♀

Hypocrea nigricans f. nigricans

Hypocrea pulvinata

Fr cushion-shaped, round to irregularly oval, often fused, ⌀ 0.5-2 cm. Upper surface rough, matt ochrous yellow to pale brown. Mostly occurring as the more common, pruinose, imperfect form.

Hypocrea citrina

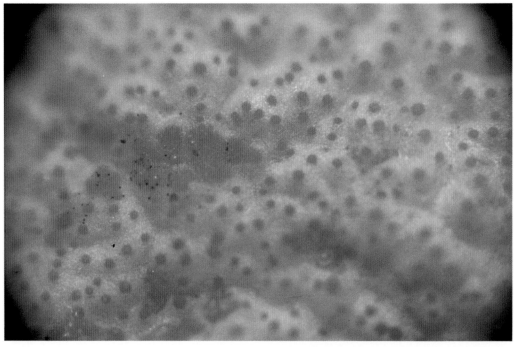

On the tube layer of old specimens of birch polypore *(Piptoporus betulinus)* (lying on the ground).

Sa

Hypocrea pulvinata

Hypocrea rufa

Fr irregularly cushion-shaped, ∅ 0.5-1 cm. Upper surface red-brown, dotted dark brown. Lower surface and margin whitish. **Fl** white. Occasionally clustered.
Often preceded by, or occurring together with, an imperfect form, the green mould *Trichoderma viride*. Common on rotting wood of broad-leaved trees.

Also *H. schweinitzii* (VR).

Sa ♀

Hypocrea rufa

Hypocreopsis lichenoides

Fr a rosette-shaped wrinkled crust, ∅ 3-10 cm. Upper surface matt, yellow-brown to reddish brown. Lower surface pale yellow-brown.

On still attached dead branches (overhanging water) or on slanting trunks of willow and birch in damp shrubberies.

VR RDL Sa

Hypocreopsis lichenoides

Creopus gelatinosus

Fr spherical to cushion-shaped, ∅ 1-3 mm. Upper surface watery creamy white to pale yellow, dotted green when ripe. Lower surface felty at the base. **Fl** gelatinous, translucent.
On trunks, stumps, branches and twigs of broad-leaved trees. Growing in clusters. Autumn to spring.

VR Sa ♀

Creopus gelatinosus

Hypomyces viridis (Peckiella viridis)

Fr spherical with papilla, ∅ 0.2-0.3 mm, in dense clusters in a crust of a few square centimetres. **Perithecia** olive yellow with olivaceous green papilla, embedded halfway in a yellow-greenish hyphal mat.

On *Russula* and *Lactarius*.

Also *H. lateritius* (VR) on gills of *Lactarius*.

VR Pa ♀

Hypomyces viridis

Hypomyces aurantius

Fr spherical with papilla, ∅ 0.3-0.4 mm, in dense clusters of a few square centimetres. **Perithecia** orange to orange-yellow, embed-

Hypomyces aurantius

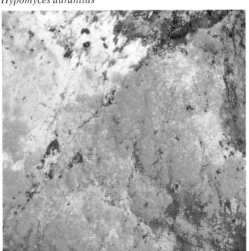

ded in a golden yellow to pale orange hyphal mat.
On old fruiting bodies of polypores and of the genus *Pleurotus*.

R Pa ♀

Hypomyces aurantius

Hypomyces rosellus

Fr spherical to pyramid-shaped with papilla, ∅ 0.1-0.2 mm, scattered on a cruSt of a few square centimetres. **Perithecia** pink-red, on hyphal mat that is white at first, rapidly becoming pink.
On old specimen of *Stereum* and *Polyporus* species, or (from the thoroughly rotted substrate) on mosses or rotting wood on the ground.

R Pa ♀

Hypomyces rosellus

Nectria cinnabarina

CORAL SPOT FUNGUS

Fr spherical to oval with papilla, ∅ 0.2-0.4 mm. **Perithecia** rough, scarlet to brown-red, breaking through the bark in raspberry-like groups. Often together with the pale orange-pink, cushion-shaped imperfect stage *Tubercularia vulgaris*. Common on (living and) dead branches of trees in woods, parks and public gardens.

Sa (Pa) ♀

Nectria cinnabarina

Nectria coccinea

Fr spherical to pear-shaped with papilla, ∅ 0.2-0.3 mm. **Perithecia** smooth, scarlet with dark papilla, solitary on bare wood, or breaking through the bark in groups. On the bark of broad-leaved trees (beech, poplar, elm, maple).

Nectria coccinea

Causes a disease in combination with attack by scale insect *Cryptococcus fagi*.

R Pa ♀

Nectria episphaeria

Fr spherical with papilla, ∅ 0.1-0.2 mm. **Perithecia** smooth, translucent, orange-red to red.

Common on *Diatrype* and *Hypoxylon* species and cancers of beech.

Pa? ♀

Nectria episphaeria

Nectria peziza

Fr spherical, top slightly depressed, with sunken papilla, ∅ 0.2-0.4 mm. **Perithecia** smooth, yellow to orange-brown. In clustering

Nectria peziza

groups. Fairly common on wood, occasionally on bark, on the ground, or on rotting polypores *(Polyporus squamosus)*.
In Britain, more than 64 species of the genus *Nectria* occur.

Sa ♀

Sordariales

A small group of species with dark or black perithecia, occurring solitary or in groups on or in the substrate (wood, plant debris, manure).

Lasiosphaeria ovina

Fr spherical with papilla, ⌀ 0.4-0.6 mm. **Perithecia** black, covered with a dingy white hyphal fur, leaving the black papilla free. In groups. Not uncommon on rotting wood of broad-leaved trees.

Sa ♀

Lasiosphaeria ovina

Trichosphaeriales

Chaetosphaerella phaeostroma

Fr spherical, ⌀ 0.2-0.5 mm. **Perithecia** rough, black, clustered on or embedded in a black hairy hyphal mat. Not uncommon on thick branches of broad-leaved trees (see also microphotograph in Chapter 1).

Sa ♀

Diatrypales

Diatrype bullata

Fr oval cushion-shaped, ⌀ 4-8 mm, rupturing the bark. Upper surface rough, evenly covered with papillae, brown-black to grey-black. **Stroma** white. On dead willow branches in damp shrubberies. Winter to spring.

R Sa ♀

Diatrype bullata

Diatrype disciformis

Fr 4- to 6-angled cushion-shaped, ⌀ 3-5 mm, rupturing the bark. Upper surface rough, evenly covered with papillae, brown-black to

Chaetosphaerella phaeostroma

grey-black. **Stroma** white. On dead beech branches.

Sa ♀

Diatrype disciformis

Diatrype stigma

Fr crust-like, ∅ from a few square centimetres to several square decimetres, spreads under the bark, and casts off the bark. Upper surface rough, evenly covered with small papillae, with a pattern of longitudinal splits and transverse cracks, black. **Stroma** creamy white.
Common on thick branches and trunks of broad-leaved trees (beech).

Sa

Diatrype stigma

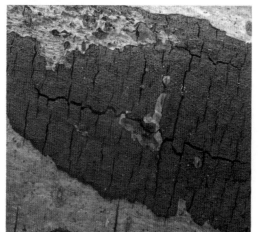

Diatrypella quercina

Fr globose cushion-shaped, ∅ 2-4 mm, rupturing the bark. Upper surface warty, papillae hardly discernible, black. **Stroma** white to light brown.

Common on dead branches, favouring oak.

Sa ♀

Diatrypella quercina

Peroneutypa heteracantha (Eutypella scoparia)

Fr bottle-shaped with long neck, ∅ 0.5-1 mm. **Perithecia** black, 2 to 8 of them together with long necks, among a few long brown hairs, breaking through the bark from a stroma. **Stroma** black.
On branches of broad-leaved trees (elm, alder). Winter to spring.

R Sa ♀

Peroneutypa heteracantha

Sphaeriales

A group of perithecial fungi, numbering a great many species, growing solitary or embedded in a stroma.
The ascospores are dark brown with an elongate germ-slit.

Hypoxylon fragiforme

Fr cushion-shaped, ∅ 4-10 mm, cinnamon to brick-red, later brown to black, rough, evenly

Hypoxylon fragiforme

Anamorf *Hypoxylon howeianum*

covered with with papillae. **Stroma** hard, brown-black to black.
Common on dead, thick branches and lying trunks of beech.

Sa ♀

Anamorf *Hypoxylon howeianum*

Fr cushion-shaped, ∅ 2-4 mm, red-brown to brown-black, rough, evenly covered with papillae. Occasionally growing on and among a root-like structure, the imperfect *Geniculosporium* stage.
Common on dead branches of broad-leaved trees. Winter to spring.

The teleomorph can only be distinguished from small specimens of *H. fragiforme* by microscopic features.

Sa ♀

Hypoxylon fuscum

Fr cushion-shaped, evenly pitted, ∅ 4-6 mm, red-brown, looks smooth due to inconspicuous papillae. **Stroma** hard, dark brown.

Common on branches of broad-leaved trees (alder, hazel).

Sa ♀

Hypoxylon fuscum

Hypoxylon multiforme

Fr elongate, rounded cushion-shaped, 2-6 x 1-3 cm, rusty brown to black, regularly undulate lumpy, with papillae.

Common on thick branches and dead trunks, favouring birch.

Sa

Hypoxylon multiforme

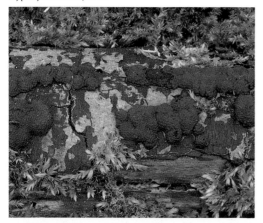

Hypoxylon rubiginosum

Fr elongate, plane, wrinkled crust-like, 5-15 x 2-5 cm, brick-red to wine red, later ochrous brown to rusty brown to black. **Stroma** ochre

to yellow-brown, exuding black droplets when damaged. On thick branches and lying trunks of broad-leaved trees from which the bark has been partly removed (see also photograph of perithecia in Chapter 1).

R Sa

Hypoxylon rubiginosum

Hypoxylon serpens

Fr irregularly winding, flattened crust-like, ∅ 1-2 x 2-4 cm, black, evenly covered with papillae. **Stroma** pallid when young. On thick branches and trunks of broad-leaved trees from which the bark has been removed.
In Britain, 18 species of the genus *Hypoxylon* occur.

R Sa

Hypoxylon serpens

Ustulina deusta

Fr irregularly crust-like, ∅ up to many square decimetres, mealy pruinose when young, light bluish grey with white growth zone, later dark grey to black, covered with scattered papillae. Perennial **stroma** black, crumbly.

Causes soft rot. At the base of the stem and on the main roots of living broad-leaved trees, favouring beech and lime, often down to below ground level, also saprophytic on remaining stumps.

Pa (Sa) ♀

Ustulina deusta

Ustulina deusta

Daldinia concentrica

KING ALFRED'S CRAMP BALLS OR
KING ALFRED'S CAKES

Fr wrinkled spherical to cushion-shaped, 2-6 x 1-3 cm. Outer surface smooth, with indistinct papillae, red-brown to black. When cut vertically, concentric circles are visible, alternately with a silvery shine and black. Fairly common

on dead branches and dead parts of trunks of broad-leaved trees, favouring ash, in broad-leaved woods, parks and ash coppice.
Also the smaller *D. vernicosa* on sites of fires on heaths or peat moors.

Sa

Daldinia concentrica

Xylaria hypoxylon

CANDLE SNUFF

Fr flattened cylindrical to narrowly club-shaped, forked to branched into an antler-shape, 3-7 x 0.5-1 cm. Upper part black, warty with ostioles, March to April with conidia

Xylaria hypoxylon

powdered white. **St** hairy, black. Common on dead branches, wood chips and stumps of broad-leaved trees (for young specimens, see photograph of *Hymenoscyphus salicinus*).

Sa

Xylaria carpophila

Fr flattened cylindrical, forked to filiform branched into antler-shape, 2-6 cm x 2-5 mm. Upper part black, conidia turning it a white to bluish grey April to May. **St** hairy, black.

Not uncommon on beech mast lying in humus or on the ground.

Sa

Xylaria carpophila

Xylaria oxyacanthae

Fr flattened cylindrical to narrowly club-shaped, forked-branched, 2-4 cm x 3-6 mm. Upper part black, conidia turning it white-

Xylaria oxyacanthae

yellow April to May. **St** hairy, black. On haws buried in humus on the edge of woods, in shrubberies (in sand dunes) and in broad-leaved woods.

R Pa

Xylaria polymorpha

DEAD MAN'S FINGERS

Fr club-shaped, 3-8 x 1-3 cm. Upper part warty, brown-black to black. **St** rough or finely pleated, black. **Fl** radially fibrillose, tough, white with black margin.

Common on dead stumps of broad-leaved trees, tufted.

Sa

Xylaria polymorpha

Xylaria longipes

Fr tongue-shaped to narrowly club-shaped, 3-8 x 0.5-1 cm. Upper part finely warty, black. **St** rough, black. **Fl** radially fibrillose, tough, white with thin black margin.

On branches and stumps of maple, plane and ash.

Sa

Xylaria longipes

Rosellinia aquila

Fr spherical with a nipple, ∅ 1-2 mm.
Perithecia dark brown to black, with papilla, usually clustered on a brown, dense hyphal mat.

Fairly common on dead branches of broad-leaved trees (favouring maple), especially on the branches at the bottom of piles of prunings. February to May.

Also *R. mammiformis* and *R. thelena*.

Sa ♀

Rosellinia aquila

Camarops polysperma

Fr flattened cushion-shaped to decurrent crust-like 5-7 x 3-4 mm. Upper surface brown-black to (shiny) black, with papillae.

On rotting trunks of broad-leaved trees (alder).
Also the much smaller, globose *C. microspora* (VR RDL).

VR RDL Sa

Camarops polysperma

Poronia punctata

Fr nail- to top-shaped or flattened bowl-shaped, ∅ 0.5-1.5 cm. Inner surface whitish to creamy yellow, dotted black. Outer surface whitish, with grey margin, **perithecia** clustered, rooting deeply in the substrate. **St** long, black. On horse manure.

Also *P. erici* (R) on rabbit and hare droppings.

R RDL Sa ♀

Poronia punctata

4 Rusts and blights (Teliomycetes)

Rusts and blights belong to the Teliomycetes, a group separate from the Basidiomycetes.

Rusts are parasites of higher plants. They occur primarily on leaves, needles and cones of broad-leaved and coniferous trees, plants and ferns, without, however, killing the host plant. The rust-coloured spores are spread by the wind.

Rusts often require two host plants. The spores of *Puccinia graminis*, for instance, germinate in spring on *Berberis* leaves and penetrate the leaf. After a few days, cup-shaped, 'male' reproductive organs or sperma-gonia with pycniospores (spermatia) appear on the upper surface of the leaf, and on the lower surface 'female' reproductive organs or aecia with receptacular hyphae. The cups exude a sugary liquid containing pycnio-spores, which attracts insects.
The insects transport the spores to the receptacular hyphae. The aeciospores, which are produced after fertilization, are spread by the wind and infect the grain. On the grain, uredinia appear, in which the summer spores or urediospores are formed, which can infect new host plants. In autumn, thick-walled winter spores are formed in so-called telia on the grain. The winter spores overwinter in the soil and in spring form a basidium with basidiospores.

Blights are spread by insects visiting flowers. They render the plant sterile. They develop mainly on the inflorescences, or in and on the reproductive organs and ovaries of plants. In doing this, they are even able to induce the female flowers to form stamens. In Europe several hundreds of species occur. The genus Ustilago is the most common, with over a 100 species on grasses (grains) and herbaceous plants.

Ustilago maydis

Fr a tumour, ∅ up to 10 cm. Whitish, then violet to black. On the inflorescence of maize, where it grows in the place of and at the expense of the reproductive organs.

Pa

Ustilago maydis

Stereum ochraceoflavum, see p. 99

5 Basidomycetes

The very extensive group of *Jelly* fungi, Aphyllophorales, Gasteromycetes, Agarics and Boleti, showing a wide variety of shapes, belongs to the Basidiomycetes.
Jelly fungi (Dacrymycetales, Auriculariales, Tremellales, Exobasidiales)

A group of Phragmobasidiomycetes, most of them with gelatinous fruiting bodies, which have the ability to regenerate after drying by absorption of moisture.

Calocera cornea

Fr cylindrical to awl-shaped, simple or rarely forked, 2-10 x 1-2 mm. Smooth, viscid, shiny egg-yellow to orange-yellow. Common on well decayed branches and trunks of broad-leaved trees. Also *C. furcata* on wood of coniferous trees (R).

Sa ♀

Calocera cornea

Calocera viscosa

Fr from a rooting stem repeatedly branched and forked, coral-shaped, 1-8 cm high. Viscid, egg-yellow to orange-yellow. **Fl** gelatinous,

tough. Common on strongly decayed coniferous stumps and trunks on dry, poor soil.

Sa

Calocera viscosa

Dacrymyces stillatus

Fr drop- or cushion-shaped to flattened cup-shaped, ∅ 2-5 mm. Slimy, gelatinous, yellow to orange-yellow, orange to orange-red when dry. Clustered in groups.

Common on well decayed coniferous (and

Dacrymyces stillatu

broad-leaved) wood, also on processed wood (fence posts, window frames, window sills).

Sa ♀

coniferous branches and trunks still covered with bark.

VR RDL Sa ♀

Femsjonia pezizaeformis

Fr top- to flattened cup-shaped, ∅ 0.5-1 cm. Upper surface bright egg-yellow. Lower surface finely downy, whitish, with pallid marginal zone. **Fl** gelatinous, translucent white, with a white core. On broad-leaved (oak) and

Femsjonia pezizaeformis

Hirneola auricula-judae

JEW'S EAR

Fr protruding or hanging, shell- to ear-shaped, ∅ 2-8 cm. Upper surface attached centrally to the substrate, finely downy, brown-pink to greyish olive brown. Lower surface wrinkled-pleated, red-brown to olive brown, occasionally whitish pruinose with spores. **Fl** gelatinous to dry horn-like. Common on branches and trunks of elder, also on other broad-leaved trees and shrubberies, especially on calcareous soil. Spring to autumn.

Pa (Sa) 🍄

Auricularia mesenterica

TRIPE FUNGUS

Fr resupinate, disc-shaped at first, then more or less bracket-like, with upper surfaces protruding up to 3 cm, ∅ a few square centimetres to several square decimetres. Upper surface

Hirneola auricula-judae

hairy-felty, undulated, with whitish grey and olive brown zones. Lower surface reticulate wrinkled-pleated, purple-brown, occasionally white pruinose with spores. **Fl** gelatinous, rubbery. Not uncommon on trunks and stumps of broad-leaved trees, favouring elm, in broad-leaved woods and parks on rich sandy and clayey soil. (Pa) Sa

Auricularia mesenterica

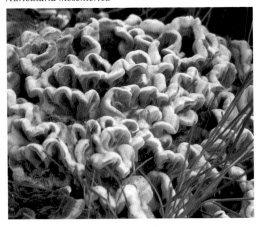

Pseudohydnum gelatinosum

JELLY TONGUE

Fr laterally attached, tongue- or fan-shaped, ⌀ 2-6 cm. Upper surface finely granular-downy, white-grey to blue-grey or green-grey or brownish. Lower surface with whitish to yellowish spines. **Spi** pointed, 3-5 mm. **Fl** translucent, gelatinous. Fairly common on well decayed stumps and trunks of coniferous trees on poor sandy soil.

Sa 🍴

Pseudohydnum gelatinosum

Exidia thuretiana

Fr flattened cushion-shaped to irregularly globose, ⌀ 1-4 cm. Upper surface white to blue-white, occasionally with pink tinge. Lower surface matt, whitish. **Fl** gelatinous, tough, becoming slimy. Fairly common on decayed branches and trunks of broad-leaved trees on moderately damp, rich soil.

Sa

Exidia thuretiana

Exidia plana

Fr complex, gelatinous brain-like, forming a thick, soft crust, 10-30 x 3-5 cm. Outer surface finely warty, shiny or dull, brown-black to black or blue-black. **Fl** 5-15 mm thick, gelatinous, soft.
Common on dead branches of broad-leaved trees (oak), often still attached to the tree. Throughout the year.

Sa

Exidia plana

Exidia truncata

Fr top-shaped to knob-like, ⌀ 1-6 cm. Upper surface matt to shiny, black to brown-black. Lower surface with obtuse spines (stubble), matt, black to brown-black. **Fl** gelatinous, tough.

Common on branches and trunks of broad-leaved trees, favouring oak.

Sa

Exidia truncata

Exidia recisa

Fr top-shaped to flattened saucer-shaped, ⌀ 0.5-3 cm. Upper surface shiny, amber to dark red-brown. Lower surface rough, matt, dark red-brown. **Fl** gelatinous, slightly elastic.

On still attached branches of broad-leaved trees.

VR SA

Exidia recisa

Myxarium nucleatum (M. hyalinum)

Fr irregularly cushion-shaped to spherical, ⌀ 0.5-1 cm. Outer surface slimy, shiny, watery white with pink or violet tinges. **Fl** translucent, with white crystal core of 1-2 mm, often becoming slimy.

Common on branches of broad-leaved trees.

Sa

Myxarium nucleatum

Tremella mesenterica

YELLOW BRAIN FUNGUS

Fr brain-like pleated-lobed, 2-6 x 2-4 cm. Outer surface shiny, pale yellow to golden yellow. **Fl** gelatinous, soft, translucent yellow. Fairly common on branches of broad-leaved trees.

Sa

Tremella mesenterica

Tremella encephala

Fr hemispherical to cushion-shaped, brain-like convoluted, ∅ 1-3 cm. Outer surface shiny, whitish or yellowish to pink-brown. **Fl** gelatinous, translucent, with hard, white core.

Not uncommon on or near fruiting bodies of *Stereum sanguinolentum* on trunks of coniferous trees.

Pa

Tremella encephala

Tremella foliacea

Fr strongly compressed folds to leaf-shaped lobes, 3-10 cm. Outer surface shiny, candy-brown to reddish orange-brown. **Fl** gelatinous, soft.
Fairly common on branches and trunks of broad-leaved trees (birch, oak) in mixed woods on sandy soil.

Sa

Tremella foliacea

Tremiscus helvelloides

Fr ear-shaped to funnel-shaped, 3-10 x 2-5 cm. Inner surface matt, occasionally whitish pruinose, orange-pink to salmon or brown-red. Outer surface smooth, orange-pink to salmon or brown-red. **Fl** gelatinous, elastic (see also photograph on front cover, top right).

VR Sa 🎏

Tremiscus helvelloides

Exobasidium vaccinii

Fr gall bladder-like, ∅ 1-2 cm. Outer surface powdery, matt, whitish to pink-red with yellowish margin. On leaves of *Vaccinium* species in coniferous woods.

In Britain, 6 species of the genus *Exobasidium* occur on *Azalea* and on *Vaccinium* species.

Pa

Exobasidium vaccinii

APHYLLOPHORALES

A group of Holobasidiomycetes exhibiting a wide variety of shapes, with fruiting bodies that are not mushroom-shaped with cap and stem and with gills or tubes, but do have an exposed hymenophore.

Corticiaceae

An extensive group of resupinate, crust-like Basidiomycetes, with smooth, wrinkled, veined, poroid or spiny hymenophores, some of them with reflexed or protruding margins or with shell-shaped, fan-shaped or ear-shaped brackets.

Hyphodontia quercina
(Kneiffiela quercina)

Fr very thin, crust-like, covering a few square centimetres to several square decimetres. Upper surface spiny, cream to creamy yellow. **Spi** awl-shaped, 1-3 mm long. On wood of broad-leaved trees.

R Sa ♀

Hyphodontia quercina

Basidioradulum radula
(Hyphoderma radula)

Fr crust-like, forming round to oval patches of a few square centimetres to several square decimetres. Upper surface spiny, whitish cream to ochraceous yellow, with white, either clearly demarcated or fibrillose margin. **Spi** obtuse to awl-shaped, 3-5 mm long. Fairly common on trunks and branches of broad-leaved trees (birch) in woods with rich soil.

Sa ♀

Basidioradulum radula

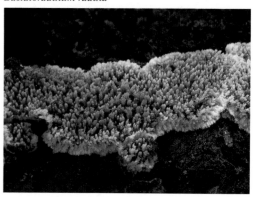

Terana caerulea
(Pulcherricium caeruleum)

Fr thin, round to elongate crust-like, waxy to hard, up to several tens of centimetres in length and a few centimetres in width. Upper surface smooth to lumpy-warty, matt, bright blue to dark blue, later blue-grey to grey-brown, with acute, occasionally felty margin. **Spo** pale blue.
On broad-leaved wood.

VR RDL Sa

Terana caerulea

Cerocorticium confluens

Fr crust-like, waxy, ∅ up to several square decimetres. Upper surface lumpy-warty, smooth, cream to grey-ochre with a hint of blue, with clearly demarcated, often ciliate margin. **Sm** of hospital disinfectants.

Common on wood of broad-leaved trees.

Sa

Cerocorticium confluens

Megalocystidium leucoxanthum (Gloeocystidiellum leucoxanthum)

Fr thick, crust-like, waxy, ∅ up to a few square centimetres. Upper surface lumpy-warty, smooth, cream to yellow-ochre or brown-ochre, with acute or ciliate, more pallid margin. **Spo** white. On dead branches and trunks of poplar and willow.

VR Sa

Megalocystidium leucoxanthum

Cerocorticium molare

Fr thick crust-like, round to elongate, ∅ up to 4 cm. Upper surface spiny, cream to dark ochre, with ciliate margin. **Spi** often with split top, 1-4 mm long.

On branches of broad-leaved trees (oak).

R Sa ♀

Cerocorticium molare

Trechispora farinacea

Fr very thin, crust-like, ∅ up to a few square centimetres. Upper surface cobweb-like or granular with fine warts or spines, white to cream, ciliate margin with white rhizomorphs. Common on half-decayed wood of broad-leaved and coniferous trees.

Sa ♀

Trechispora farinacea

Phlebiella vaga (Trechispora vaga)

Fr thin, crust-like, ∅ a few square centimetres to several square decimetres. Upper surface granular at the centre, honey-yellow to brownish, hairy-warty towards the margin, sulphur-yellow, with whitish to yellow rhizomorphs. Not uncommon on (the underside of fallen) wood of broad-leaved and coniferous trees.

Sa

Phlebiella vaga

Rogersella sambuci (Hyphoderma sambuci)

Fr thin, crust-like, like a streak of paint, ∅ several square decimetres. Upper surface slightly warty, matt, white to light cream. Common on elder branches and trunks without bark. Throughout the year.

Sa

Rogersella sambuci

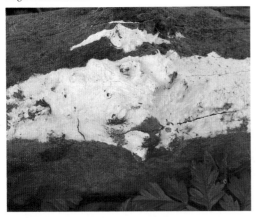

Meruliopsis corium (Byssomerulius corium)

Fr crust-like, leathery, elongate, with reflexed margins forming brackets, up to several tens of centimetres in lenght and a few centimetres in width. Brackets protruding far from the substrate, upper surface hairy-felty, zoned, white to ochraceous. Lower surface wrinkled-veined, strongly warty, whitish to ochrous, later brownish.
Common on the underside of fallen branches of broad-leaved trees.

Sa

Meruliopsis corium

Merulius tremellosus

Fr elastic, crust-like, with margins protruding up to 5 cm, forming strips up to several decimetres in length. Upper surface of the flexible, semicircular brackets hairy-felty,

Merulius tremellosus

white. Lower surface pleated-veined, forming a poroid net, yellow or orange to salmon, later dark orange, with a silky, hairy, pleated-furrowed, pale white margin. **Spo** white.

Common on strongly decayed stumps and on the underside of lying trunks of broad-leaved trees, favouring birch.

Sa

Peniophora incarnata

Fr thin, crust-like, ∅ up to several square decimetres. Upper surface smooth to lumpy, pale or bright orange to salmon-pink. **Spo** light pink.

Common on branches and trunks of broad-leaved trees (alder) (see also photograph of *Datronia mollis*).

Sa

Peniophora quercina

Fr thick crust-like with upturned margins, forming strips a few centimetres to several decimetres in length. Upper surface of the

brackets matt, dark brown to black. Lower surface smooth or cracked, purple or blue-lilac to pinkish grey-brown. **Spo** white. Common on (hanging) oak branches.

Sa

Peniophora quercina

Peniophora rufomarginata

Fr crust-like, ∅ up to a few square centimetres. Upper surface smooth, somewhat cracked when dry, bumpy-undulate, matt,

Peniophora incarnata

grey-pink to bluish grey-brown. **Spo** white. On (hanging), dead lime branches.

R Sa

Peniophora rufomarginata

Peniophora laeta

Fr crust-like, rupturing the bark, ∅ up to several square centimetres. Upper surface smooth, with bulges up to 1-3 mm thick, light orange to cream. On dead, hanging branches of broad-leaved trees, favouring hornbeam.

In Britain, 20 species of the genus *Peniophora* occur.

R Sa

Peniophora laeta

Mycoacia uda

Fr waxy, thin, crust-like, up to several cm long. Upper surface densely covered with with spines, sulphur-yellow or waxy yellow to ochraceous yellow. Spi pointed, 1-2 mm long. **Spo** white.

Fairly common on lying wood of broad-leaved trees, especially on the underside.

Also *M. aurea* (R) and *M. fuscoatra* (R).

Sa

Mycoacia uda

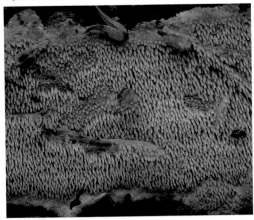

Phlebia radiata

Fr crust-like, oval to irregularly elongate, ∅ several square centimetres to several square decimetres. Upper surface irregularly radially pleated-veined to ridged, bright orange to dull flesh or violet-grey, with ciliate margin. **Spo** white. Common on dead branches (attached to the tree) and on trunks (rupturing the bark) of broad-leaved trees (oak).
In Britain, X species of the genus *Phlebia* occur.

Sa

Phlebia radiata

Plicaturopsis crispa

Fr pleated to undulate shell- or fan-shaped, with lateral stem, ∅ 1-2 cm. Upper surface felty, concentrically zoned, whitish to ochraceous brown or red-brown. Lower surface with gill-like ridges; ridges undulate-forked, interconnected, dingy white to grey-ochre, with appendiculate, rolled in margin. **Spo** white. On trunks and branches of birch, beech and hazel.

VR Sa

Plicaturopsis crispa

Auriculariopsis ampla

Fr ear-shaped to flattened saucer-shaped, pendulous, ∅ 10-15 mm. Upper surface of the bracket felty hairy, attached nearly centrally, dingy white. Lower surface smooth to wrinkled, light ochre to cinnamon. **Fl** thin, elastic. **Spo** white. On dead, often still attached branches and twigs of broad-leaved trees, favouring poplar.

R Sa

Auriculariopsis ampla

Schizophyllum commune

SPLIT-GILL

Fr shell- to fan-shaped, often lobed, laterally attached, ∅ 1-4 cm. Upper surface of the bracket covered with hairy down protruding over the margin, white or grey-white, occasionally with purple tinge. Lower surface bearing radially arranged 'pseudo-gills', split lengthwise with reflexed edges, pale flesh to violet-grey. **Fl** tough. **Spo** white. Common on (piles of thick) trunks and branches of broad-leaved trees.
Sa

Schizophyllum commune

Steccherinum bourdotii

Fr crust-like with brackets on the upper margin, 3-6 x 1-2 cm. Upper surface of the brackets, which protrude up to 1 cm, hairy, cream to greyish. Lower surface densely spiny, creamy buff. **Spi** 2-3 mm. **Spo** white.

Fairly common on wood of broad-leaved trees

Steccherinum bourdotii

(alder). Also *S. ochraceum* (R) and *Steccherinum laeticolor* (VR).

Sa ♀

Steccherinum fimbriatum

Fr thin, leathery crust-like with ciliate margin, ∅ 3-6 cm. Upper surface veined, warty, spiny, grey-red or grey-violet to flesh-brown. Mycelium strands white to grey-reddish. **Spi** warty, obtuse, 1 mm. **Spo** white.

On fallen branches of broad-leaved trees in damp woods with rich soil.

R Sa ♀

Steccherinum fimbriatum

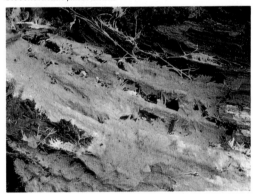

Chondrostereum purpureum

SILVER-LEAF FUNGUS

Fr crust-like, with undulate margins protruding up to 2 cm, ∅ 2-4 cm. Upper surface of the brackets hairy-downy, concentrically zoned, hairs white. Lower surface smooth, dark violet

Chondrostereum purpureum

or brown-violet to brown. **Spo** white. Common on fresh trunks and stumps of broad-leaved trees. Causes silver-leaf disease in cherry trees.

Pa (Sa)

Stereum hirsutum

HAIRY STEREUM

Fr leathery crust-like, with brackets protruding up to 2 cm, 3-10 x 1-4 cm. Upper surface of the brackets hairy, zoned, ochre to brown, with pallid margin, often green due to algal growth. Lower surface smooth, bright yellow to dull brown or grey-yellow. **Spo** white. Common on wood of broad-leaved trees, especially on piles of wood or firewood. Sa

Stereum hirsutum

Stereum gausapatum

Fr leathery crust-like, with margins slightly upturned, ∅ 1-4 cm. Upper surface of the brackets finely hairy, zoned, greyish ochraceous brown, whitish margin. Lower

Stereum gausapatum

surface smooth, pallid to dark yellow-brown or chestnut, bleeding red when damaged. **Spo** white. Common on trunks and stumps of broad-leaved trees, favouring oak.

Sa

Stereum ochraceoflavum (S. rameale)

Fr leathery crust-like, with brackets protruding up to 1 cm, forming strips a few centimetres wide and from a few centimetres to decimetres in length. Upper surface of the brackets hairy-felty, hairs grey-white to ochraceous white, with ciliate margin. Lower surface smooth, brown-ochre to grey-ochre. **Spo** white. Common on branches and twigs of broad-leaved trees.

Sa

Stereum ochraceoflavum

Stereum rugosum

Fr crust-like, forming irregularly strips of a few decimetres in length. Outer surface smooth, whitish-yellowish to grey-pink, bleeding red when damaged. **Spo** white. Common on wood of broad-leaved trees, especially on dead, standing or fallen trunks.
Also *S. sanguinolentum* on fresh coniferous trunks and branches (see photograph of *Tremella encephala*).

Sa

Stereum rugosum

Stereum subtomentosum

Fr leathery crust-like, with strongly protruding, fan-shaped, undulate brackets, ∅ 3-7 cm. Upper surface of the brackets hairy-felty, concentrically zoned, brown-orange or grey-orange to ochrous yellow, often green due to algal growth, with whitish growth zone. Lower surface smooth, yellow to grey-yellow or ochraceous, becoming bright yellow when damaged. **Spo** white. Fairly common on branches and trunks of broad-leaved trees (alder, willow).

Sa

Stereum subtomentosum

Xylobolus frustulatus

Fr crust-like, cracking mosaic-like, consisting of polygonal blocks of 1-3 mm. Upper surface smooth, buff to grey-pinkish ochre. Lower surface brown to black. **Spo** white.
The fruiting bodies grow very slowly and can

Xylobolus frustulatus

reach an age of over 20 years. On bare heartwood of very old, lying or standing dead oak.

VR RDL Sa ♀

Vuilleminia comedens

Fr crust-like, making the bark curl and drop off, covering several square decimetres. Upper surface smooth, matt to shiny, whitish to pale flesh or grey with lilac tinges. **Spo** white.

Common on dead, attached or fallen broad-leaved branches, favouring oak.

Sa

Coniophora arida

Fr felty, crust-like, ∅ up to a few square centimetres. Upper surface warty-felty, ochraceous brown to olivaceous brown, with an irregular white-fibrillose margin. **Spo** light brown.
In the wood, the wet form of brown rot is visible.

Not uncommon on wood of coniferous trees,

Vuilleminia comedens

occasionally on wood of broad-leaved trees. Also *C. olivacea* (VR) and *C. putanea*.

Sa

Coniophora arida

Leucogyrophana romellii

Fr leathery, soft, crust-like, strongly veined-pleated or with angular, wide pores, spreading over several square decimetres. Upper surface bright orange to salmon, with hairy-fibrillose, white margin. **Spo** light yellow. On (burnt) branches of coniferous and broad-leaved trees, occasionally on the ground or on mosses.

R Sa

Leucogyrophana romellii/Trechispora mollusca

Trechispora mollusca

Fr fibrillose soft, honeycomb-shaped crust-like, ∅ up to a few square centimetres. Upper surface with fine, irregular pores, snow-white to white-ochre, with fibrillose-hairy margin. **Po** ∅ 0.3-1 mm. **Spo** white. On half-decayed (or burnt) wood lying in a sheltered location and on litter of broad-leaved and coniferous trees.
In Britain, X species of the genus Trechispora occur.

R Sa ♀

Serpula himantioides

Fr soft leathery crust-like, spreading over several square decimetres. Upper surface felty, labyrinthine to reticulate, veined-pleated, mustard-yellow to rusty brown or olivaceous brown, with woolly-felty, somewhat free, wide white marginal zone. **Spo** yellow-brown. On wood of coniferous trees in coniferous woods with poor soil. Also Dry-rot Fungus *(Serpula lacrymans)*, which is becoming increasingly common on processed wood in buildings.

R Sa

Serpula himantioides

Thelephoraceae

A small group of Basidiomycetes, laciniate appearance or with laciniate tips to the usually branched fruiting bodies.

Thelephora terrestris

EARTH FAN

Fr fan- to rosette-shaped, often fused to large, semicircular or elongate plaques covering several square decimetres. Upper surface radially hairy-fibrillose, concentrically zoned, grey-brown to rusty brown with light, ciliate margin. Lower surface warty-wrinkled, bright or dark cinnamon to grey brown. **Fl** fibrous, tough. **Sm** faintly earthy. **Spo** purple-brown.

Common near (young) broad-leaved and coniferous trees in woods and on heaths on poor soil, often on litter or on and around small trunks.

M

Thelephora terrestris

Thelephora palmata

Fr tufted, strongly branched coral-shaped, 4-7 x 4-7 cm. Upper surface branched once or repeatedly, each branch with a flattened to fan-shaped, ciliate-dentate tip, whitish when young, later darker grey-brown to lilac-brown, tips remaining whitish. **Fl** corky, tough.

Thelephora palmata

Sm unpleasant. **Spo** brown. Near coniferous trees on humous soil with plenty of litter.

R RDL M

Thelephora anthocephala

Fr tufted coral-shaped or flattened rosette-shaped, repeatedly branched, 3-6 x 2-4 cm. Upper surface branched once or repeatedly, flattened cylindrical with pointed, whitish tip, or flattened wide spatula-shaped with white fringe, matt, olivaceous grey to lilac-brown. **Fl** elastic, dark brown. **Sm** none. **Spo** brown. Near broad-leaved trees (beech, willow) in broad-leaved woods on rich clay and humous sandy soil.

In Britain, 10 species of the genus Thelephora occur.

R RDL M

Thelephora anthocephala

Hydnaceae, Boletopsidiaceae, Auriscalpiaceae

A group of Basidiomycetes with spines, or, exceptionally, with shallow pores (Boletopsis) on the underside of the cap.

Hydnellum aurantiacum

Fr top- to funnel-shaped, up to 6 cm high. **C** ⌀ 2-7, irregularly round, lumpy, with undulate and appendiculate margin, felty, white when young, later with faint concentric zones, centre orange-yellow to orange-brown, towards the margin light orange-yellow to whitish. **Spi** up to 5 mm long, decurrent, whitish or grey-brown to orange-brown. **St** finely felty, swollen at the base, 2-5 x 0.5-2 cm, orange-brown to dark brown. **Fl** white to pale orange or orange-brown. **Spo** light brown.

Near Scots pine in sparse fir woods on very poor sand.

RDL M

Hydnellum aurantiacum

Hydnellum caeruleum

Fr top-shaped, up to 6 cm high. **C** ⌀ 3-7 cm, irregularly round, with undulate, irregularly appendiculate margin, downy-velvety to smooth, undulate-wrinkled, grey-blue when young, later brownish at the centre, with whitish margin. **Spi** up to 5 mm long, decurrent, brown-bluish to grey-white or brown. **St** rudimentary, conical, 2-3 x 2-3 cm, brown-red. **Fl** red-brown or orange-brown to grey-blue or black-blue, with darker zones. **Sm** of cucumber. **Spo** light brown.

Hydnellum caerulum

Near Scots pine in fir woods on very poor, dry, shifting sandy soil.

RDL M

Hydnellum ferrugineum

Fr top-shaped, up to 6 cm high. **C** ⌀ 3-10 cm, irregularly round, when young cushion-shaped, velvety, white to pinkish, exuding red guttation drops, later flattened to funnel-shaped, rough, red-brown, with undulate-appendiculate, pallid margin. **Spi** up to 5 mm long, decurrent, whitish to red-brown. **St** 1-5 x 1-3 cm, red-brown. **Fl** pale red-brown. **Spo** light brown.

Among heather near Scots pine and spruce in coniferous woods.

Also *H. compactum* (R RDL), *H. concrescens* (R RDL) and *H. spongiosipes* (R RDL).

VR RDL M

Hydnellum ferrugineum

Phellodon niger

Fr top-shaped to funnel-shaped, up to 6 cm high. **C** ⌀ 3-8 cm, irregularly round, velvety, undulate-lumpy, occasionally with upturned scales at the centre, concentrically zoned, blue-black or brown-black to black, with acute, light grey-blue to whitish marginal zone. **Spi** up to 3 mm long, whitish to blue-grey or grey-brown. **St** felty, cylindrical, 2-5 x 1-2 cm, black. **Fl** tough, with black and brown zones. **Sm** spicy, of lovage. **Spo** whitish. Near broad-leaved trees (oak, beech), occasionally near coniferous trees (fir) in woods on poor, shifting sandy soil and in poor roadsides with old trees.

VR RDL M

Phellodon niger

Phellodon confluens

Fr top-shaped to flattened funnel-shaped, margins often fused, up to 5 cm high. **C** ⌀ 3-9 cm, confluent to ⌀ 15 cm, round to oval, lumpy-grooved, downy, whitish to grey-brown or black-brown, with whitish marginal zone. **Spi** 2-4 x 1-2 cm, felty, grey-brown to dark brown. **Fl** zoned, pink-brown to grey brown or black-brown. **Sm** spicy, of lovage. **Spo** whitish.

Near broad-leaved trees (oak, beech), occasionally near coniferous trees (fir) in woods on poor, shifting sandy soil and in poor roadsides with old trees.

VR RDL M

Phellodon tomentosus

Fr flattened funnel-shaped, often with many caps fused together, up to 4 cm high. **C** ⌀ 2-6 cm, confluent to ⌀ 10-20 cm, irregularly round, with fine radial wrinkles, felty, matt, concentrically zoned, becoming darker towards the centre, hazel to grey-brown or reddish brown, margin smooth, white.

Spi up to 3 mm long, smooth, bright to dark brown. **Fl** zoned, light brown to red-brown or black-brown. **Sm** spicy, of lovage. **Spo** white.

Occasionally growing in fairy rings.

Phellodon confluens

Near Scots pine in coniferous woods on dry, very poor, shifted sandy soil.

Also *P. melaleucus* (VR RDL M)

ZZ RL M

Phellodon tomentosus

Sarcodon imbricatus

Fr top- to funnel-shaped, up to 9 cm high. **C** ∅ 10-20 cm, irregularly round, with large, erect scales in concentric rows, velvety-felty, pale pink to flesh-brown, scales red-brown to dark-brown, with rolled in, more pallid margin. **Spi** up to 1 mm, whitish to grey-brown or purple-brown. **St** 4-7 x 2-4 cm, velvety, white to brownish. **Fl** white. **Sm** faint, pleasantly spicy. **Spo** brown. Near fir in

Sarcodon imbricatus

coniferous woods on very poor shifting sand deficient in humus.

VR RDL M 🍄

Sarcodon scabrosus

Fr flattened funnel-shaped, up to 12 cm high. **C** ∅ 4-14 cm, irregularly round, with flattened scales gradually becoming erect, velvety-felty, light chestnut, occasionally with pink tinge, scales dark chestnut to black-brown, margin undulate, pallid. **Spi** up to 1 mm, light grey-pink to purple-brown with white tip. **St** 3-10 x 1-3.5 cm, longitudinally striate, with dark scales, pale pink-brown to dark brown with grey-green base. **Fl** whitish to pink, in the base of the stem blue-green. **Sm** mealy. **Spo** brown.

Near oak and beech in broad-leaved woods and in roadsides with old trees on poor sandy soil.

Also *S. foedes* (VR RDL) and *S. lepidus* (VR RDL).

R RDL M †

Sarcodon scabrosus

Boletopsis grisea

Fr flattened funnel-shaped, up to 10 cm high. **C** ∅ 4-10 cm, irregularly round, smooth, undulate, whitish to light grey-brown, with acute, undulate margin. Lower surface with irregular angular, shallow, decurrent pores, ∅ 0.3-1 mm, whitish to pink. **St** 3-7 x 1-3 cm, smooth to finely scaly, whitish to light grey-brown. **Fl** whitish to pink. **Spo** whitish.

Near coniferous trees (and broad-leaved trees) on poor sandy soil.

May be confused with or is possibly a pallid variety of *B. leucomeleana* (VR RDL).

RDL M?

Boletopsis grisea

Hydnum repandum

HEDGEHOG FUNGUS

Fr top- to funnel-shaped or flattened funnel-shaped, up to 8 cm high. **C** ∅ 3-15 cm, irregularly round, occasionally slightly furrowed, faintly felty, matt, cream or apricot to mustard-yellow or ochre yellow, with inrolled, appendiculate margin. **Spi** fragile, soft, awl-shaped, decurrent, up to 6 mm long, creamy white to salmon-pink. **St** 2-6 x 2-3 cm, finely downy, white, yellow at the base. **Fl** soft, white. **Sm** pleasant. **Spo** white. Not uncommon near broad-leaved trees (beech), rarely near coniferous trees in broad-leaved woods and

Hydnum repandum

avenues on moderately to slightly acid, sandy or loamy soil. Also an orange-red to reddish brown species (or variety), *H. rufescens* (VR RDL).

RDL M ⦾

Auriscalpium vulgare

EAR-PICK FUNGUS

Fr laterally attached, leathery cap on a stem, up to 8 cm high. **C** ∅ 1-2 cm, ear- to kidney-shaped, covered with yellow-brown to chestnut or black-brown hairs, with ciliate margin. **Spi** 2-3 mm long, pointed, pink-brown to grey-brown. **St** 2-6 cm x 1-3 mm, hairy-felty, bristly at the swollen base, dark brown to black-brown. **Spo** white. On fir (and spruce) cones lying on the ground or shallowly buried in coniferous or mixed woods on slightly acid to alkaline, often calcareous sandy or loamy soils.

R RD Sa

Auriscalpium vulgare

Hericiaceae

A small group of Basidiomycetes with long spines on the lower surface of the bracket-like or branched, spatula-shaped caps.

Creolophus cirrhatus

Fr consisting of irregularly semicircular to shell-shaped caps, often imbricated, growing laterally from a bracket-like core. **C** 3-8 cm wide, undulately curved, granular-warty, whitish to cream or ochre, later orange-brown, often with incurved margin. **Spi** 1-1.5 cm long, awl-shaped, creamy yellow to pale salmon. **Fl** thick, soft, white to cream. **Sm** pleasant. **St** white.

On wounds on trunks and on living and dead trunks and thick branches of old broad-leaved trees (beech) in parks and open woodland.

R RDL Sa (Pa)

Creolophus cirrhatus

Hericium erinaceus

Fr cushion-shaped to bracket-like, ∅ up to 25 cm. **C** bulbous, surrounded by pendulous spines, stem short or absent. **Spi** up to 6 cm

Hericium erinaceus

long, white to cream, dingy yellow or dingy orange-yellow. **Fl** white. **Spo** white.

On wounds on trunks of broad-leaved trees (beech) in parks and along avenues.

R RDL Pa (Sa) 🍄

Hericium coralloides

Fr growing from a thick stem, coral-shaped, repeatedly branched, with pendulous spines in irregular groups hanging from branches, ∅ 5-30 cm. Stem ∅ 1-4 cm, creamy white to pale yellow. Branches angular, flattened, 5-10 mm thick, creamy white to pale yellow. **Spi** awl-shaped, 5-10 mm long, creamy white. **Spo** white.
On big, strongly decayed trunks of beech in parks and broad-leaved woods.

VR RDL Sa

Hericium coralloides

Hymenochaetaceae

A group of Basidiomycetes showing a rich variety in shapes, including *Hymenochaete* species, with crust-like fruiting bodies and brackets without tubes, *Coltricia* species, with top-shaped fruiting bodies, with stem, with tubes on the underside of the cap, *Inonotus* species, with annual, cushion-shaped, bracket-like to hoof-shaped or imbricated fruiting bodies, tubes and pores with a sheen, and *Phellinus* species, with hard, perennial, bulbous to bracket-like or hoof-shaped fruiting bodies with several tube layers.

Hymenochaete rubiginosa

Fr crust-like, with imbricated brackets, 2-6 x 2-4 cm. Upper surface of the brackets concentrically zoned, velvety to smooth, dark rusty brown or date-brown to black. Lower surface smooth, red-brown to orange-brown, with undulate, acute margin. **Spo** whitish to light yellowish olive.

Not uncommon on wood or broad-leaved trees, favouring oak.

Sa

Hymenochaete tabacina

Fr crust-like, occasionally with brackets, which protrude up to 1 cm, spreading over a few square centimetres to a length of several decimetres. Upper surface of brackets zoned, felty, orange-brown to grey-brown. Lower surface concentrically undulate, finely felty, matt, tobacco-brown or rusty brown to coffee-brown, with acute, appendiculate margin. **Spo** whitish.
Not uncommon on wood of broad-leaved trees (willow) in damp, rich shrubberies.

Hymenochaete tabacina

Also *H. cinnamomea* (VR), *H. corrugata* (VR) and *H. cruenta* = *mougeotii* (VR).

Sa

Hymenochaete rubiginosa

Coltricia perennis

Fr top-shaped to flattened funnel-shaped, with stem, up to 6 cm high. **C** ∅ 2-8 cm, with concentric zones, finely velvety to smooth, chestnut or rusty brown to ochre or pale grey. **Tu** 2-3 mm long, decurrent, brown or grey-buff. **Po** 2-4 per mm, irregularly angular, cinnamon, white pruinose. **St** 2-4 cm x 2-6 mm, velvety, rusty brown. **Spo** ochrous brown.
Near coniferous and broad-leaved trees in open fir woodland, mixed woods and heaths on dry, poor sandy soil.

R RDL M

Coltricia perennis

Coltricia confluens

Fr top-shaped to flattened funnel-shaped, with stem, usually with caps fused into plaques, on several stems, up to 5 cm high. **C** ∅ 4-6 cm,

Coltricia confluens

fused up to ∅ 15 cm, not or only very slightly zoned, finely velvety to smooth, red-brown to rusty brown to ochrous grey. **Tu** 2-3 mm long, decurrent, brown. **Po** 2-3 per mm, irregularly angular, cinnamon. **St** 1-3 cm x 2-4 mm, velvety, rusty brown to dark brown. **Spo** ochrous brown.

On coarse leaf litter and wood chips in parks and scrub with young trees and shrubberies.

Also *C. cinnamomea* (VR RDL).

Z Sa

Inonotus hispidus

Fr annual, hoof-shaped to bracket-like, 10-30 x 6-20 cm, 4-10 cm thick. Upper surface felty-hairy bristly, ochrous brown to dark brown or black-brown, with sulphur-yellow to yellow-brown margin when young. **Tu** 1-4 mm long, rusty brown. **Po** 2-3 per mm, circular to angular, white-yellowis to greyish ochrous brown, often guttate. **Spo** yellow-brown.

Not uncommon on trunks of living broad-leaved trees (apple, walnut, ash, elm, plane) in parks, orchards, avenues and public gardens.

RDL Pa

Inonotus hispidus

Inonotus radiatus

Fr annual, flattened bracket-like, usually imbricated, 3-10 x 2-6 cm, 1-2 cm thick. Upper surface finely felty to smooth, radially wrinkled, occasionally with concentric zones, rusty brown with yellow-white marginal zone,

Inonotus radiatus

later dark brown to black-brown with acute, more pallid margin. **Tu** 3-10 mm long, rusty brown. **Po** 3-4 per mm, circular to angular, silvery white to yellow-grey. **Spo** yellowish. The bulbous fruiting bodies often exude large guttation drops when young. Common on trunks, stumps and branches of broad-leaved trees (alder, birch).

Pa

Inonotus radiatus

Inonotus nodulosus

Fr annual, cushion-shaped to bracket-like, imbricated on a common, poroid base, 2-3 x 1-3 cm. Upper surface irregularly undulate, felty, orange-yellow to dark brown, with pallid margin. **Tu** 5-6 mm long, cream to brown. **Po** 3-4 per mm, circular, cream with silvery sheen to ochrous brown. **Spo** pale yellow.

On rotted saw cuts and wounds on the trunks of living and dead beech.

R Pa (Sa)

Inonotus nodulosus

Inonotus rheades

Fr annual, flattened bracket-like, usually with several imbricated caps, 4-15 x 2-9 cm. Upper surface velvety felty, yellow-orange or orangey sorrel-red to red-brown, with undulate, pallid margin. **Tu** 5-15 mm long, red-brown. **Po** 2-3 per mm, angular, cream or light yellow to ochrous brown. **Spo** brown.

On trunks of poplar in open scrub and tree clusters.

Also *I. cuticularis*, *I. dryadeus* (R RDL),

Inonotus rheades

I. hastifer (see photograph of *Antrodiella hoehnelii*, VR), and *I. obliquus* (R).

R RDL Pa

Phellinus igniarius

Fr perennial, hard, hoof-shaped to bracket-like, 10-40 x 5-20 cm, 5-15 cm thick. Upper surface concentrically grooved-ridged, smooth, cracking, rusty brown to grey-black or black, with lighter, obtuse margin. With several horizontal tube layers. **Tu** each layer 1-5 mm long, rusty brown. **Po** 5-6 per mm, circular, rusty brown to brown-grey. **Spo** white. Not uncommon on trunks of often still living trees (poplar, birch, willow, rowan) in open broad-leaved woods and lines of trees.

RDL Pa

Phellinus hippophaecola

Fr perennial, hard, hoof-shaped to bracket-like, 3-6 x 2-4 cm, 2-4 cm thick. Upper surface velvety to smooth, yellow-brown to rusty brown, often green due to algal growth, with acute, rusty brown margin. With several tube layers. **Tu** each layer 2-3 mm long, cinnamon.

Po 5-7 per mm, circular, buff to rusty brown or dark brown. **Spo** white. Common on trunks and branches of hawthorn, especially in dune scrub.

Pa

Phellinus hippophaecola

Phellinus tuberculosus (P. pomaceus)

Fr perennial, hard, thick, cushion- to hoof-shaped, 3-10 cm. Upper surface smooth, matt, grey to reddish brown, often green due to algal

Phellinus igniarius

growth. With several tube layers. **Tu** each layer 2-3 mm long, rusty brown. **Po** 4-5 per mm, circular, buff to cinnamon or grey-brown. **Spo** white.

Not uncommon on trunks and on the underside of branches of fruit trees (cherry, apple, pear) in orchards, public gardens and open woodland. Also *P. torulosus* (VR), on broad-leaved trees (*Robinia*).

Pa

Phellinus tuberculosus

Phellinus robustus

Fr pernnial, hard, bulbous to hoof-shaped or bracket-like, 8-25 x 5-10 cm, 5-20 cm thick. Upper surface smooth, rusty brown to grey-

Phellinus robustus

brown or black-brown, with obtuse, yellow-brown margin. With several tube layers. **Tu** each layer 3-5 mm, yellow-brown. **Po** 5-6 per mm, circular, yellow-brown to rusty brown. **Spo** white, On trunks of old broad-leaved trees, favouring oak, in avenues or open woodland.

R RDL Pa

Phellinus trivialis

Fr perennial, hard, bracket-like, 10-20 x 5-20 cm. Upper surface smooth, concentrically zoned, cracked, grey-brown to black, with pallid margin. With several, decurrent, slanting tube layers. **Tu** each layer 3-5 mm, dark rusty brown. **Po** 5-6 per mm, circular, buff to cinnamon or rusty brown. **Spo** white. On trunks of willow, occasionally hanging from a slanting trunk.

VR Pa

Phellinus trivialis

Phellinus conchatus

Fr perennial, hard, thick, crust-like, occasionally with several imbricated, bracket-like caps of 1-4 x 1-2 cm. Upper surface concentrically zoned and dark brown to black-brown. With several, stratified tube layers.
Po 3-6 per mm, angular to dentate, rusty brown to grey-brown. **Spo** pale yellow.
On trunks of dead and living broad-leaved trees (willow, poplar) in mixed woods on calcareous soil.

Also *P. contiguus* (R) on oak and *P. nigri-*

tolimitatus (VR) and *P. pini* (VR RDL) on coniferous trees.

R Pa (Sa)

Phellinus conchatus

Phellinus ferruginosus

Fr annual to perennial, hard, crust-like, forming strips measuring a few square centimetres to several decimetres in length, 1-10 mm thick, with felty marginal zone. With several tube layers. **Tu** each layer 1-4 mm long, red-brown. **Po** 5-6 per mm, circular, yellow-brown to red-brown or grey-brown. **Spo** white. Not uncommon on trunks and branches of broad-leaved trees (oak, beech, willow, hawthorn) on rich soil.

Sa ♀

Phellinus ferruginosus

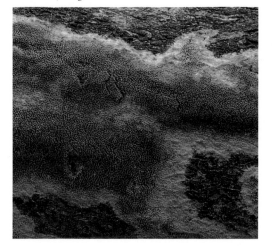

Phellinus ferreus

Fr perennial, hard, crust-like, forming strips measuring a few square centimetres to several decimetres in length, 5-15 mm thick, with light yellow-brown, felty marginal zone. With several tube layers. **Tu** each layer 1-3 mm long, mustard-yellow. **Po** 3-5 per mm, circular to angular, yellow-brown to dark brown. **Spo** white. Not uncommon on branches and trunks of broad-leaved trees (oak) in broad-leaved woods on poor soil.

Can be distinguished with certainty from *Phellinus ferruginosus* only by microscopic features. Also *P. punctatus* (VR).

Sa ♀

Phellinus ferreus

Phylloporia ribis f. evonymi (Phellinus ribis)

Fr annual to perennial, corky, shell- to fan-shaped, 3-15 x 2-10 cm, 1-2 cm thick. Upper surface concentrically zoned, finely felty, red-brown to black-brown, often green due to algal growth. **Tu** each layer 1-3 mm long, rusty brown. **Po** 6-8 per mm, circular, cinnamon to reddish brown. **Spo** light yellow.

At the base of the stem of living shrubs (*Celastraceae*).

Also *P. ribis* f. *ribis* (VR) on berry bushes.

R Pa

Polyporaceae

An extensive group of annual to perennial *Polyporus* species, exhibiting a large variety of species and shapes, fruiting bodies shell-shaped, fan-shaped, broadly spatula-shaped or tongue-shaped, or flattened funnel-shaped, saddle-shaped, hoof-shaped or bracket-like, occasionally imbricated, with a poroid or lamelliform hymenium.

Bjerkandera adusta

Fr annual, usually imbricated, leathery caps on a leathery, poroid crust spreading over the substrate. **C** 2-6 x 1-3 cm, 3-6 mm thick. Upper surface usually concentrically zoned, felty-chamois-like, ochraceous grey or brown-grey to black, with acute white, later black margin. **Tu** 1-2 mm long, grey. **Po** 4-6 per mm, circular, light to dark grey, becoming black when damaged, more pallid towards the margin. **Fl** thin, tough, whitish. **Sm** somewhat sour, mushroomy. **Spo** white to light yellow.
Common on stumps and standing and fallen trunks and branches of broad-leaved trees, occasionally on spruce.

Sa

Bjerkandera adusta

Phylloporia ribis

Bjerkandera fumosa

Fr annual, single to imbricated, bracket-like caps. **C** 10-15 x 4-8 cm, 2-3 cm thick. Upper surface velvety, matt, usually not zoned, ochrous to coffee-brown, with acute, undulate, pallid margin. **Tu** 2-4 mm long, brownish. **Po** 2-4 per mm, circular to angular, whitish to cream, becoming brownish when damaged. **Fl** thick, mushroomy, ochrous brown. **Sm** pleasantly sweetish. **Spo** white.

Common on stumps and trunks of broad-leaved trees.

Sa

Oligoporus caesius
(Tyromyces caesius)

Fr annual, semicircular fan-shaped to bracket-like. **C** 2-6 x 1-4 cm, 1-2 cm thick. Upper surface hairy, white, later blue-grey to brownish, with acute white margin. **Tu** 1-5 mm long, white. **Po** 4-5 per mm, circular to angular, white to grey. **Fl** fibrillose, white. **Spo** white.

Common on trunks, stumps and branches of coniferous trees.

Oligoporus caesius

Also the smaller *O. subcaesius*, especially on wood of broad-leaved trees.

Sa

Bjerkandera fumosa

Oligoporus stipticus
(Tyromyces stipticus)

Fr annual, cushion-shaped, bracket-like to kidney-shaped. **C** 3-12 x 2-5 cm, 1-4 cm thick. Upper surface finely felty, white to ochrous cream, with acute margin. **Tu** 3-10 mm long, white. **Po** 3-4 per mm, circular to elongate, white to cream. **Fl** crumbly, white. **Sm** sweetish, pungent. **Ta** bitter. **Spo** white. Common on stumps, trunks (also on saw cuts), and branches of coniferous trees, occasionally on wood of broad-leaved trees.
Sa

Oligoporus stipticus

Oligoporus tephroleucus
(Tyromyces tephroleucus)

Fr annual, bulbous to bracket-like. C 4-10 x 2-5 cm, 2-4 cm thick. Upper surface finely felty to smooth, whitish to grey-yellow or grey-brown, with acute margin. **Tu** 6-10 mm long,

Oligoporus tephroleucus

whitish. **Po** 4-5 per mm, circular to angular, white. **Fl** crumbly, white. **Sm** sweetish, pungent. **Ta** mild. **Spo** white. Fairly common on trunks, stumps and branches of broad-leaved trees (birch, beech, poplar).
Also *Tyromyces chioneus*.

Sa

Oligoporus ptychogaster
(Tyromyces ptychogaster)

Fr annual, hemispherical to cushion-shaped, ⊘ 3-6 cm, or with caps up to 2 cm thick and measuring 1-4 x 1 cm. Upper or outer surface hairy-felty, white to pale brown, staining brown when damaged. The imperfect form *Ptycogaster fuliginoides* occasionally with yellowish guttation drops, disintegrating into a powdery, brown ball. Spores (Chlamydospores) yellow-brown to dark brown. The perfect stage with 2-5 mm long tubes. **Po** 2-4 per mm, angular, white to cream. **Fl** concentrically zoned, fibrillose, whitish to yellow-brown. **Spo** white. The photograph shows both the imperfect stage and the teleomorph. The imperfect stage is not uncommon on branches, trunks and stumps of coniferous trees.

R Sa

Oligoporus ptychogaster

Oligoporus fragilis
(Tyromyces fragilis)

Fr annual, with several bracket-like to fan-shaped caps on a soft, poroid crust. **C** 2-6 x 2-3 cm, 5-10 mm thick. Upper surface not zoned to faintly zoned, finely felty, yellow-ochre to orange-brown, with white margin. **Tu** 2-5 mm long, white. **Po** 2-4 per mm, angular to maze-like, white. **Fl** fibrillose, elastic, white. **Spo** white. On trunks and branches of coniferous trees.

In Britain, more than 20 species of the genera *Ceriporiopsis*, *Leptosporus*, *Tyromyces* and *Oligoporus* occur.

R Sa

Oligoporus fragilis

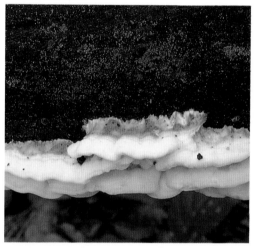

Antrodiella hoehnelii
(Trametes hoehnelii)

Fr annual, semicircular bracket-like. **C** 2-4 x 1-3 cm, up to 1 cm thick. Upper surface undulate, velvety matt, white or cream to

Antrodiella hoehnelii

yellowish, with obtuse, yellow margin. **Tu** 2-4 mm long, cream. **Po** 3-5 per mm, irregularly circular, white to ochrous yellowish. **Fl** elastic, tough, cream. **Spo** white. Often on or near old fruiting bodies of *Inonotus* species, such as *Inonotus hastifer*, which can be seen at the right in the photograph, on trunks and stumps of broad-leaved trees, favouring alder.

R RDL Sa (Pa?)

Antrodiella semisupina
(Antrodia semisupina)

Fr annual, fan- to shell-shaped. **C** 0.5-2 x 0.5-1.5 cm, 1-3 mm thick. Upper surface occasionally faintly concentrically zoned, smooth, translucent pale cream to yellowish, with thin, undulate margin. **Tu** up to 1 mm long, whitish. **Po** 5-7 per mm, circular to angular, cream. **Fl** thin, very tough, whitish to cream. **Spo** white. Fairly common on branches and trunks of broad-leaved trees (willow, birch).

Also the crust-like *A. romelii* (VR).

Sa

Antrodiella semisupina

Donkioporia expansa

Fr perennial, flattened cushion-shaped, forming strips measuring a few square centimetres to 1 m in length, 1-2.5 cm thick, with velvety, light growth zone. **Tu** each layer 2-7 mm long, tobacco-brown. **Po** 4-5 per mm, circular, whitish to light or dark brown with a silvery sheen. **Spo** white. On (processed) oak wood, in buildings.

VR Sa ♀

Donkioporia expansa

Datronia mollis

Fr annual, crust-like, forming strips measuring a few square centimetres to several decimetres in length, with rows of shelf-like brackets. **C** protruding up to 2 cm. Upper surface with undulate zones, finely felty to smooth, brown to black, with undulate and white margin. **Tu** of variable depth, grey-brown to ochrous brown. **Po** irregular, 1-2 per mm, up to 1 mm

Datronia mollis

wide and up to 5 mm long, often distant, slot-like-dentate to maze-like, grey-ochre to light brown. **Fl** leathery tough to hard and crumbly, cream to ochraceous with black dividing line. **Spo** white. Fairly common on the sides and on the undersides of branches and trunks of broad-leaved trees.
Also young fruiting bodies of *Peniophora incarnata*.

Sa

Dichomitus campestris

Fr annual to perennial, crust-like to cushion-shaped, 4-15 x 2-10 cm, 5-15 mm thick, with blackening margin. **Tu** each layer 1-3 mm long, light ochre. **Po** 1-2 per mm, irregularly polygonal, cream to pale wood-coloured or orange-brown. **Fl** corky, light wood-coloured to ochrous. **Spo** white. On dead and living branches of broad-leaved trees (oak, beech, alder, hazel).

R RDL Pa

Dichomitus campestris

Lenzites betulinus

Fr annual, fan- to rosette-shaped, usually attached laterally, occasionally somewhat centrally, often in overlapping tufts. **C** 3-10 x

2-5 cm, 1-2 cm thick. Upper surface concentrically zoned, finely felty, buff to grey-ochre or light brown, often green due to algal growth, with acute margin. **Po** 12-15 per cm, up to 10 mm wide, elongate with transverse walls to lamelliform, often forked, cream to ochre or grey-brown. **Fl** corky, tough, whitish. **Spo** white. Fairly common on stumps, trunks and branches of broad-leaved trees (birch, oak, beech), parasitizing on the mycelium of *Trametes* species.

Sa (Pa)

Lenzites betulinus

Pycnoporus cinnabarinus

CINNABAR POLYPORE

Fr annual, semicircular bracket-like to fan-shaped. **C** 2-10 x 2-6 cm, 1-2 cm thick. Upper surface concentrically undulate, warty, flattened felty to smooth, orange to orange-red, with

Pycnoporus cinnabarinus

acute margin. **Tu** 4-6 mm long, orange-red. **Po** 2-3 per mm, circular or angular to elongate, orange-red. **Fl** corky, tough, orange-red. **Spo** white. On branches and trunks of broad-leaved trees (birch, mountain ash, cherry).

R Sa

Trametes versicolor

MANY-ZONED POLYPORE

Fr annual, fan- to rosette-shaped, usually growing in large groups in rows or imbricated. **C** 2-7 x 1-5 cm, 1-5 cm thick. Upper surface concentrically zoned, undulate, velvety, with black, bluish, brown, reddish and yellowish zones, often with a sheen, with acute, appendiculate, whitish margin. **Tu** 0.5-4 mm long, whitish. **Po** 2-4 per mm, circular to angular, white or cream to yellowish ochre. **Fl** thin, leathery, tough, whitish. **Spo** white. Common on stumps, trunks and branches of broad-leaved trees, occasionally on coniferous trees (spruce). In the wood in the top right corner of the photograph white rot is visible. Also *T. multicolor*.

Sa ♀

Trametes versicolor

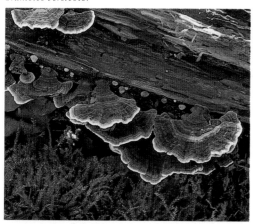

Trametes hirsuta

Fr annual, fan- to rosette-shaped. **C** 3-10 x 2-6, 5-10 mm thick.
Upper surface concentrically zoned, bristly to hairy-felty, with whitish, cream, ochraceous yellow and yellow-brown zones, often green due to algal growth, with acute, appendiculate-ciliate margin. **Tu** 1-4 mm long, whitish to cream. **Po** 2-4 per mm, whitish or

Trametes hirsuta

cream to brownish with greyish tinge. **Fl** corky, elastic, tough, whitish to cream.
Spo white. Common on stumps, trunks and branches of broad-leaved trees (birch, alder, beech) and fence posts. Also *T. pubescens* (R).

Sa (Pa) ♀

Trametes gibbosa

Fr annual, bracket-like to semicircular saucer-shaped. **C** 10-20 x 5-15 cm, 1-4 cm thick.

Upper surface undulate, occasionally zoned, with thick umbo at the side the cap is attached, velvety-felty to smooth, whitish to buff or yellowish brown, often green due to algal growth, with acute, appendiculate, whitish to brown margin. **Tu** 5-10 mm long, white to cream. **Po** 1-2 per mm, up to 4 mm long, elongate to lamelliform at the margin, whitish or cream to grey-ochre. **Fl** tough, elastic, white to cream. **Spo** white.
Common on stumps and trunks of broad-leaved trees (beech, poplar, maple, ash). Parasitizing on the mycelium of *Bjerkandera adusta*.

Sa (Pa)

Trametes suaveolens

Fr annual, thick, cushion-shaped to bracket-like. **C** 2-12 x 2-8 cm, 2-4 cm thick. Upper surface velvety-felty, whitish cream to ochraceous brownish, with obtuse margin. **Tu** 5-10 mm long, white. **Po** 1-3 per mm, circular or angular to elongate, white to cream. **Fl** corky, tough, white. **Sm** of aniseed, of iodine when dry. **Spo** white. On trunks, stumps and pollarded trees (willow, poplar) in osier beds and marshland scrub.

Pa

Trametes gibbosa

Trametes suaveolens

Coriolopsis trogii (Trametes trogii)

Fr annual, semicircular bracket-like, often growing in rows. **C** 4-10 x 2-6 cm, 1-3 cm thick. Upper surface coarsely bristly-hairy, grey-ochre to brownish, with acute margin. **Tu** 4-8 mm long, often decurrent on substrate, whitish to cream. **Po** 1-2 per mm, circular to angular, dentate, with fringe, cream to ochraceous, occasionally with pink tinge. **Fl** corky, tough, whitish cream. **Spo** white.

Coriolopsis trogii

On trunks and branches of poplar. Also *C. gallica* (R RDL).

R RDL Pa

Trichaptum abietinum

Fr annual, leathery crust-like, with shelf-like, fan-shaped caps in rows. **C** protruding up to 2.5 cm. Upper surface concentrically zoned, hairy-felty to smooth, grey-whitish to brownish, often green due to algal growth, broadly

Trichaptum abietinum

attached, with acute, appendiculate, pallid margin. **Po** 3-4 per mm, reticulate to labyrinthine, dentate, violet to brown-violet or yellow-brown. **Spo** white.

Common on trunks, stumps and branches of coniferous trees.

Sa ♀

Skeletocutis amorpha

Fr annual, leathery crust-like, with shelf-like, shell-shaped caps. **C** 1 x 2.5 cm. Upper surface faintly zoned, finely felty, whitish, with acute margin. **Tu** up to 1 mm long, yellowish. **Po** 3-4 per mm, circular to angular, whitish to yellow-pink or orange-pink to salmon. **Fl** fibrillose to gelatinous. **Spo** white. On stumps, trunks and branches of coniferous trees, favouring fir.

In Britain, X species of the genus *Skeletocutis* occur.

R Sa ♀

Skeletocutis amorpha

Ceriporia reticulata

Fr annual, waxy, crust-like, ∅ up to several square centimetres, up to 1 mm thick, with whitish, fibrous margin. **Po** circular to polygonal, reticulate, whitish or cream to pale grey. **Spo** white. On the underside of strongly

decayed branches of broad-leaved trees in damp woods.
In Britain, X species of the genera *Cerioporia* and *Ceriporiopsis* occur.

R Sa ♀

Ceriporia reticulata

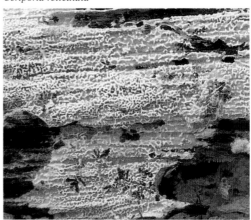

Physisporinus sanguinolentus (Rigidoporus sanguinolentus)

Fr annual, waxy, crust-like, forming strips measuring a few centimetres to several decimetres in length, 2-4 mm thick, with acute, clearly demarcated margin. **Tu** 1-2 mm long, watery white. **Po** 3-5 per mm, circular to angular, white to creamy white, becoming red to brown when touched. **Sm** faint. **Spo** white. Common on stumps and on the underside of branches of broad-leaved trees lying on the ground.

Sa ♀

Physisporinus sanguinolentus

Physisporinus vitreus
(Rigidoporus vitreus)

Fr annual, waxy, crust-like, forming strips measuring a few square centimetres to several decimetres in length, 3-8 mm thick, clearly demarcated margin, occasionally with brown rhizomorphs. **Tu** 2-4 mm long, watery white. **Po** 3-6 per mm, circular, glassy creamy white to ochrous, becoming faintly brownish when touched. **Sm** unpleasant. **Spo** white. Not uncommon on stumps of broad-leaved trees (beech, birch), occasionally spreading onto the fore **St** floor.

Sa ♀

Physisporinus vitreus

Schizopora paradoxa

Fr annual, leathery crust-like, forming strips up to 5 decimetres in length, up to 5 mm thick, with pallid, ciliate or clearly demarcated, occasionally incurved margin. **Tu** 1-4 mm long, creamy white to pale yellow. **Po** 1-3 per mm, highly variable, angular to labyrinthine, slantingly dentate, tiered on perpendicular substrates, white or cream to pale yellow. **Spo** white. Common on branches, trunks and stumps of broad-leaved trees (oak, beech, birch, alder), occasionally on wood of coniferous trees. Also *S. radula* (VR).

Sa ♀

Schizopora flavipora (S. phellinoides)

Fr annual, leathery crust-like to flattened cushion-shaped, forming strips up to many decimetres in length, 2-6 mm thick, with pallid margin. **Tu** 2-6 mm long, cream to yellowish

orange. **Po** 4-7 per mm, circular to angular, cream of yellowish orange to flesh or ochraceous brownish. **Spo** white. Fairly common on branches of broad-leaved trees (oak, birch), occasionally on wood of coniferous trees.

Sa ♀

Schizopora flavipora

Daedalea quercina

MAZE-GILL

Fr annual to perennial, hoof-shaped to semicircular bracket-like, 10-30 x 10-20 cm, 3-7 cm thick. Upper surface lumpy-undulate,

Schizopora paradoxa

123

faintly concentrically zoned, felty, light brown to grey-brown, acute margin. **Tu** irregularly lamelliform, 1-3 mm wide, 1-2 mm thick, light brown. **Po** labyrinthine, walls 1-2 mm apart, buff, occasionally with pink tinge. **Fl** corky, tough, light brown to coffee-brown. **Sm** pleasant. **Spo** white. Common on stumps, trunks or dead parts of oak, occasionally on beams (see photograph of underside in Chapter 1).

Sa (Pa)

Daedalea quercina

Daedaleopsis confragosa

BLUSHING BRACKET

Fr annual, fan-shaped to semicircular, 4-15 x 3-10 cm, 2-4 cm thick. Upper surface concentrically zoned, smooth, matt, ochrous to brown, brown-red towards to the centre, with acute, white-yellowish to brown margin. **Tu** 5-10 mm long, grey-ochre to brown-ochre. **Po**

Daedaleopsis confragosa

irregular, up to 1 mm wide, circular or angular to lamelliform elongate, whitish, grey or light grey to grey-brown, becoming pink-brown when damaged. **Fl** corky, tough, grey-ochre to brown-ochre. **Sm** none. **Spo** white. Common on trunks, branches and stumps of broad-leaved trees (willow, alder, birch). Also *D. tricolor* (VR) with dark red cap and entirely lamelliform hymenium on hazel branches.

Pa (Sa)

Fomes fomentarius

TINDER FUNGUS OR HOOF FUNGUS

Fr perennial, hoof-shaped to bracket-like, 10-30 x 5-20 cm, 10-25 cm thick, with an obtuse, felty growth zone. Upper surface concentrically zoned, smooth, with 1-2 mm thick, dark brown crust, ochraceous brown or red-brown to light or dark grey. **Tu** each layer 2-8 mm, light brown. **Po** 3-4 per mm, circular, cream to light ochre or brownish. **Fl** corky to fibrillose, tough, light brown. **Sm** pleasant. **Spo** white. Fairly common on trunks of birch and beech, occasionally on oak and lime (see photographs of geotropism and of white rot in birch in chapter 1).

Pa (Sa)

Fomes fomentarius

Fomitopsis pinicola

Fr perennial, bracket-like to hoof-shaped, 5-20 x 5-10 cm, 3-15 cm thick, with white, rounded growth zone. Upper surface concentrically zoned, smooth, hard due to resin-like top layer, orange-red to yellow-pink or grey-pink, becoming grey to grey-black at the centre. **Tu** 1-2 mm long, cream to ochrous yellow. **Po** 3-4 per mm, circular, cream or yellowish to brownish, often with yellowish guttation drops. **Fl** hard, tough, cream to ochraceous. **Sm** somewhat sour, irritating. **Spo** white. On often still living trunks of coniferous trees (spruce), occasionally on broad-leaved trees (beech, birch, oak, maple). Also *Fomitopsis* or *Lariciformes officinalis* (VR) on larch.

R RDL Pa (Sa)

Fomitopsis pinicola

Gloeophyllum sepiarium

Gloeophyllum sepiarium

Fr annual to perennial, bracket-like or fan- to shell-shaped, often with caps fusing or growing in rosettes, in rows or imbricated, 6-20 x 2-8 cm, 6-10 mm thick. Upper surface concentrically zoned, bristly-hairy to smooth, tobacco-brown or yellow-brown to red-brown or dark brown, with white to yellow-brown marginal zone. **Po** lamelliform, 5-20 per cm, 4-10 mm wide, often strongly decurrent on the substrate, creamy ochre to grey-brown. **Fl** thin, tough, tobacco-brown. **Spo** white. Fairly common on trunks and stumps of coniferous trees in woods and on fence posts and processed wood of coniferous trees in buildings.

Sa

Gloeophyllum abietinum

Fr annual to perennial, bracket-like or fan- to shell-shaped, occasionally with caps fusing or growing in rosettes, in rows or imbricated, 4-8 x 2-5 cm, 5-10 mm thick. Upper surface concentrically zoned, bristly-hairy to smooth, tobacco-brown or red-brown to brown-black, with whitish to yellow-brown marginal zone.

Po lamelliform, 8-13 per cm, 4-10 mm wide, often decurrent on substrate, cream to grey-brown. **Fl** thin, tough, tobacco-brown. **Spo** white. On trunks and processed wood of coniferous trees.
Also the strongly scented *G. odoratum* (R) and *G. trabeum* (R).

R Sa

Gloeophyllum abietinum

Abortiporus biennis (Heteroporus biennis)

Fr annual, fan- to rosette-shaped in stemmed tufts, diameter 8-20 cm, with thin, undulate margin. **C** 3-9 cm long, 5-30 mm thick. Upper surface finely velvety-felty, whitish or ochraceous to red-brownish. **Tu** 2-5 mm long, white. **Po** 1-3 per mm, irregularly reticulate to labyrinthine, whitish, staining pink-reddish

Abortiporus biennis

brown on bruising. **St** usually sunk into the soil, 4-7 x 2-3 cm, covered with soil. **Fl** soft to hard, white. **Sm** unpleasant. **Spo** white. Occasionally together with the anamorph *Ceriomyces terrestris* in the form of white bulbs with red guttation drops. Fairly common on stumps or apparently on the ground on tree roots and buried wood of (living) broad-leaved trees (poplar, beech, oak). Summer to autumn.

Pa (Sa)

Grifola frondosa

Fr annual, fan-shaped to broadly tongue- or spatula-shaped, with several leathery caps growing from a single central, repeatedly branched stem, Ø 20-50 cm. **C** 4-10 cm wide, 5-10 mm thick, with lateral stem. Upper surface fibrillose-wrinkled, cream or ochrous brown to grey-brown. **Tu** 2-5 mm long, whitish. **Po** 2 per mm, circular to polygonal, whitish to cream. **Fl** fibrillose, white. **Sm** pleasantly fresh. **Spo** white. At the base and on the roots or stumps of old oak. Summer to autumn.
Also *Polyporus umbellatus* (VR RDL), which shows more branching.

R RDL Pa 🐷

Grifola frondosa

Hapalopilus rutilans (H. nidulans)

Fr annual, cushion-shaped to semicircular bracket-like or kidney-shaped. **C** 3-12 x 2-8 cm, with acute, incurvate margin. Upper surface velvety-felty, cinnamon to ochraceous brown. **Tu** 4-10 mm long, grey-brown. **Po** 2-4 per mm, circular to polygonal, grey-brown to cinnamon. **Fl** fibrillose to corky, tough, pale cinnamon. **Sm** sweetish. **Spo** white. Fairly common on branches and trunks of broad-leaved trees (birch, oak, mountain ash). Geotropism due to tilting of the substrate.

Sa

Hapalopilus rutilans

Heterobasidion annosum

ROOT FOMES

Fr perennial, thick, crust-like with free, semicircular, flattened bracket-like cap or caps. **C** 5-15 x 3-10 cm, up to 3 cm thick. Upper surface concentrically grooved-zoned, a fairly smooth, hard crust, light brown or red-brown to dark brown or black, with acute,

Heterobasidion annosum

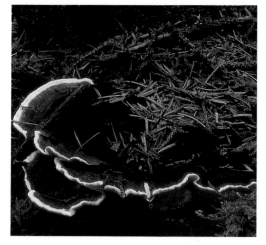

white to red-brown growth zone. **Tu** each layer 3-6 mm long, cream to pale ochre. **Po** 3-5 per mm, circular to angular, whitish to ochre. **Fl** woody, whitish to cream. **Sm** strong, sweetish. **Spo** white. Common on stumps and trunks and at the base of living coniferous trees, occasionally on broad-leaved trees.

Pa (Sa)

Ischnoderma benzoinum

Fr annual, flattened bracket-like to fan-shaped. **C** 4-20 x 3-15 cm. Upper surface concentrically undulate, radially furrowed, rough to felty, later smooth, dark red-brown to black, with acute, undulate, whitish to yellow-brown margin. **Tu** 5-8 mm long, light ochre. **Po** 4-6 per mm, circular, white to ochrous, staining brown when touched. **Fl** juicy, light ochre. **Spo** white.
Fairly common on stumps and trunks of coniferous trees.

Sa

Ischnoderma benzoinum

Laetiporus sulphureus

SULPHUR POLYPORE

Fr annual, semicircular bracket-like to fan-shaped, often imbricated. **C** 10-30 cm wide, 1-5 mm thick. Upper surface irregularly undulate, velvety, sulphur-yellow to orange, zoned towards the downcurved margin. **Tu** 3-5 mm long, sulphur-yellow. **Po** 3-5 per mm, circular to elongate, sulphur-yellow, occasionally with guttation drops. **Fl** juicy, sulphur-yellow, later crumbly like goat's cheese, whitish grey. **Spo**

white. Common on trunks and stumps of living broad-leaved trees (oak, willow, Robinia, cherry) in open landscapes. Spring to autumn.

Pa 🔕

Laetiporus sulphureus

Ceriomyces aurantiacus

An anamorph or imperfect form of Sulphur Polypore (Laetiporus sulphureus) also occurs. **Fr** annual, bulbous or flattened cushion-shaped, 5-15 x 3-7 cm, 2-5 cm thick, soft, velvety, sulphur-yellow to yellow-brown, often with large, pale guttation drops, disintegrating to a cinnamon mass. (Chlamydo)-spores cinnamon. In hollows in oak trunks.

VR Pa?

Meripilus giganteus

GIANT POLYPORE

Fr annual, in a tuft consisting of multiple, imbricated, fan-shaped to semicircular caps, ⌀ 20-80 cm. **C** 10-30 cm wide, 1-3 cm thick. Upper surface undulate, concentrically zoned, felty, yellow to dark red-brown, growing from a bulb, with acute, undulate, appendiculate, whitish to black margin. **Tu** up to 10 mm long, whitish cream. **Po** 3-5 per mm, white to cream, becoming brown-black when touched. **Fl**

fibrillose, soft, whitish cream. **Sm** mushroomy. **Spo** white. Common at the base and apparently on the ground on roots of old, living broad-leaved trees (beech, oak, lime). Summer to autumn.

Pa

Meripilus giganteus

Phaeolus schweinitzii

Fr annual, fan-shaped to flattened funnel-shaped, stem attached centrally or eccentrically, occasionally fused together. **C** ⌀ 8-30 cm, 1-

Ceriomyces aurantiacus

4 mm thick. Upper surface concentrically zoned, felty, orange to dark brown or red-brown or black, with a sulphur-yellow to green-yellow, acute marginal zone. **Tu** 5-10 mm long, brown. **Po** maze-like, green-yellow. **St** 3-8 x 2-5 cm, brown. **Fl** juicy, brown. **Sm** somewhat sour. **Spo** white. Fairly common at the base or on the roots of living coniferous trees, also on stumps. Summer to autumn.

Pa

Phaeolus schweinitzii

Piptoporus betulinus

BIRCH POLYPORE OR RAZOR-STROP POLYPORE

Fr annual, flattened cushion-shaped to bracket-like or fan-shaped, laterally attached. **C** 5-30 x 5-20 cm, 2-5 cm thick. Upper surface smooth, creamy white to ochrous brown or grey-brown, with rolled in margin. **Tu** 4-8 mm long, creamy

Piptoporus betulinus

white. **Po** 3-4 per mm, circular to angular, white to creamy white. **Fl** corky, soft, white. **Sm** pleasant. Common on trunks and thick branches of living and dead birch (see photograph of brown rot in birch in Chapter 1). Summer to autumn.

Pa (Sa)

Polyporus squamosus

DRYAD'S SADDLE OR SCALY POLYPORE

Fr annual, funnel-shaped to circular or oval fan-shaped with lateral to central stem *(f. rostkovii)*. **C** ⌀ 5-60 cm, 1-5 cm thick. Upper surface with concentric rings of fibrillose, dark brown scales, cream to ochraceous yellow, with acute margin. **Tu** 3-10 mm long, decurrent, yellow. **Po** 0.5-1 per mm, irregularly angular-oval, whitish to creamy ochre. **St** 3-10 x 2-6 cm, creamy ochre with brown-black base. **Fl** leathery, white to cream. **Sm** mealy. **Spo** white. Common on stumps, trunks and wound areas on the trunks of living and dead broad-leaved trees (ash, elm, beech, willow, maple, poplar). Often two fruitings per year. Spring to autumn.

Pa (Sa)

Polyporus squamosus

Polyporus brumalis

Fr annual, flattened funnel-shaped with central stem. **C** ⌀ 2-7 cm. Upper surface faintly zoned, finely felty, grey-brown to red-brown or dark brown, with acute, appendiculate margin. **Tu** 2-4 mm long, somewhat decurrent, creamy white to ochre. **Po** 2-3 per mm, circular or angular to elongate, creamy white to ochre. **St** 1-7 cm x 2-8 mm, finely felty-scaly, brown to grey-brown. **Fl** leathery, tough, whitish. **Spo** white.

Common on dead branches, trunks and stumps of broad-leaved trees (birch, ash, oak, beech). Winter (see photograph of pores in Chapter 1).

Sa ♀

Polyporus brumalis

Polyporus ciliatus f. *ciliatus*

Fr annual, (flattened) funnel-shaped with central stem. **C** ∅ 1-4 cm. Upper surface occasionally concentrically zoned, velvety to finely scaly, olive brown or grey-brown to yellow-brown, with acute, strongly ciliate margin. **Tu** 1-2 mm long, white. **Po** 5-6 per mm, circular, white. **St** 2-3 cm x 1-3 mm, felty, matt, brown to brown and yellow-brown dotted zones. **Spo** white. On branches lying on the ground (alder). Summer.

R Sa ♀

Polyporus ciliatus f. *ciliatus*

Polyporus ciliatus f. *lepideus*

Fr annual, (flattened) funnel-shaped with centrally attached stem. **C** ∅ 4-8 cm. Upper surface occasionally concentrically zoned, velvety to finely scaly, olive brown or grey-

Polyporus ciliatus f. *lepideus*

brown to yellowish or yellow-brown, with acute, faintly ciliate to not-ciliate, inrolled margin. **Tu** 1-3 mm long, somewhat decurrent, white. **Po** 5-6 per mm, circular, white. **St** 2-5 cm x 5-12 mm, felty, matt, with brown and yellow-brown dotted zones, with pallid, swollen base. **Spo** white. Common on branches, trunks and stumps of broad-leaved trees (alder, willow, birch, beech, oak). Spring.

Sa ♀

Polyporus ciliatus f. *lepideus*

Polyporus badius

Fr annual, (flattened) funnel- to fan-shaped with central or eccentric stem. **C** ∅ 2-25 cm. Upper surface smooth, shiny, dark red-brown with light red-brown to yellowish marginal zone and undulate, acute margin. **Tu** 0.5-2 mm long, decurrent, ochre. **Po** 6-8 per mm, circular to angular, white or cream to light brown. **St** 1-5 x 0.5-2 cm, velvety, brown-black. **Spo** white.

Polyporus badius

Polyporus tuberaster

Common on dead branches, trunks and stumps of broad-leaved trees (poplar, willow, ash, beech). Spring to autumn.

Sa ♀

Polyporus tuberaster

Fr annual, (flattened) funnel-shaped with central stem. **C** ∅ 3-10 cm, 10-15 mm thick. Upper surface with more or less concentric, adpressed, pointed, dark yellow-brown scales, hairy at the tips, yellow-brown to orange-brown with a cream to ochre background, with undulate, acute, fringed margin. **Tu** 1-4 mm long, strongly decurrent, whitish cream. **Po** 0.5-2 per mm, circular to elongate, dentate, cream to yellowish. **St** 1-6 cm x 5-15 mm, pale yellow, with white, downy base. The stem can root through the substrate and end in a deeply buried **bulbous** sclerotium. **Fl** soft, elastic, white. **Sm** mushroomy. **Spo** white.

Not uncommon on branches, trunks and stumps of various broad-leaved trees (maple, willow, alder, beech) on rich (clayey) soil. Spring to summer.

Sa ♀

Polyporus varius

Fr annual, slantingly funnel- to kidney- or fan-shaped, with eccentric to central stem. **C** ∅ 1-8 cm. Upper surface smooth, matt, ochraceous yellow to pale brown or orange-brown with acute, undulate, appendiculate margin. **Tu** 0.5-2 mm long, decurrent, cream to ochre. **Po** 4-6 per mm, circular to angular, whitish or cream to ochraceous brown or grey-brown. **St** 1-5 cm x 3-10 mm, smooth, matt, cream to brown, with clearly demarcated, black margin or lower part. **Fl** corky, tough, white. **Sm** pleasant. **Spo** white. Common on branches, stumps and trunks of broad-leaved trees (beech, willow, poplar, ash). Summer to autumn.

Also *P. arcularius* (R) and *P. melanopus* (VR).

Sa ♀

Polyporus varius

Ganoderma lipsiense (G. applanatum)

Fr perennial, thick to flattened bracket-like. **C** ∅ 10-70 x 5-30 cm, 2-10 cm thick. Upper surface concentrically grooved, lumpy, smooth, with impressible crust, light brown or cinnamon to grey-brown to black, often powdered rusty brown with spores, with undulate, white margin becoming acute. **Tu** each layer 5-20 mm long, red-brown. **Po** 5-6 per mm, cinnamon, white to cream, becoming permanently brown when damaged, occasionally with nipple-shaped galls. **Fl** corky-fibrillose, red-brown to dark brown. **Sm** mushroomy. **Spo** (light) brown. Common on trunks and stumps of broad-leaved trees, occasionally on coniferous trees (see photographs of pores and nipple-shaped galls in Chapter 1, and the photograph on p. 6).

Pa (Sa)

Ganoderma lipsiense

Ganoderma australe (G. adspersum)

Fr perennial, bracket-like. **C** 10-30 x 10-25 cm, 4-10 cm thick. Upper surface irregularly undulate, cru **St** hard, not impressible, matt, yellow-brown to dark brown or black-brown, often powdered rusty brown

Ganoderma australe

with spores, with obtuse, cream to yellowish growth zone. **Tu** each layer 10-15 mm long, red-brown. **Po** 4-5 per mm, circular, white to cream, becoming permanently brown when damaged, without galls. **Fl** corky, tough, dark red-brown. **Sm** faint. **Spo** brown.

Fairly common on trunks of living broad-leaved trees or stumps of broad-leaved trees (willow, beech, oak, maple, horse chestnut, Catalpa).

Pa (Sa)

Ganoderma lucidum

Fr annual, fan- to kidney-shaped, with eccentric stem. **C** Ø 10-25 cm, 2-3 cm thick. Upper surface concentrically furrowed-zoned, smooth, impressible crust, shiny as if varnished, ochre or orange-brownish red to purple-brown or black-brown, with whitish or yellowish to brown-red marginal zone. **Tu** 5-20 mm long, cream to yellowish. **Po** 4-5 per mm, circular, whitish or cream to yellow-brown. **St** 10-25 x 1-3 cm, smooth, shiny, dark brown-red. **Fl** corky, tough, cream. **Spo** white. At the base of or in hollows of trunks, and on stumps of broad-leaved trees (beech, oak).

R Pa (Sa)

Ganoderma lucidum

Ganoderma pfeifferi

Fr perennial, bracket-like. **C** Ø 15-25 x 10-15 cm, 8-15 cm thick. Upper surface smooth, shiny, with impressible crust, copper-red-brown to violet-brown or purple-brown, with a yellow, waxy resinous layer under the crust, which is inflammable if you hold a lighted match to it, with obtuse, yellow-orange growth zone. **Tu** each layer 10-15 mm long, red-brown. **Po** 4-5 per mm, circular, whitish to

Ganoderma pfeifferi

yellowish. **Fl** corky, tough, red-brown. **Sm** pleasant. **Spo** brown. On trunks and stumps of old broad-leaved trees (beech, oak) in parks and on country estates on clay.
Also *G. resinaceum* (R).

Fistulina hepatica

Fr annual, bracket-like to tongue-shaped, laterally attached. **C** ∅ 7-20 x 10-20 cm, 2-5 cm thick. Upper surface rough, salmon or orange-red to vinaceous red or rusty brown, often slimy-viscid, occasionally with moisture dripping from the margin, with acute margin. **Tu** 5-10 mm long, whitish cream. **Po** 2-3 per mm, circular, whitish to yellowish, often with guttation drops. **Fl** juicy, soft, white-yellow to orange-red or wine red. **Sm** pleasant. **Ta** somewhat sour. **Spo** white.

Common at the base of or on wounds on the trunks of living oak and on oak stumps.

Pa ⑭

Fistulina hepatica

Clavariaceae, Ramariaceae

A group of Basidiomycetes with annual, more or less stemmed, club-shaped, or repeatedly branched, coral-shaped fruiting bodies. Spore print white, yellowish, ochrous brown.

Typhula erythropus

Fr stemmed, club-shaped, 1-3 cm high. Upper quarter to half cylindrical, 0.5-1 mm thick, with round top, smooth, white. **St** filiform, 0.1-0.3 mm thick, finely hairy, red-brown,

with an oval, red-brown **sclerotium** at the dark base.

Common on leaf stems and twigs of broad-leaved trees and occasionally on the stems of grass, ferns and stinging nettles.

Sa ♀

Typhula erythropus

Typhula phacorrhiza

Fr filiform, 2-8 cm x 0.5-1 mm. Upper two thirds with obtuse, pallid or pointed dark top, smooth, cream to honey-yellow. **St** smooth, yellow, with a lentil-shaped, 2-4 mm long, pale brown **sclerotium** at the faintly felty base. Common on fallen leaves and humus of broad-leaved trees. In large groups.

Typhula phacorrhiza

Also *Macrotyphula juncea* = *Clavariadelphus junceus* without sclerotia.
In Britain, about 15 species of the genus *Typhula* occur.

Sa

Macrotyphula fistulosa (Clavariadelphus fistulosus)

Fr slender, club-shaped, 3-20 x 0.5-1 cm, hollow. Upper two thirds with obtuse top, matt, ochraceous yellow or chamois-coloured to reddish ochraceous brown. **St** matt, ochraceous yellow to reddish ochraceous brown, with tapering, felty-woolly base. Fairly common on dead trunks, branches and twigs of broad-leaved trees (alder, birch). The small, squat, occasionally branched variety contorta occurs on small branches.

Sa

Macrotyphula fistulosa

Clavaria argillacea

MOOR CLUB

Fr club-shaped, 3-8 cm x 2-8 mm. Upper part with obtuse top, matt, pale dingy yellow to green-yellow. **St** smooth, bright yellow. Not uncommon on poor, acid sandy soil, along heath paths, in sand drifts and sand dunes.

RDL Sa

Clavaria argillacea

Clavaria falcata (C. acuta)

Fr slender, clubs, 1-8 cm x 1-3 mm. Upper part matt, white. **St** smooth, white. On the ground in poor pastures and meadowlands, roadsides and open woodland.

A white *Typhula* with pale grey stem is also visible.

R Sa

Clavaria falcata

Clavaria daulnoyae

Fr club-shaped, 3-5 cm x 3-4 mm. Upper part somewhat flattened, with rounded apex, matt, white or whitish grey to dingy grey-yellow. **St** smooth, whitish grey to dingy grey-yellow. On soil rich in minerals or nutrients on bare patches in grasslands and open woodland.

In Britain, more than 15 species of the genus *Clavaria* occur.

R Sa

Clavaria daulnoyae

Clavulinopsis corniculata

Clavulinopsis corniculata

Fr growing from a stem, once or repeatedly branched, with antler-like, forked tips, 2-5 cm high. Branches 2-4 mm thick, tips forked, U-shaped, with obtuse apex, smooth, egg-yellow to ochraceous yellow, with more pallid margin. **St** smooth, egg-yellow. **Fl** fragile, yellowish. Not uncommon on the ground among grass and moss in unmanured, poor pasture and meadowlands, roadsides, dykes and open edges of woods.

RDL Sa

Clavulinopsis helveola

Fr slender, club-shaped, often curved/twisted, 1-6 cm x 2-4 mm. Upper part with acute apex, smooth, egg-yellow. **St** smooth, egg-yellow with pale yellow base. **Floccose** firm, fibrillose, pale yellow.
Not uncommon on the ground among grass and moss in open edges of woods, grassy roadsides, dykes, pasture and meadowlands.

In Britain, 10 species of the genus *Clavulinopsis* occur.

RDL Sa

Clavulinopsis helveola

Clavariadelphus pistillaris

GIANT CLUB

Fr slender to broad club-shaped, 10-20 x 2-6 cm, with rounded apex. Outer surface longitudinally wrinkled, matt, light yellow to orange-brown or brown-yellow, occasionally cinnamon with lilac tinge, darker at the tapering base. **Fl** mushroomy, soft, white, becoming violet-brown when cut. **Sm** faint, pleasant. On litter or wood chips in broad-leaved woods and parks on calcareous soils.

VR RDL Sa ⑨⑩

Clavariadelphus pistillaris

Clavulina coralloides (C. cristata)

CRESTED CORAL FUNGUS

Fr growing from one or several stems, repeatedly branched, coral-shaped, with apices branched once or repeatedly, 2-8 cm high. Branches 5-10 mm thick, with branched tips, tips pointed or dentate, smooth, white to cream or pale ochre. **Fl** fragile, white. **Sm** none. Common on humous soil in broad-leaved woods and shrubberies, often along paths and the sides of ditches. Often in groups.

Sa (M?) ⑩

Clavulina coralloides

Clavulina cinerea

GREY CORAL FUNGUS

Fr growing from a short stem, repeatedly branched, coral-shaped, 3-10 cm high. Branches

Clavulina cinerea

4-8 mm wide, round to flattened, forking, with round to dentate tip 1-2 mm wide, ochre with lilac tinge to grey-lilac or violet-grey. **St** whitish to grey-lilac. **Fl** tough, white. **Sm** musty. Fairly common on the ground among humus in broad-leaved and coniferous woods.

Sa (M) 🔪

Clavulina rugosa

WRINKLED CLUB

Fr sparsely-branched, antler-shaped, 5-6 x 0.5-1 cm. Branches slender, club-shaped or flattened, twisted, sparsely-branched or branched at the tip, tips round to flattened, wrinkled, dingy white to ochre. **Fl** elastic, white. **Sm** none. Not uncommon on humus-rich soil in broad-leaved woods and avenues (oak).

Sa (M) 🔪

Clavulina rugosa

Ramaria abietina (R. ochraceovirens)

Fr growing from a common base, repeatedly branched, coral-shaped, with ends branched once or repeatedly, 3-6 cm high. Branches 2-5 mm thick, round to flattened, ochrous to olive yellow, the pointed tips in particular becoming green-blue when touched and with age. **St** 3-14 mm thick, olive yellow, with white mycelium strands. **Fl** tough, white. Fairly common on litter of coniferous trees (spruce), occasionally of broad-leaved trees (hawthorn, *Salix repens*).

Sa

Ramaria flava

Fr repeatedly branched, coral-shaped, 6-15 cm high, 10-15 cm wide. Branches 1-3 cm thick, repeatedly branched U- or V-shaped, usually ending in a double, pointed tip, sulphur-yellow to light egg-yellow. **St** 5-7 cm thick, sulphur-yellow, white at the base. **Fl** soft, whitish.

On the ground in broad-leaved and coniferous woods in the Ardennes and in alpine regions.

M 🔪

Ramaria flava

Ramaria formosa

Fr repeatedly branched, coral-shaped, 10-15 cm high, 10-20 cm wide. Branches 1-2 cm thick, repeatedly branched U-shaped, usually ending in a double or triple, pointed tip, salmon-yellow to salmon-orange with yellow tips. **St** 4-5 cm thick, salmon to salmon-

Ramaria abietina

yellow, with whitish, tapering base. **Fl** soft, white. On the ground in avenues with broad-leaved trees (beech, oak) on poor, calcareous soils.

VR RDL M? Deadly †

Ramaria formosa

Ramaria stricta

Fr repeatedly branched, coral-shaped, 4-10 cm high, 3-8 cm wide. Branches 1-5 mm thick, with perpendicular, parallel branches, with repeatedly branched, thorn- or tooth-like tips, yellow-ochre with flesh tinge to light cinnamon, with yellowish tips. **St** 1-4 cm x 5-15 mm, ochre to flesh, occasionally with vinaceous red tinge, with tapering base with white rhizomorphs. **Fl** tough, white to pale

Ramaria stricta

yellow. Fairly common on plant debris (marram grass, *Ammophila arenaria*) and branches, wood chips and stumps of broad-leaved trees (see also photograph of *Lepiota aspera*).
In Britain, X species of the genera *Ramaria* and *Ramariopsis* occur.

Sa

Pterula multifida

Fr repeatedly branched, hairy-bristly, 3-8 cm high. Branches 1 mm thick, repeatedly forked-branched, with pointed tips, ochraceous brown to lilac-brown, with whitish ends. **St** short, ochraceous brown to lilac-brown. **Fl** elastic, whitish. On litter of coniferous trees, occasionally on humus of broad-leaved trees (willow, poplar). Often in groups.
Also the much smaller *P. gracilis* (R), on dead plant stems.

R RDL Sa

Pterula multifida

Sparassis crispa

CAULIFLOWER OR BRAIN FUNGUS

Fr globose to cushion-shaped, cauliflower-like or like a natural sponge, 10-50 x 10-30 cm, 10-15 cm high. Branches lobed, leaf-shaped to broad spatula-shaped, curly, smooth, cream or pale ochre to dark yellow-brown, margin becoming brown. **St** short, yellow-brown. **Fl** tough, pale yellow. **Sm** pleasantly sweetish. **Spo** white to pale yellow.
Fairly common on roots of coniferous trees on

(loamy) sandy soil. Also *S. spathulata* = *laminosa* (VR), on roots of broad-leaved and coniferous trees.

Pa 🍴

Sparassis crispa

Cantharellaceae

A group of Basidiomycetes with a cap and a stem and with the hymenium on folds, ribs or ridges under the cap.

Cantharellus cibarius

Cantharellus cibarius

CHANTERELLE

Fr flattened funnel-shaped. **C** ∅ 3-10 cm, plane, with inrolled, undulate margin, pale to deep egg-yellow. Lower surface with irregularly forked, decurrent, vein-like ridges, egg-yellow. **St** 3-8 cm x 5-15 mm, with tapering base, egg-yellow. **Fl** fibrillose, yellowish. **Sm** faint, agreeable. **Ta** watery-peppery. **Spo** ochre. Fairly common near coniferous and broad-leaved trees (fir, oak, birch, beech) on poor, acid sandy soil.

RDL M 🍴

Cantharellus tubaeformis

Fr trumpet- to funnel-shaped. **C** ∅ 2-6 cm, depressed, smooth to scaly, with irregularly undulate margin, yellow-brown to dark dingy brown. Lower surface with narrow, irregularly branched, decurrent, lamelliform ridges, yellowish to grey-brown. **St** 2-10 cm x 5-10 mm, hollow, grooved or flattened, dingy yellow to olivaceous yellow. **Fl** tough, yellowish. **Sm** faint. **Ta** mild. **Spo** yellowish. Near beech and oak in broad-leaved woods, avenues and wooded banks on poor, acid sandy soil. Often in groups.

R RDL M 🍴

Cantharellus tubaeformis

Cantharellus aurora (C. lutescens)

Fr trumpet- to funnel-shaped. **C** Ø 2-6 cm, depressed, matt, with irregularly undulate margin, yellow-brown to orange-brown. Lower surface with irregularly branched, decurrent wrinkles, light to dark orange-pinkish yellow. **St** 2-7 cm x 5-10 mm, hollow, grooved, light to dark golden yellow or orange-yellow. **Fl** fibrillose, yellowish. **Sm** pleasant. **Ta** mild. **Spo** yellowish. In broad-leaved and coniferous woods.

M (Y)

Cantharellus aurora

Craterellus cornucopioides

HORN OF PLENTY

Fr trumpet-shaped to depressed funnel-shaped. **C** Ø 2-8 cm, depressed, radially striate-grooved, with a curled, undulate margin, greyish brown to black. Lower surface with irregularly branched, close ribs and ridges, pruinose, matt, grey to grey-brown or

grey-black. **St** 3-10 cm long, hollow, grey-brown to black. **Fl** fibrillose, grey. **Sm** pleasant. **Ta** mild. **Spo** white. Near beech and *Quercus robur* on poor sandy or loamy soils. Often in tufts or groups.

VR RDL M (Y)

Craterellus cornucopioides

Pseudocraterellus undulatus (P. sinuosus)

Fr trumpet- to funnel-shaped. **C** Ø 1-5 cm, depressed, with appendiculate, undulate, lighter margin, loam-coloured grey-brown or nut-brown to sepia. Lower surface irregularly veined-ribbed, buff to grey-buff. **St** 3-6 cm x 3-8 mm, hollow, grooved, sand-yellow to brown-buff, with tapering base. **Fl** soft, fibrillose, grey-brown. **Sm** fruity. **Spo** white. Near broad-leaved trees (oak, beech) in woods and avenues on clay and poor sandy or loamy soils. Often in tufts or groups.

VR RDL M (Y)

Pseudocraterellus undulatus

GASTEROMYCETES

A highly diverse group of Basidiomycetes with fruiting bodies in which the spores are formed on an internal hymenium, not exposed to the air.

Hymenogastrales

A small group of Gasteromycetes growing either entirely underground or in the soil at surface level.

Rhizopogon luteolus

OKERKLEURIGE VEZELTRUFFEL

Fr irregularly globose to bulbous, ∅ 2-8 cm, partly above the surface. Outer surface covered with sparse, branched, brown mycelium strands, dingy white to dingy yellow or brownish. **Fl** with irregular, close cavities, white, deliquescing olive green. **Sm** disagreeably garlicky.
Not uncommon in fir woods on dry, acid sandy soil.

In Britain, X species of the genera *Hymenogaster*, *Melanogaster*, *Octavianina* and *Rhizopogon* occur.

RDL M

Rhizopogon luteolus

Nidulariales

A group of Gasteromycetes in which the spores are packaged in 'eggs' or balls which are launched by rain drops or projected.

Crucibulum crucibuliforme (C. laeve)

COMMON BIRD'S-NEST

Fr closed globose to top-shaped, ∅ 4-8 mm, 3-7 mm high. Outer surface felty, whitish to dingy yellow, with a felty, ochrous yellow membrane, which peels loose at the margin, covering the top of a cup. Cup with dingy white, lens-shaped 'eggs' 1-2 mm in diameter,

Crucibulum crucibuliforme

142

attached to the inner surface with a mycelium strand, inner surface silvery white. Common on branches, twigs and chips of broad-leaved and coniferous trees and on plant stems. In groups.

Sa ♀

Cyathus olla

Fr closed ovoid to top-shaped, ∅ 8-12 mm, 8-15 mm high. Outer surface felty, yellowish grey, with a downy, whitish, irregularly rupturing membrane. Cup with buff 'eggs', 2-3 mm in diameter, attached to to the inner surface by a strand, inner surface smooth, silvery grey. Common on the ground on coarse litter, trunks, stumps and branches of broad-leaved trees and shrubs and plant stems. Usually in groups.
Also *C. stercoreus* (VR RDL).

Sa ♀

Cyathus olla

Cyathus striatus

Fr closed top- to cup-shaped, ∅ 6-8 mm, 7-10 mm high. Outer surface bristly-hairy, brown, with a white, irregularly rupturing membrane. Cup with grey-white 'eggs' 1-2 mm in diameter, attached by a strand, Inner surface striate-furrowed, shiny, light to dark brown-grey.
Common on chips, stumps, coarse litter, branches and twigs of broad-leaved trees and shrubs.

Sa ♀

Nidularia deformis (N. farcta)

Fr globose to ovoid, ∅ 2-10 mm. Outer surface pruinose to smooth, pale yellow-brown or flesh-brown to cinnamon. Rupturing, revealing the yellow-brown, lens-shaped 'eggs' of 1-2 mm in diameter.

On damp twigs and branches of broad-leaved and coniferous trees and fir needles lying on the ground, occasionally on sites of fires.

R Sa ♀

Nidularia deformis

Sphaerobolus stellatus

Fr closed spherical, ∅ 1-2 mm. Outer surface whitish to ochrous yellowish, splitting into 5 to 9 golden yellow or orange-yellow rays, revealing a brown-black ball 1 mm in diameter. After the ball has been projected, the reversed membrane becomes a glassy

Cyathus striatus

white sphere at the centre of the fruiting body. Common on damp, decayed wood of broad-leaved and coniferous trees, occasionally on manure and plant debris.

Sa ♀

Sphaerobolus stellatus

Geastraceae

A group of Gasteromycetes with a sphere at the centre of the stellate fruiting bodies which on ripeness release clouds of dry, brown spores through one central or several scattered openings, when touched or hit by rain drops.

Geastrum triplex

Fr closed onion-shaped, ⌀ 3-5 cm, splitting into 4-8 pointed, fleshy rays, usually with an upturned collar around the parchment-like sphere, with a central opening, which comes loose from the inner surface of the rays, measuring ⌀ 5-15 cm by that time. Lower surface of the rays smooth, cracked, brown to yellow-brown. Inner surface and collar matt, buff to yellow-brown. Sphere ⌀ 15-35 mm, stem absent, with pallid areola around the ciliate opening, light grey-brown.
Fairly common on the ground in broad-leaved and coniferous woods, avenues, parks, dune scrub, dune pastures, churchyards and heaps of rubble.

Sa

Geastrum coronatum

Fr closed globose, with 7-12 pointed rays, ⌀ 4-10 cm. Lower surface of the rays grey, with attached soil. Inner surface light buff or brownish to dull white or light grey-brown.

Geastrum triplex

Sphere ⌀ 15-30 mm, with a clearly de-marcated stem, with a ciliate opening, mealy, light grey or cream to brownish or dark grey. On rich, calcareous sandy soils in broad-leaved woods (ash, elm) and dune-scrub.

R RDL Sa

Geastrum coronatum

whitish or buff to brownish. Sphere ⌀ 10-16 mm, stem absent, with a furrowed areola around the high, conical, ciliate opening, very finely felty, light brown-cream.

On humous, sandy or loamy soil in old broad-leaved woods *(Robinia)*.

VR Sa

Geastrum lageniforme

Geastrum lageniforme

Fr closed onion- to bottle-shaped, with 6-10 slender, long pointed rays, ⌀ 3-6 cm. Lower surface of the rays smooth, blotched yellow-brown to light dingy brown. Inner surface

Geastrum schmidelii (G. nanum)

Fr closed globose, with 6-9 rays, ⌀ 2-4 cm. Lower surface of the rays pale brown, with attached soil. Inner surface light cream with

Geastrum schmidelii

pink tinge to pale brown. Sphere ⌀ 6-11 mm, with clearly demarcated short stem, with a ring-shaped furrow around the broad to high conical, strongly pleated furrowed opening, mealy to smooth, light grey to light brown or light grey-brown or dingy brown. On dune sand deficient in humus in unmanured dune pastures, dune heaths, dunes covered with marram grass *(Ammophila arenaria)* and open dune scrub.

R RDL Sa

Geastrum pectinatum

Fr closed globose to onion-shaped, with 6-10 rays, ⌀ 3-11 cm. Lower surface cream to brownish, with attached soil. Inner surface cream to buff-brown. Sphere ⌀ 14-20 mm, with long stem, with strongly pleated-furrowed opening, mealy, grey-brown to brown-black. On damp sandy, clayey and loamy soils with a thick layer of litter or humus under coniferous trees in coniferous or mixed woods.

R RDL Sa

Geastrum pectinatum

Geastrum quadrifidum

Fr closed globose, with 4 erect rays, attached at the points, ⌀ 2-4 cm. Lower surface whitish to light brown. Inner surface whitish or cream to brown. Sphere ⌀ 5-15 mm, with a clearly demarcated stem, with an areola or ring-shaped furrow around the conical, ciliate opening, mealy, buff-grey to dark grey or pale brown.

On dry to moderately damp sandy soil in coniferous woods with a thick layer of litter.

VR RDL Sa

Geastrum quadrifidum

Geastrum fimbriatum (G. sessile)

Fr closed globose to onion-shaped, with 6-10 rays reflexed downwards, ⌀ 2-4 cm. Lower surface fibrillose, brownish cream, with attached soil. Inner surface white or light cream to light brown. Sphere ⌀ 6-18 mm, stem absent, with conical, ciliate opening, smooth, white to light brown-grey or grey-brown. Not uncommon on sandy or loamy soils or clayey soils in coniferous woods (spruce, fir), occasionally in broad-leaved woods, (dune) shrub, parks and avenues.

Sa

Geastrum fimbriatum

Geastrum rufescens (G. vulgatum)

Fr closed globose, with 5-9 rays, ⌀ 5-12 cm. Lower surface brown and with attached soil. Inner surface cream or pinkish to winered or brown-red. Sphere ⌀ 20-40 mm, stem short or absent, with ciliate opening, felty round smooth, light brown, occasionally with pink tinge.
On fairly rich, humous (dune) sand in broad-leaved woods, parks and avenues (oak, elm), rarely under coniferous trees.

R RDL Sa

Geastrum rufescens

Geastrum campestre

Fr closed globose, with 7-10 occasionally reflexed rays, ⌀ 15-35 mm. Lower surface pale brown with attached soil. Inner surface light cream to dark brown. Sphere ⌀ 9-16 mm, short-stemmed, with a ring zone around the flattened conical, distinctly pleated-furrowed

Geastrum campestre

opening, warty rough, grey or grey-brown to dark brown or black-brown. On (dune) sand deficient in lime and humus in mossy grasslands, hawthorn scrub, in clearings and along paths in broad-leaved and coniferous woods.
In Britain, 16 species of the genus *Geastrum* occur.

VR RDL Sa

Myriostoma coliforme

Fr closed globose to top-shaped, with 6-12 rays, ⌀ 4-12 cm. Outer surface smooth, yellowish to brown. Inner surface whitish or yellowish to brownish or brown-black. Sphere ⌀ 25-50 mm, with 3 to 15 stems, with 3 to 25 preformed, circular openings, granular, light grey to brownish, often with silvery sheen. On dry, calcareous sandy soil with thin layer of litter, especially in sunny locations in dune scrub.

R RDL Sa

Myriostoma coliforme

Myriostoma coliforme

Sclerodermataceae and Lycoperdaceae

A group of Gasteromycetes with fruiting bodies of which the top ruptures to create a wide, deep bowl-shaped, cup-like opening, or developing a small, central opening at the top, through which the olive brown to dark brown spores are expelled when touched or hit by rain drops.

Disciseda bovista

Fr closed globose, ∅ 1-3 cm, growing partly below the surface. When ripe, the leathery outer membrane ruptures at the base and the sphere, on the saucer-shaped covering with reflexed margin, rises above the surface, on which the fruiting body is usually reversed. Inner surface of the saucer grey-brown to red-brown or dark brown. Sphere with irregular, small, central opening, matt, yellow-brown or grey-brown to light grey.
On dry dune sand deficient in humus, on sandy or moss- and grass-covered, sheltered, sunny locations.

Also *D. candida* = *calva* (VR RDL), which can only be distinguished by microscopic features.

VR RDL Sa

Disciseda bovista

Scleroderma citrinum

COMMON EARTH-BALL

Fr irregularly globose to bulbous, ∅ 4-10 cm. Outer surface coarsely scaly, dingy yellow or green-yellow to ochrous brown. **Fl** purple-black, white-veined. Common near broad-leaved trees (oak, birch), occasionally near coniferous trees, on humous sandy soils in woods, parks, avenues, heaths and shrubberies.

M †

Scleroderma citrinum

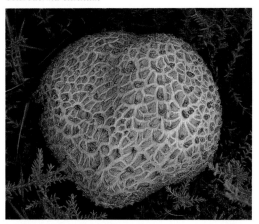

Scleroderma areolatum

Fr irregularly globose to bulbous, ∅ 1-4 cm, short-stemmed. Outer surface covered with flat, dark scales surrounded by a lighter ring, producing a leopard-skin pattern, yellow-brown. **St** 1-2 cm long, rooting with mycelium strands, grooved, smooth, yellowish. **Fl** deeply purple-brown.
Common in broad-leaved and mixed woods, shrubberies, parks and avenues.

M †

Scleroderma areolatum

Scleroderma verrucosum

Fr irregularly globose to bulbous, ∅ 3-7 cm, long-stemmed. Outer surface smooth at first, later covered with small, brownish scales, yellowish to brown. **St** 2-4 cm long, rooting with yellowish mycelium strands, grooved, smooth, whitish cream to yellowish. **Fl** olivaceous brown. Common near broad-leaved trees on rich, humous soils in woods, parks, avenues, heaths and shrubberies. Also *S. bovista* and *S. cepa* (R RDL).

M †

Scleroderma verrucosum

Bovista plumbea

Fr globose, ∅ 2-3 cm, with white mycelium strand. Outer surface matt, white, coming loose in scales or plaques, revealing the green-grey to leaden inner layer. With central opening. **Fl** grey-brown to olive brown. Common on dry to damp sandy soil in haylands, often mowed grasslands, roadsides and dykes and in clearings and along paths in woods and dune scrub.

Sa

Bovista plumbea

Bovista nigrescens

Fr irregularly globose, ∅ 3-6 cm, with white mycelium strand. Outer surface matt, white to yellowish, coming loose in plaques, revealing the dark purple-brown to black inner layer. With large, irregularly rupturing opening. **Fl** dark purple-brown.
Not uncommon on (loamy) sand and clay in moderately manured, grazed grasslands, in clearings in woods, on heaths and in roadsides.

In Britain, 6 species of the genus *Bovista* occur.

Sa

Bovista nigrescens

Calvatia excipuliformis

Fr broadly globose to cushion-shaped, with broad, long stem, ∅ 5-12 cm, up to 15 cm high. Upper surface with spines, which soon disappear, whitish pale grey to brownish, with paper-like, yellowish inner layer. **St** 7-10 cm high, up to 5 cm thick, with disappearing spines, granular, whitish pale grey to light brown, with hollow, pleated, tapering base. **Fl** purple-brown, spongy in the stem, brown.

Common among coarse litter and on especially sandy soils in woods, shrubberies, parks and dry, unmanured grasslands.

Sa 🍽

Calvatia excipuliformis

Calvatia utriformis

Fr squat pear-shaped to broad cushion-shaped with narrow base, with broad, short stem, ⌀ 5-15 cm, up to 15 cm high. Upper part with flat, pyramidal, scaly warts forming a hexagonal

Calvatia utriformis

pattern, white or cream to pale grey-brown, with parchment-like, grey-brown inner layer. **St** 5-8 cm high, whitish cream to grey-brown, with tapering, pleated base. **Fl** olive brown.

Common on usually sandy soil in sparsely manured, dry grasslands, in mossy spots in sand dunes, in broad-leaved and mixed woods and parks.

Sa 🍽

Langermannia gigantea

GIANT PUFFBALL

Fr irregularly to regularly globose, ⌀ 10-80 cm. Outer surface leathery, wrinkled or smooth, matt, white, with mycelium strands at the base. **Fl** white, when ripe sulphur-yellow to olivaceous brown.

Common on rich (sandy) clayey and peaty soil in highly manured pastures, in orchards, roadsides and parks, also in broad-leaved woods and shrubberies, often on recently disturbed ground or dried mud.

Sa 🍽

Langermannia gigantea

Lycoperdon perlatum

Fr pear-shaped to globose, ⌀ 2-6 cm, 3-8 cm high, with stem. Upper part with evanescent spines and conical warts, leaving a regular, reticulate pattern, whitish to yellowish or greyish brown, with a central opening. **St** 2-5 cm high, up to 3 cm thick, warty to smooth, whitish to yellowish grey-brown. **Fl** white to olivaceous brown. Common on humous, usually sandy soil in woods, shrubberies and parks.

Sa 🎨

Lycoperdon perlatum

Lycoperdon pyriforme

Fr pear-shaped, ⌀ 2-4 cm, 1-6 cm high, with stem. Upper part granular, whitish or buff-flesh to chestnut, with a central opening. **St** 1-3 cm long, with fine, dark scales, whitish or buff to brown, with whitish rhizomorphs. **Fl** white to olive brown, white in the stem.

Common on decayed stumps and wood of broad-leaved trees on rich soil. In groups.

Sa 🎨

Lycoperdon pyriforme

Lycoperdon foetidum

Fr spherical to top-shaped, ⌀ 2-5 cm, with short, tapering stem. Outer surface with evanescent, light to dark brown, pyramidal, pointed spines, leaving a regular, reticulate pattern, cream to light or black-brown, with a central opening. **Fl** olive brown.
Common on somewhat acid, humous soils in broad-leaved and mixed woods (oak), shrubberies, parks, poor grasslands and sand valleys.

Sa

Lycoperdon foetidum

Lycoperdon echinatum

Fr spherical to pear-shaped, ⌀ 2-6 cm, with short stem. Outer surface with evanescent spines, 3-6 mm long, pointed, dense, light to

Lycoperdon echinatum

dull brown, leaving a regular reticulate pattern, light to dark brown, with a central opening. **Fl** olivaceous yellow to brown.

On humus-rich, calcareous soil in broad-leaved woods (beech).

VR Sa

Lycoperdon mammiforme (L. mammaeforme)

Fr broadly pear-shaped, ∅ 3-6 cm, 4-8 cm high, with short, broad stem. Outer surface with evanescent, woolly, white to cream warts, remaining at the (base of) the stem in the form of a ring, whitish to pinkish ochraceous brown, with central opening. **Fl** white to yellow-brown.

On rich river clay or calcareous soil in avenues and broad-leaved woods (beech, hornbeam).
In Britain, 13 species of the genus *Lycoperdon* occur.

VR RDL Sa

Lycoperdon mammiforme

Vascellum pratense

Fr spherical to flattened pear- or top-shaped, ∅ 2-5 cm, with short stem. Outer surface granular-spiny, rough, pleated at the transition zone between fruiting body and stem, white or yellowish to olive brown, with broad, central opening. **St** with tapering

pleated base, white or yellowish to brown. **Fl** white to olivaceous brown. Common in roadsides, sparsely manured grasslands, on mossy lawns and close-grazed spots in woods, in shrubberies, parks, heaths and roadsides.

Sa

Vascellum pratense

Tulostomatales

A small group of Gasteromycetes with fruiting bodies in the form of a sphere with a central opening, on a long stem remaining deeply sunk into the soil, with red-brown spores.

Tulostoma melanocyclum

Fr globose to apple-shaped, ∅ 10-20 mm, with long stem. Outer surface smooth, parchment-like, light brown or red-brown to creamy yellow, with a central, papilla-like opening

Tulostoma melanocyclum

surrounded by a brown, ring-shaped zone, ⌀ 1 mm. **St** 2-8 cm x 2-4 mm, tough, yellow-brown with red-brown scales, largely remaining below the surface.

On dry, calcareous dune sand deficient in humus, among mosses and in unmanured, dry grasslands in sand dunes and dune scrub.

R Sa

Tulostoma brumale

Fr globose to apple-shaped, ⌀ 6-15 mm, with long stem. Outer surface smooth, parchment-like, cream or light ochrous brown to whitish, with a central, papilla-like opening surrounded by a yellow to brown ring-shaped zone, ⌀ 1.5 mm. **St** 2-5 cm x 1-3 mm, tough, smooth, ochre, brown towards the base, with basal bulb, largely remaining below the surface.
On dry, calcareous sandy and loamy soil deficient in humus, among mosses in sand dunes, in dune pastures and calcareous grasslands on sunny slopes and on sand drifts covered with vegetation.

Also *T. fimbriatum* (R RDL).

R RDL Sa

Tulostoma brumale

Phallales

A group of Gasteromycetes showing a wide variety of shapes with fruiting bodies on which the spores are released in a slimy substance, after which they are spread by insects attracted by the fetid smell.

Clathrus archeri

Fr growing from a whitish, leathery egg which develops below the surface, ⌀ 2-4 cm, emerging with the extremities of the arms connected. The 4 to 6 arms, on a central stem 2-5 cm high, spread cuttlefish-like and curved downward. Arms 4-7 cm long, fragile, deep-red, with olivaceous green, stinking slime on the reticulately grooved upper surface.

On rich or loamy sand, often on wood chips or decayed wood in roadsides and the edge of broad-leaved woods. Summer to autumn.

Also *C. ruber* (VR) (see photograph of mycophilately).

VR Sa

Clathrus archeri

Mutinus caninus

DOG STINKHORN

Fr growing from a whitish, leathery 'devil's egg' which develops below the surface, ⌀ 2-4 cm, rupturing the outer membrane with a disc or egg tooth. 'Devil's egg' with long, white mycelium strand. **Fr** 8-12 cm high. Upper part conical acorn-shaped, with dark olive green slime with faint smell, below that shallowly honeycombed, orange-red, with ring-shaped disc at the apex. **St** 6-9 x 1-2 cm, mushroomy, hollow, whitish to pale yellow-brown or pale orange. Common on sawdust, coarse humus,

on or near strongly decayed wood of broad-leaved trees in woods, avenues and parks. Summer to autumn.
Also *M. elegans* (VR) and *M. ravenelii* (R).

Sa

Phallus impudicus

STINKHORN

Fr growing from a grey-whitish, leathery 'devil's egg' which develops mostly below the surface, ∅ 3-6 cm, rupturing the outer membrane with a disc or egg tooth. 'Devil's egg' with long, white mycelium strand. **Fr** 10-25 x 2-4 cm. Upper part conical-bell-shaped, with dark olive green

Phallus impudicus

Mutinus caninus

slime with a sweetish stench, below that with wide, deep honeycomb-shapes, white, with ring-shaped disc at the apex. **St** 8-20 x 2-4 cm, spongy, hollow, white. Common on humous, sandy or loamy soil, or on or near strongly decayed wood in woods, shrubberies, parks and gardens. Summer to autumn.

Sa M? 🍴

Phallus hadriani

Fr growing from a whitish, pink to red-violet-tinged 'devil's egg' which develops below the surface, ∅ 3-6 cm, rupturing the outer membrane with a disc or egg tooth. 'Devil's egg' with white mycelium strand. **Fr** 10-15 x 2-3 cm. Upper part conical-bell-shaped, with dark olivaceous green slime with a pleasantly sweetish smell, below that with wide, deep honeycomb-shapes, white, with ring-shaped disc at the apex. **St** 7-11 x 2-3 cm, spongy, hollow, white. On dry, calcareous dune sand deficient in lime, near marram grass *(Ammophila arenaria)* in the outer coastal sand dunes. Summer to autumn.
Also *P. duplicatus = Dictyophora duplicata* (VR) (see photograph of mycophilately).

R RDL Pa

Phallus hadriani

AGARICS AND BOLETI

A group of Basidiomycetes with a cap and a central to eccentric stem or with a shell- or fan-shaped sessile cap and with lamellae or gills on the lower surface of the cap (agarics), or with a cap and a central stem with tubes on the lower surface of the cap (Boleti).

Limacella

A small group of agarics with slimy-viscid caps and free gills, with a ring or ring zone on the stem. **Spo** white.

In Britain, X species of the genus *Limacella* occur.

Limacella guttata

C ovoid at first, then convex to flattened, ⌀ 6-12 cm, slimy-viscid, velvety matt when dry, Isabella or yellow-brown to flesh or brown-pink. **G** narrow, white, occasionally shedding tears when moist. **St** 10-15 x 1-2 cm, whitish, with membranous, whitish ring with droplets

Limacella guttata

leaving grey-brown dots. **Fl** white. **Sm** mealy. In broad-leaved and coniferous woods (spruce) on clay, loam and humus-rich sand.

R RDL Sa (M) 🍄

Limacella glioderma

C campanulate at first, then convex to flattened, ⌀ 3-6 cm, shiny, slimy-viscid, matt when dry, red-brown to orange-brown. **G** wide, whitish to light yellow or cream. **St** 4-6 cm x 7-12 mm, smooth, whitish with pink tinge, woolly-floccose below the evanescent woolly white ring. **Fl** whitish. **Sm** mealy.

In broad-leaved woods on calcareous loam and clay.

VR RDL Sa

Limacella glioderma

Limacella ochraceolutea

C hemispherical at first, then conical to flattened, ⌀ 3-6 cm, shiny, strongly slimy-viscid, viscid when dry, light to ochrous yellow with orange-yellow centre. **G** wide, white to cream. **St** 3-6 cm x 6-10 mm, smooth, whitish yellowish, ochrous yellow to yellow-brown below the slimy ring zone, slimy, with brown fibrils when dry. **Fl** whitish. **Sm** mealy. In broad-leaved woods on calcareous clay or loam.

VR RDL Sa.

Amanita

A group of agarics with a universal veil, usually leaving warts or scales on the cap and/or a volva around the base of the stem, and usually also a partial veil, remaining as a ring on the stem, with free, white gills. **Spo** white. Mycorrhizal.

In Britain, 20 species of the genus Amanita occur.

Amanita muscaria

FLY AGARIC

C globose, then expanded to plane, ∅ 8-20 cm, smooth, bright red, becoming pale orange-yellow, with evanescent, pyramidal and white warts. **G** white. **St** 8-18 x 1-2 cm,

Amanita muscaria

white, floccose at the base, with white to yellowish ring. **Fl** white. **Sm** faint. Common in woods and avenues near broad-leaved trees (birch, oak, beech, lime) and coniferous trees (fir, spruce) on sandy and peaty soil.

M †

Amanita phalloides

DEATH CAP

C globose, then expanded to plane, ∅ 4-12 cm, smooth, finely radially striate, white (var. alba) to greenish or yellowish with olivaceous sheen. **G** close, white. **St** 7-10 x 1-2 cm, smooth, below the pendulous, membranous, white ring smooth or membranous-floccose, around the bulbous base white, with a white to cream volva. **Fl** white. **Sm** sickly sweet. Fairly common in broad-leaved woods and avenues, particularly near oak, on rich soil.

M Lethally †

Amanita phalloides

Amanita citrina var. *citrina*

FALSE DEATH CAP

C globose, then convex to plane, ∅ 4-10 cm, smooth, ivory-white to pale lemon-yellow at the centre, often covered with white to yellowish brown patches. **G** white. **St** 6-8 cm x 8-12 mm, striate above the membranous, white ring, ivory-white, yellowish at the apex, the large, bulbous base encased in a volva. **Fl** white. **Sm** of raw potatoes. Common in broad-leaved and mixed woods (oak and beech), on sandy soil.

M 🚫

Amanita citrina var. *citrina*

Amanita citrina var. alba

C globose, then convex to plane, ⌀ 4-10 cm, smooth, white, frequently covered with white to yellowish patches. **G** white. **St** 6-8 cm x 8-12 mm, smooth, white below the membranous, white ring with floccose zones, the large, bulbous base encased in a white volva. **Fl** white. **Sm** faint, of raw potatoes. In broad-leaved and mixed woods, particularly near oak and beech, on sandy soil.

R M 🚫

Amanita citrina var. *alba*

Amanita pantherina

PANTHER CAP

C globose, then convex to expanded, ⌀ 6-10 cm, smooth, ochraceous to dark brown, with white, warty scales. **G** close, white. **St** 9-13 cm x 10-15 mm, smooth, white, with frayed, pendulous white ring, with ring-like floccose zones at the base and the strongly swollen base encased in a white volva. **Fl** white. **Sm** faint, pleasant. Fairly common to rare near broad-leaved trees (oak, beech, birch), occasionally near coniferous trees, in broad-leaved and mixed woods and avenues.

M †

Amanita pantherina

Amanita rubescens

THE BLUSHER

C globose, then convex to plane, ⌀ 5-15 cm, smooth, pink-brown to flesh, with white to pink-red patches. **G** white, staining wine red when damaged. **St** 7-12 x 1-2 cm, smooth,

Amanita rubescens

white below the membranous, pendulous, striate white ring (occasionally yellow ring: var. *annulosulphurea*), scaly-felty, white to red-brown, with bulbous base with velar remnants. **Fl** white, becoming pink-red. **Sm** faint. Common in broad-leaved and coniferous woods and avenues on poor soil.

M ⊕

Amanita gemmata

C hemispherical, then convex to plane, ⌀ 5-7 cm, smooth, pale ochrous yellow to lemon-yellow, with white patches and a pallid, striate margin. **G** white. **St** 7-10 cm x 8-12 mm, smooth, white, pale yellow at the apex, with an evanescent, white ring, the large bulbous base encased in a membranous volva. **Fl** white. **Sm** faint. Fairly common in broad-leaved and coniferous woods and avenues, near beech, oak and fir, on poor, acid soil. Summer to autumn.

RDL M †

Amanita porphyria

C obtusely conical, then convex to plane, ⌀ 5-9 cm, smooth, silky, grey-brown to red-brown. **G** white. **St** 10-13 cm x 8-15 mm, striate,

whitish with grey-violet base, with thin, striate, grey-violet ring and a pronouncedly rimmed, bulbous base, encased in a volva. **Fl** white. **Sm** musty. In broad-leaved and coniferous woods (fir) and avenues on poor sandy soil.

R RDL M 🔟

Amanita ceciliae (A. inaurata)

C conical, then wide campanulate to expanded, ⌀ 7-12 cm, smooth, ochrous brown to dark grey-brown, with striate margin and

Amanita porphyria

large, dingy grey patches. **G** white. **St** 10-13 cm x 15-30 mm, pale yellow-brown, with horizontal, floccose, whitish zones, at the base 2 to 3 ring-like zones and a bulbous base encased in a volva. **Fl** white. **Sm** faint. Near broad-leaved trees, particularly oak, in broad-leaved woods and avenues on river clay.

VR RDL M

Amanita ceciliae

Amanita lividopallescens

C conical, then campanulate, ∅ 8-12 cm, smooth, light or dark greyish or salmonpink-ochrous yellow to brown-grey, occasionally with dingy white patches, with faintly striate margin. **G** white to cream. **St** 7-12 x 1-3 cm,

Amanita lividopallescens

white, with whitish or yellowish scales in belts forming a ring zone at the base, with the base encased in a membranous, whitish volva. **Fl** white. **Sm** faint, unpleasant.
Near old broad-leaved trees (oak) in avenues on river clay.

VR RDL M

Amanita fulva

C ovoid, then plane with raised centre, ∅ 4-9 cm, smooth, orange-brown to red-brown, with striate, pallid margin. **G** white. **St** 7-10 cm x 10-15 mm, smooth, white to cream with orange-brown tinge, with base encased in a large sac-like, membranous, whitish to pale orange-brown volva. **Fl** white. **Sm** faint. Common near broad-leaved trees (birch, oak, beech), occasionally near coniferous trees in woods and avenues on sandy soil. Summer to autumn.
Particularly near poplar also *A. vaginata*.

M

Amanita fulva

Macrolepiota and Lepiota

A large group of agarics with large *(Macrolepiota)* or small *(Lepiota)* fruiting bodies, free, white to cream or pale yellow gills, with a membranous, occasionally double ring, occasionally movable on the stem, or a ring zone. **Spo** white.

In Britain, 45 species of the genera *Macrolepiota* and *Lepiota* occur.

Macrolepiota procera

PARASOL MUSHROOM

Fr at first appearance resembling a drumstick, **C** globose, then plane with raised centre, ⌀ 10-25 cm, light yellow-brown to grey-brown, concentrically zoned with dark brown, large scales. **G** white. **St** 15-30 x 1-3 cm, cream, with felty, grey-brown, horizontal zones, a large, double ring, white on upper surface and brown below, movable on the stem, and a bulbous swollen base. **Fl** white. **Sm** faint.

Common in unmanured or sparsely manured grasslands and roadsides and broad-leaved and mixed woods on poor soil.

Sa ⑭

Macrolepiota procera

Macrolepiota rachodes (M. rhacodes)

SHAGGY PARASOL

C ovoid, then convex to nearly plane with raised centre, ⌀ 5-15 cm, pale brown, smooth centre, towards margin reflexed, membranous, brown scales on a whitish background, hanging from the edge like rags. **G** white, staining red when damaged. **St** 10-15 x 1-2 cm, smooth, with fibrillose base, dingy white to pink-brown, with a membranous, double ring,

movable on the stem, and an eccentric, thick bulbous base staining red-brown on bruising. **Fl** white, staining saffran-yellow to reddish orange on bruising. **Sm** strong, pleasant.

Common in woods, avenues, parks, orchards and gardens on rich soil.

Sa ⑭

Macrolepiota rachodes

Macrolepiota excoriata

C ovoid, then convex with raised centre, ⌀ 6-10 cm, smooth, white to cream, often with brownish centre, with adpressed, ochrous yellow to pale brown scales overhanging the margin. **G** white to cream. **St** 4-6 cm x 8-10 mm, smooth, whitish cream, with narrow ring and bulbous base staining brown. **Fl** white. **Sm** faint.

Macrolepiota excoriata

Not uncommon in unmanured grasslands and roadsides.

RDL Sa ⑨

Macrolepiota mastoidea
(M. gracilenta)

C globose, then convex with central, acute papilla, ∅ 8-11 cm, with smooth, buff-brown centre, white to creamy ochre, with fine, pale ochraceous to light brown, granular scales and overhanging scales producing a denticulate margin. **G** white to cream. **St** 8-11 cm x 8-14 mm, cream to pale brown, with whitish, granular scales and a thick, white ring, slightly swollen white-felty base. **Fl** white to pink-brown. **Sm** faint.

In grazed dune pastures, roadsides and mixed woods on dry, poor sandy soil.

R RDL Sa ⑨

Macrolepiota mastoidea

Lepiota aspera

C conical or campanulate to expanded, ∅ 6-8 cm, light to dark brown, with dark brown, upturned, acute scales on a white to cream background and with a shaggy margin. **G** forked, white. **St** 8-10 x 1-2 cm, white at the apex, below the membranous, white ring cream to pale brown with brown, upturned scales and a slightly swollen base. **Fl** white. **Sm** disagreeably pungent.

Not uncommon on humus or litter in broad-leaved and coniferous woods, parks and gardens on rich soil (see also the photograph of a partial veil in Chapter 1).

On the left in the background *Ramaria stricta*.

Sa †

Lepiota aspera

Lepiota echinacea

C globose, then expanded with obtuse umbo, ∅ 2-5 cm, creamy brown, with dark brown, conical or plane, upturned scales. **G** white to cream. **St** 3-6 cm x 3-6 mm, smooth, cream, below the woolly ring zone light brown with brown, floccose scales, with swollen, white-

Lepiota echinacea

161

felty base. **Fl** whitish. **Sm** disagreeably pungent. On humous soil in broad-leaved woods and near wildshoots of young trees on chalk slopes and slag heaps, on rich loamy or clayey soil.

R RDL Sa

Lepiota alba

C campanulate, then expanded with obtuse umbo, ⌀ 3-5 cm, finely felty, white to creamy white with yellow-brown centre, with floccose margin. **G** white to cream. **St** 4-6 cm x 4-7 mm, smooth, white, below the evanescent, floccose ring pale yellow-brown with white warts. **Fl** white. **Sm** disagreeably pungent.

Not uncommon in close-grazed dune vegetation and dry calcareous grasslands on calcareous sand.

Sa 🍄

Lepiota alba

Lepiota cristata

C campanulate, then expanded with umbo, ⌀ 2-5 cm, smooth centre, red-brown, with red-brown scales on a white to cream background, with floccose margin. **G** white. **St** 2-4 cm x 3-4 mm, whitish with dingy pink tinge, with evanescent, yellowish white ring. **Fl** white. **Sm** disagreeably pungent. Common on humus, rich soil in broad-leaved and coniferous woods, urban parks and avenues. Summer to autumn.

Sa 🍄

Lepiota cristata

Lepiota clypeolaria

C campanulate, then conical expanded with umbo, ⌀ 4-8 cm, centre smooth, ochraceous brown, with concentric, upturned, pale ochraceous brown scales on a cream background, with floccose, torn margin. **G** white. **St** 5-10 cm x 4-8 mm, cottony-woolly, white to straw-yellow. **Fl** w. **Sm** spicy.

On calcareous, loamy to clayey soil thickly covered with leaf litter, under broad-leaved trees (beech, hornbeam, oak).

R Sa 🍄

Lepiota clypeolaria

Lepiota castanea

C conical, then expanded with umbo, ⌀ 2-4 cm, ochraceous yellow or orange-ochre to red-brown, with red-brown to black-brown, adpressed scales and more pallid at the margin. **G** cream to ochrous yellow. **St** 3-5 cm x 2-4 mm, creamy ochre with orange tinge, below the evanescent woolly ring zone with red-brown to dark brown, woolly scales. **Fl** cream. **Sm** unpleasant. Not uncommon on humous soils covered with leaf litter in broad-leaved and coniferous woods and in young scrub (willow, birch).

Sa Deadly †

Lepiota castanea

Lepiota felina

C campanulate, then expanded with umbo, ∅ 2-3 cm, with dark brown to black scales on a whitish to cream background. **G** white. **St** 3-5 cm x 2-3 mm, fibrillose, whitish yellowish, with a membranous ring. **Fl** white. On litter-covered soil in coniferous and broad-leaved

Lepiota felina

woods on calcareous sand, in young scrub (willow, birch) on slag heaps.

R RDL Sa

Lepiota boudieri (L. fulvella)

C hemispherical, then expanded with umbo, ∅ 2-5 cm, smooth to fibrillose, deep ochraceous brown to orange-brown. **G** white to yellowish. **St** 3-6 cm x 3-6 mm, whitish, below the ring zone orange-brown woolly-felty. **Fl** white to brown. **Sm** strongly mushroomy.
On humus-rich soils in broad-leaved and coniferous woods.

R Sa

Lepiota boudieri

Leucoagaricus

A group of large agarics resembling *Lepiota*, *Macrolepiota* or *Agaricus*, occasionally becoming brown or red when damaged, with caps that are smooth to granular or covered with small or large warts, and white to cream or pale yellow gills free or ending in a ring distant from the stem. **Spo** white or cream to pale yellow.
In Britain, 10 species of the genus *Leucoagaricus* occur.

Leucoagaricus leucothites (L. pudicus)

C globose, then convex to plane, ∅ 5-8 cm, smooth, whitish to flesh or light creamy ochre.

G white to flesh. **St** 6-8 x 1-2 cm, white, with narrow, protruding, white ring. **Fl** white, becoming brown. **Sm** faint. Fairly common on humous soil, at the edges of broad-leaved and coniferous woods, in roadsides, parks and in grassy, rich locations.

RDL Sa 🍴

Leucoagaricus leucothites

Cystolepiota

A group of small agarics resembling *Macrolepiota* or *Lepiota,* with mealy pruinose or woolly-floccose caps and free or almost free gills. **Spo** white to creamy yellow.

In Britain, 5 species of the genus *Cystolepiota* occur.

Cystolepiota bucknallii

C campanulate, then expanded, ∅ 1-4 cm, matt, finely granular-mealy, light violet, later cream to light ochre. **G** quite distant, creamy white to yellowish. **St** 4-8 cm x 2-4 mm, pruinose, lilac-violet, whitish to cream at the apex. **Fl** whitish to creamy yellow. **Sm** highly unpleasant, slightly gas-like.

On very humous, occasionally somewhat muddy soil in woods on chalk slopes and woods on river clay.

R RDL Sa

Cystolepiota bucknallii

Cystolepiota hetieri

C globose, then hemispherical to expanded, ∅ 3-5 cm, mealy or finely felty, creamy white or ochraceous to pale pink, staining pink-brown, with floccose margin. **G** white, becoming orange-red. **St** 3-6 cm x 3-5 mm, creamy white to pale pink, with floccose ring zone. **Fl** white, with pink-brown tinge. **Sm** pleasant.
On rich soil mixed with humus or well-decayed wood, on calcareous loam or sand and river clay.

R RDL Sa

Cystolepiota hetieri

Cystolepiota seminuda (C. sistrata)

C hemispherical, then expanded with umbo, ⌀ 8-12 cm, mealy, white, with buff centre, floccose dentate margin. **G** whitish. **St** 2-3 cm x 1 mm, white, with lilac-grey background. **Fl** thin, whitish. **Sm** faint. Common on very rich, humous and loose soil in broad-leaved and coniferous woods, often under stinging nettles.

Sa ♀

Cystolepiota seminuda

Melanophyllum

A genus of small agarics resembling *Macrolepiota* and *Lepiota*, with red or green gills. **Spo** yellow.

Melanophyllum haematospermum (M. echinatum)

C conical, then expanded, ⌀ 2-5 cm, warty to granular-mealy, matt, dingy grey-buff to light brown, with membranous velar remnants on margin. **G** carmine to brown-red. **St** 3-5 cm x 3-5 mm, hollow, fragile, vinaceous red at the apex, below ring zone vinaceous red, dingy grey-buff pruinose, swollen to bulbous base. **Fl** white, becoming red when damaged. **Sm** mushroomy. Not uncommon on humus-rich soil in parks, gardens and broad-leaved woods on rich clay and sand.

Also *M. eyrei* (VR RDL).

Sa 🍴

Cystoderma

A small group of agarics with floccose-granular caps and white to cream gills, adnate

Melanophyllum haematospermum

or decurrent with a tooth. **Spo** white. In Britain, 6 species of the genus *Cystoderma* occur.

Cystoderma amianthinum

C campanulate, then expanded with umbo, ∅ 2-5 cm, pruinose, matt, ochraceous yellow to yellow-orange, floccose at the margin. **G** close, white to creamy yellow. **St** 3-5 cm x 5-8 mm, ochraceous yellow to creamy yellow, orange-brown pruinose to floccose below the evanescent ring. **Fl** yellowish orange. **Sm** faint, musty. Common on humus, moderately rich sand or coarse litter and among mosses in broad-leaved and coniferous woods and in poor grasslands and roadsides.
Also a completely white form, forma *album* (R).

Sa 𝕸

Cystoderma amianthinum

Cystoderma carcharias

C campanulate, then expanded with umbo, ∅ 2-6 cm, granular-mealy, dingy white or buff to flesh or light grey with pink tinge, floccose at the margin. **G** white to cream. **St** 3-6 cm x 3-7 mm, smooth, white, below the upturned, membranous ring granular-floccose zones, whitish to cream. occasionally with swollen base. **Fl** whitish. **Sm** unpleasant.
On humous soil and litter in coniferous and broad-leaved woods, heathland and roadsides with poor soil and grasslands on sandy and loamy soil

R Sa 𝕸

Armillaria

A group of agarics often growing in tufts, with scaly-floccose caps, adnate to slightly decurrent white gills and a ring or ring zone around the stem. **Spo** whitish cream. In Britain, 5 species of the genus *Armillaria* occur.

Armillaria mellea (Armillariella mellea)

HONEY FUNGUS

C convex, then irregularly plane, ∅ 4-15 cm, matt, dark scales particularly at the centre, honey-yellow or yellow-brown to olivaceous yellow or olivaceous brown, with white margin. **G** whitish, staining red-brown. **St** 6-16 cm x 5-15 mm, whitish to flesh, with thick, membranous, white ring with a yellow marginal zone on the lower surface, base tapering or swollen, often with rhizomorphs. **Fl** white to flesh. **Sm** musty. Common on roots and stumps and at the base of the trunk of mainly broad-

Armillaria mellea

Cystoderma carcharias

leaved trees on rich soil. In tufts (see photo-graph rhizomorphs in Chapter 1).

Pa

Armillaria lutea
(Armillariella bulbosa)

C obtusely conical, then expanded, ∅ 5-18 cm, yellowish brown to olive green, with brown scales. **G** white. **St** 8-15 cm x 2-3 mm, whitish woolly, ochrous yellow-brown, with yellow velar remnants on the evanescent, whitish ring and on the stem, bulbous base swollen, becoming olive green. **Fl** white. **Sm** faint, musty. Common on wood, both buried and above ground, and on dead parts or at the base of especially broad-leaved trees on rich soil. Singl y or in groups.

Sa

Armillaria lutea

Armillaria ostoyae
(Armillariella obscura)

C obtusely conical, then expanded, ∅ 4-20 cm, light flesh to red-brown with dark brown, fibrillose scales and velar remnants at the more pallid, translucent striate margin. **G** whitish or grey-whitish to cream. **St** 6-15 x 1-3 cm, whitish-floccose, below the mem-branous, white, dentate ring with dark brown to black scales on the lower surface, white-fibrillose, yellow-brown to brown-black, often with rhizomorphs. Common on the trunk, at the base of and on the roots and stumps of broad-leaved and coniferous trees on acid sandy soil. In tufts.

Pa

Oudemansiella, Xerula and Megacollybia

Genera of agarics with slimy, shiny or velvety caps with wide, obese, free, white to whitish gills and tough, often deep-rooting stems occasionally rooting with mycelium strands. **Spo** white. In Britain, 5 species of the genera *Oudemansiella*, *Xerula*, and *Megacollybia* occur.

Oudemansiella mucida

POACHED EGG GUNGUS

C globose, then expanded, ∅ 3-12 cm, light grey when young, later ivory-white with yellow-greyish centre, semi-translucent, slimy. **G** white. **St** 5-14 cm x 4-12 mm, striate or scaly, white, with membranous, white ring. **Fl**

Oudemansiella mucida

Armillaria ostoyae

white. **Sm** faintly acid. Common on branches and trunks of old beech, rarely on oak.

Sa (Pa)

Xerula radicata
(Oudemansiella radicata)

C campanulate, then flattened convex with a wide umbo, ∅ 5-8 cm, smooth, radially wrinkled, pale ochraceous to hazel. **G** white. **St** 8-20 cm x 5-10 mm, yellow-brown, white, striate at the apex, and grey-brown base rooting up to 10 cm deep. **Fl** white. **Ta** faintly fruity. Common at the base of or on the roots of beech, usually some distance away from the tree.

Also *X. kuehneri* (VR RDL) and *X. pudens* = *longipes* (R RDL).

Sa (Pa)

Xerula radicata

Megacollybia platyphylla
(Oudemansiella platyphylla)

C hemispherical, then flattened expanded, ∅ 4-12 cm, smooth, radially fibrillose striate, scaly, light to dark grey-brown with ochraceous or pale olive green tinge, with torn, appendiculate margin. **G** distant, whitish

cream. **St** 3-5 cm x 10-14 mm, tough, striate, whitish pruinose, light grey-brown, with white mycelium strands. **Fl** white. **Sm** faint, musty. Common on wood debris, buried wood of broad-leaved trees and woodland litter. Summer to autumn.

Sa

Megacollybia platyphylla

Tricholoma

A group of agarics with large, fleshy fruiting bodies, gills sinuate, with stem, ring usually absent. **Spo** white. Mycorrhizal. In Britain, about 50 species of the genus *Tricholoma* occur.

Tricholoma album

C campanulate convex, then irregularly expanded, ∅ 7-9 cm, matt, white with straw-yellow centre, staining yellow when damp. **G**

Tricholoma album

white with pink tinge. **St** 6-8 cm x 10-15 mm, white pruinose at the apex, white with pink tinge. **Fl** whitish cream. **Sm** unpleasant, earthy smell.

Near broad-leaved trees (birch, oak) in broad-leaved and mixed woods and avenues on sandy or clayey soil.

R M 🚫

Tricholoma argyraceum var. scalpturatum

C hemispherical, then irregularly expanded, ∅ 4-7 cm, dark grey to brown-grey with fine scales on a lighter background, pallid at the margin. **G** white, staining yellow. **St** 4-8 cm x 6-12 mm, white with grey-brown tinge. **Fl** white. **Sm** mealy.

Fairly common near broad-leaved trees (oak, beech, poplar) and coniferous trees in avenues and woods.

M 🍴

Tricholoma argyraceum var. scalpturatum

Tricholoma cingulatum

C convex, then expanded with umbo, ∅ 3-6 cm, grey-brown, with fine, felty, light grey-brown scales. **G** whitish. **St** 5-8 cm x 8-12 mm, whitish, scaly below the woolly, white ring. **Fl** white. **Sm** mealy. Not uncommon near willow species (favouring *Salix repens*) in willow shrubberies and willow woodland in coastal sand dunes, on river clay and on rich, humus soil.

M 🚫

Tricholoma equestre (T. flavovirens)

C conical, then expanded, ∅ 5-8 cm, bright yellow with light olive brown, scaly centre. **G** sulphur-yellow to lemon-yellow. **St** 5-10 cm x 8-12 mm, pale yellow, with brownish scales. **Fl** whitish yellow. **Sm** faint. Near fir in coniferous woods on dry, poor soil deficient in humus.

R RDL M 🍴

Tricholoma equestre

Tricholoma fulvum

C irregularly convex to expanded with umbo, ∅ 4-8 cm, yellow-brown to red-brown, with yellow-brown margin. **G** yellowish, staining brown. **St** 3-7 cm x 8-15 mm, fibrillose, yellow-brown to red-brown. **Fl** whitish to yellow. **Sm** mealy.

Tricholoma cingulatum

Fairly common near birch and oak in broad-leaved and mixed woods and poor roadsides.

RDL M

Tricholoma focale

C expanded to plane with umbo, ⌀ 10-12 cm, copper-like brown with olivaceous or brick-red tinge, with inrolled margin. **G** cream with red-brown edge and blotches. **St** 10-12 cm x 2-3 mm, pruinose, whitish cream at the apex, below the membranous, woolly, protruding ring copper-like, brown, scaly, zoned, on a whitish cream background, with tapering, curved base. **Fl** white. **Sm** mealy.

Near Scots pine in young or old coniferous woods on poor soil deficient in humus.

VR RDL M

Tricholoma myomyces

C convex with low, broad umbo, ⌀ 4-7 cm, downy to felty, light to dark grey. **G** whitish to

Tricholoma focale

Tricholoma myomyces

grey. **St** 3-8 cm x 10-15 mm, silky, white, with remnants of cortina on stem. **Fl** whitish grey. **Sm** faint, mealy. Near fir in coniferous woods and roadsides on calcareous soil.

RDL M 🍴

Tricholoma sulphureum

C convex to plane, ∅ 3-8 cm, sulphur-yellow with red-brown or olivaceous tinge. **G** sulphur-yellow. **St** 2-7 cm x 10-17 mm, sulphur-yellow, with white-downy base. **Fl** sulphur-yellow. **Sm** unpleasant, of coal gas or coal tar.

Not uncommon near broad-leaved trees (oak, beech) in broad-leaved woods and avenues on rich loamy or sandy soil.

RDL M †

Tricholoma sulphureum

Tricholoma ustale

C convex, then expanded, ∅ 4-8 cm, viscid when damp, chestnut, with creamy white margin. **G** creamy white, staining rusty brown. **St** 4-9 cm x 10-15 mm, fibrillose, red-brown, more pallid at the apex. **Fl** creamy white, staining brown. **Sm** faint, mealy.
Not uncommon near beech in avenues and broad-leaved woods on sandy or loamy soil.

Also *T. ustaloides* (R).

M †

Calocybe

A group of saprophytic, *Tricholoma*-like agarics, gills sinuate or decurrent with a tooth. **Spo** white to cream.
In Britain, 5 species of the genus *Calocybe* occur.

Calocybe gambosa

C globose, then convex to expanded, ∅ 5-15 cm, white to buff, with inrolled margin. **G** close, whitish. **St** 3-7 cm x 10-25 mm, white. **Fl** soft, white. **Sm** mealy.
On the ground on wood edges and in shrubberies on calcareous humus-rich sandy soil. Spring.

Sa 🍴

Calocybe gambosa

Tricholoma ustale

Calocybe carnea

C convex to plane, ∅ 2-4 cm, finely felty, matt, flesh-pink with pink-brown centre and incurvate margin. **G** white. **St** 2-4 cm x 3-7 mm, whitish to flesh-pink. **Fl** white. **Sm** faint.

On the ground in grassland and grassy roadsides, gardens, parks and open broad-leaved woods on humous, rich soil.

Sa 🚫

Calocybe carnea

Calocybe ionides

C convex to plane with umbo, ∅ 2-5 cm, finely felty, matt, lilac to violet-brown, more pallid at the margin. **G** white to cream. **St** 3-5 cm x 3-7 mm, dark violet to lilac-brown. **Fl** whitish to pale lilac. **Sm** mealy.

On litter or on the ground in broad-leaved and coniferous woods on calcareous, sandy soil.

R Sa 🚫

Calocybe ionides

Lyophyllum and Hypsizygus

A group of *Tricholoma*-like agarics, usually tufted, with large, tough, fleshy fruiting bodies and usually adnate gills. **Spo** white to pale cream.

In Britain, 10 species of the genus *Lyophyllum* and *Hypsizygus* occur.

Lyophyllum decastes

C convex to irregularly plane with umbo, ∅ 6-15 cm, smooth, with a lubricous gloss, grey to hazel. **G** whitish. **St** 5-18 x 1-2 cm, often twisted, striate, pruinose at the apex, whitish to greyish whitish. **Fl** tough, white. **Sm** none.

Common, usually on buried wood or on stumps and roots of broad-leaved trees in woods, parks and avenues on rich soil. Usually in clusters.

Sa 🍴

Lyophyllum decastes

Lyophyllum fumosum

C convex to irregularly plane, ∅ 3-13 cm, smooth, matt, light to dark yellowish or hazel. **G** light cream to pale brown. **St** 3-10 x 6-15 mm, striate, pruinose at the apex, whitish or cream to light brown, ending in a common swollen bulbous base. **Fl** whitish to brownish. **Sm** somewhat sour.

Not uncommon on buried wood or on stumps and roots of broad-leaved trees in woods,

parks and avenues on rich soil. Usually in dense clusters.

Sa 🐞

Lyophyllum connatum

C convex to plane, ∅ 3-7 cm, matt, pruinose, white to dingy white. **G** white to creamy yellow. **St** 3-6 cm x 8-15 mm, white. **Fl** white. **Sm** pleasant, nutty. Not uncommon on humous, rich soil in broad-leaved woods, tangled growth and roadsides. In clusters or groups.

Sa †

Lyophyllum connatum

Hypsizygus ulmarius
(Lyophyllum ulmarius)

C hemispherical, then convex, ∅ 8-15 cm, smooth, matt, cream to brown with grey tinge, with reflexed margin. **G** white to creamy yellow. **St** 8-15 x 1-3 cm, striate-grooved, pale cream. **Fl** tough, white. **Sm** somewhat sour. Often high up on the trunk of living or recent-

Hypsizygus ulmarius

ly dead elms or on stumps in parks and along roads. Usually tufted.

R Pa (Sa) 🗡

Tricholomopsis

A genus of brightly coloured, large *Tricholoma*-like agarics, growing on wood of coniferous trees, with sinuate, golden yellow gills. **Spo** white to creamy white. In Britain, 3 species of the genus *Tricholomopsis* occur.

Tricholomopsis rutilans

PLUMS AND CUSTARD

C convex to expanded with broad umbo, ⌀ 4-12 cm, with orange-red or wine red to purple, woolly fibrils on a yellow background, fibrillose at the margin. **G** golden yellow. **St** 3-12 x 1-3 cm, yellow, with downy orange-red or wine red to purple scales. **Fl** pale yellow to cream. **Sm** faintly nutty.

Common on coniferous trunks and stumps in coniferous and mixed woods on sandy soil.

Also *T. decora* (VR RDL).

Sa 🗡

Tricholomopsis rutilans

Tricholomopsis rutilans

Melanoleuca

A group of sombrely coloured, saprotrophic *Tricholoma*-like agarics, with sinuate, golden yellow gills. **Spo** white to creamy white.

In Britain, 10 species of the genus *Melanoleuca* occur.

Melanoleuca polioleuca
(M. melaleuca)

C convex, then plane, often with flattened umbo, ⌀ 3-8 cm *(f. polioleuca)* smooth, dark

Tricholomopsis rutilans

brown to brown-black. **G** close, whitish to cream. **St** 4-9 cm x 8-15 mm, longitudinally striate, with dark brown fibrils and bulbous base. **Fl** white to ochrous brown. **Sm** faint.
Common on the ground in broad-leaved and mixed woods, parks, avenues, roadsides, grasslands, gardens and kitchen gardens on rich sand. Summer to autumn.

Sa

Melanoleuca polioleuca

Melanoleuca brevipes

C flattened expanded, ∅ 8-11 cm, smooth, matt, grey-brown or buff-brown to ochraceous brown. **G** white-cream to pale buff with lilac tinge. **St** 3-5 cm x 10-15 mm, yellowish fibrillose, creamy buff, with swollen base. **Fl** white to cream. **Sm** faint, mushroomy. Not uncommon on rich soil in broad-leaved woods (poplar) and coniferous woods (spruce), wooded banks, avenues, roadsides, along shell

Melanoleuca brevipes

paths and also on slag heaps. Spring to autumn.

Sa

Melanoleuca cinereifolia

C expanded, with broad umbo, ∅ 8-12 cm, matt, grey-brown. **G** grey. **St** 8-10 x 1-2 cm, light grey, half buried in dune sand. **Fl** whitish cream. **Sm** faint.
On sand deficient in humus in outer coastal sand dunes or calcareous dune sand under gorse scrub.
With a small, fully developed fruiting body on the cap!

R Sa

Melanoleuca cinereifolia

Clitocybe

A group of agarics with depressed or flattened funnel-shaped fruiting bodies and (deeply) decurrent gills. **Spo** white to cream.

In Britain, 55 species of the genus *Clitocybe* occur.

Clitocybe ditopa

C convex to flattened funnel-shaped, ∅ 2-5 cm, smooth, grey-brown when damp; grey-buff when dry, with translucent striate margin. **G** adnate to decurrent, grey-brown. **St** 2-5 cm x 3-6 mm, white-fibrillose, grey-brown, with mycelium fluff at the base. **Fl** watery grey-brown. **Sm** mealy-rancid. Fairly common among needles (spruce, Douglas fir) and leaves (birch, oak, alder) on rich sand.

Sa 🔏

Clitocybe ditopa

Clitocybe vibecina

C flattened funnel-shaped, ∅ 2-5 cm, smooth, translucent striate, grey-brown to buff-brown when damp; whitish buff with striate margin when dry. **G** deeply decurrent, grey-brown to buff. **St** 3-6 cm x 3-8 mm, grey-brown, whitish fibrillose. **Fl** watery grey-brown. **Sm** faint, mealy.

Common among leaves and needles in woods on poor sand or loam.

Sa 🔏

Clitocybe vibecina

Clitocybe diatetra

C convex-umbilicate to funnel-shaped, ∅ 4-5 cm, smooth, translucent caramel-coloured buff when damp; dull pink when dry. **G** broad, whitish to creamy buff. **St** 3-4 cm x 3-4 mm, whitish cream to pale brown. **Fl** creamy buff. **Sm** mushroomy.
Fairly common on leaves and needles in woods on moderately rich sand or loam.

Sa

Clitocybe diatetra

Clitocybe phyllophila

C convex-umbilicate to flattened, ∅ 2-8 cm, smooth, with matt silky gloss, white. **G** slightly decurrent, white to cream. **St** 3-10 cm x 5-10 mm, elastic, white, with mycelium fluff at the swollen base. **Fl** white. **Sm** strong,

Clitocybe phyllophila

mushroomy. Common among leaves and needles on moderately rich sand or loam.

Sa †

Clitocybe clavipes

CLUB FOOT

C depressed or flattened funnel-shaped with obtuse umbo, ⌀ 3-8 cm, smooth, grey-brown to ochrous brown, lighter at the margin. **G** broad, sickle-shaped decurrent, white to pale yellow. **St** 3-10 cm x 5-16 mm, fibrillose, brownish striate on whitish yellow background, with white-felty, strongly bulbous swollen base. **Fl** whitish. **Sm** pleasant, spicy. Common among leaves and needles on moderately rich sand or loam.

Sa 🚫

Clitocybe clavipes

Clitocybe odora

ANISEED TOADSTOOL

C irregularly flattened, ⌀ 3-7 cm, matt, green-blue (var. *odora*) to grey-ochre with a blue-green tinge. **G** broad, adnate to slightly decurrent, cream to grey-green. **St** 3-4 cm x 3-6 mm, smooth, whitish to blue-greenish, with white-felty base. **Fl** white to pale green. **Sm** strong, of aniseed.
Fairly common among leaves on moderately rich sand or loam.

Sa 🍴

Clitocybe geotropa

C plane with depressed centre and with umbo, ⌀ 10-25 cm, felty, whitish to pale cream, with inrolled margin. **G** broad, deeply decurrent, creamy buff. **St** 6-15 x 2-3 cm, finely felty striate or smooth, whitish to cream, with white-felty base. **Fl** white. **Sm** faint, sweetish.

Among leaves on rich loam or clay. Often in groups or fairy rings.

R RDL Sa 🍴

Clitocybe geotropa

Clitocybe odora

Clitocybe nebularis
(Lepista nebularis)

CLOUDED AGARIC

C flattened, occasionally with somewhat depressed centre and umbo, ∅ 7-18 cm, finely felty, dark grey-brown to pale grey-brown or buff-brown, with incurvate margin. **G** faintly decurrent, cream to yellowish. **St** 5-12 x 2-5 cm, grey-brown fibrillose on paler background, with white-felty base. **Fl** whitish. **Sm** unpleasant, sweetish.

Common among leaves, occasionally among needles on moderately rich soil. In groups or fairy rings. (For dry specimens, see the photograph of a fairy ring in Chapter 1).

Sa ⑪(Suspect)

Pseudoclitocybe

Pseudoclitocybe cyathiformis

C funnel-shaped, ∅ 3-9 cm, dark grey-brown when damp; more pallid when dry, with inrolled margin. **G** distant, sickle-shaped, somewhat decurrent, pale grey to brownish. **St** 4-9 cm x 5-10 mm, grey-brown, silky white-fibrillose, with dark, swollen base. **Fl** whitish to grey-buff. **Sm** faint, pleasant. **Spo** white. Among leaves and needles on rich loam and clay.

Also *P. obbata*, growing among grass and mosses in dune pastures (R).

R RDL Sa ⑪

Pseudoclitocybe cyathiformis

Lepista

A group of large, saprophytic agarics with flattened to broad funnel-shaped fruiting bodies. **Spo** white to pale pink.
In Britain, 10 species of the genus *Lepista* occur.

Lepista flaccida
(L. gilva, L. inversa)

C flattened convex to broadly depressed funnel-shaped, ∅ 5-9 cm, smooth, pale pink-yellow or ochrous brown to yellow-brown or orange-brown, with incurvate, pallid margin. **G** forked, close, deeply decurrent, cream to light buff-red. **St** 2-5 cm x 5-15 mm, pale ochre to pale orange-brown, with white-felty base. **Fl** cream. **Sm** faint, sweetish.

Common among leaves and needles and in humus of broad-leaved and coniferous woods on rich soil. Summer to autumn.

Sa ⑪

Lepista flaccida

Lepista nuda

WOOD BLEWIT

C undulate flattened convex, ∅ 6-12 cm, smooth, purple-lilac to violet-brown. **G** close, purple-lilac to pink-brown. **St** 5-9 cm x 15-25 mm, white-fibrillose, purple. **Fl** lilac. **Sm** pleasant. Common on humus in broad-leaved and coniferous woods and open vegetation on nutrient- and nitrogen-rich locations. Often in groups. Summer to autumn.
Sa ⑪

Lepista sordida

C undulate convex to plane, ∅ 3-8 cm, smooth, lilac to lilac-brown. **G** lilac to pale lilac-brown. **St** 4-6 cm x 5-8 mm, fibrillose, lilac to lilac-brown, often with somewhat swollen base. **Fl** greyish lilac. **Sm** pleasant.

Fairly common on humus in woods, parks, public gardens and grasslands on rich locations, occasionally on old manure and compost. Often in groups. Summer to autumn.

Sa ⑭

Lepista sordida

Laccaria

A group of small, pink, red-brown or orange-brown, brick-red and purple-brown or purple

Lepista nuda

179

agarics with distant gills. Mycorrhizal. **Spo** white.

In Britain, 10 species of the genus *Laccaria* occur.

Laccaria amethystina

AMETHYST DECEIVER

C convex to plane, ∅ 1-6 cm, scurfy, purple-lilac to pale lilac. **G** distant, purple-lilac, powdered white with spores. **St** 4-10 cm x 5-10 mm, purple-lilac to purple-brown, whitish fibrillose at the base, with purple mycelium fluff. **Fl** lilac. **Sm** faint.
Common in coniferous and mixed woods and avenues (beech, oak) on dry sandy soil.

M

Laccaria proxima

C convex to plane, ∅ 2-7 cm, scurfy-scaly, drying orange-brown to dark ochraceous yellow. **G** distant, pale pink, white with spores. **St** 3-12 cm x 2-5 mm, fibrillose, reddish brown, with white mycelium fluff at the base. **Fl** pale red-brown. **Sm** faint.

Common near young to old broad-leaved trees (birch, oak) and coniferous trees (fir) in broad-leaved and mixed woods, peat bogs and heaths on poor, dry sandy soil.

M

Laccaria proxima

Laccaria amethystina

Laccaria bicolor

C convex to plane, often centrally depressed, ∅ 2-5 cm, scurfy, orange-brown to red-brown, drying pink-yellow to ochraceous yellow, with pallid margin. **G** distant, pale lilac, white with spores. **St** 5-14 cm x 4-10 mm, fibrillose, ochraceous to red-brown, with felty, lilac mycelium at the base, which is often deeply buried in litter. **Fl** whitish, with yellow or pink tinge. **Sm** faint.
Fairly common in coniferous woods (fir) and mixed woods (beech) on dry sandy soil.

M

Collybia

A group of saprotrophic agarics with smooth caps, often with close, non-decurrent gills and fleshy, tough stems. **Spo** whitish to pale pink. In Britain, 25 species of the genus *Collybia* occur.

Collybia butyracea var. butyracea

BUTTER CAP

C convex to plane, ∅ 3-7 cm, lubricous-greasy, smooth, brown or reddish brown to dark ochraceous yellow, drying creamy brown to ivory, with light, striate margin. **G** free, close, whitish. **St** 3-5 cm x 5-10 mm, tough, reddish brown to ochraceous yellow, with white, woolly hairs and swollen base. **Fl** whitish yellow. **Sm** faintly rancid. Common on coarse litter of broad-leaved trees (oak, birch, beech) and coniferous trees (spruce, larch) in woods, avenues and parks on poor sand or loam.

Sa

Collybia butyracea var. *butyracea*

Laccaria bicolor

Collybia amanitae (C. cirrhata)

C convex to plane, ⌀ 1-2 cm, white, with buff centre. **G** close, white. **St** 1-2 cm x 1 mm, velvety, whitish buff, sclerotia absent. **Fl** white.
Common on humus and mummified agarics (*Lactarius* and *Russula* species), on poor sand and loam.

Sa ♀

Collybia amanitae

Collybia tuberosa

C convex to plane, ⌀ 3-13 cm, white, with yellow-brown tinge at the centre. **G** close, white. **St** 15-25 x 1 mm, white or pallid, on a red-brown sclerotium. **Fl** white.

Common on mummified agarics (*Lactarius* and *Russula* species), or on humus or coarse litter on poor sand or loam. In groups.

Sa ♀

Collybia tuberosa

Collybia confluens

CLUSTERED TOUGH-SHANK

C convex, ⌀ 3-5 cm, matt, dingy flesh-yellowish when damp; whitish when dry. **G** narrow, close, dingy pink. **St** 3-6 cm x 2-5 mm, hollow, compressed, tough, downy, dark dingy pink to brown. **Fl** white. Common on coarse litter of broad-leaved trees (beech, oak) and coniferous trees (spruce). In dense tufts or clusters, often in fairy rings.

Sa 🚫

Collybia confluens

Collybia dryophila

C irregularly convex to plane, ⌀ 2-5 cm, smooth, pale ochre to reddish brown, with pallid, striate margin. **G** whitish yellowish. **St** 4-6 cm x 2-5 mm, hollow, smooth, creamy buff to orange-brown. **Fl** whitish.
Common on humus and coarse litter of broad-

Collybia dryophila

leaved trees (oak, beech), rarely of coniferous trees in woods, parks, public gardens, heaths and poor acid grasslands.

Sa 🐾

Collybia ocior
(C. dryophila var. funicularis)

C convex to plane, ∅ 2-5 cm, smooth, reddish brown to black-brown, with yellowish margin. **G** yellow. **St** 4-6 cm x 2-5 mm, smooth, yellow-brown to orange-brown.

On humus, decayed wood and coarse litter in woods and dune scrub on dry soil.

R Sa 🐾

Collybia maculata

SPOTTED TOUGH-SHANK

C irregularly convex to plane, ∅ 4-10 cm, matt, white to creamy white, staining red-brown when damaged or with age, with splitting margin. **G** close, white to cream, staining rusty brown. **St** 5-10 cm x 8-25 mm, white, with tapering base, slightly rooting. **Fl** white. **Sm** unpleasant.

Common on litter and humus of broad-leaved trees (oak, beech) and coniferous trees. Often in fairy rings.

Sa 🐾

Collybia maculata

Collybia ocior

Thephrocybe

A group of small, grey or brown, saprotrophic or parasitic agarics. **Spo** white. In Britain, 15 species of the genus *Thephrocybe* occur.

Tephrocybe anthracophila

C convex to plane, ⌀ 1.5-2.5 cm, striate, dark ochraceous brown with brown-black centre when damp; ochraceous brown when dry. **G** distant, decurrent with a tooth, whitish cream to buff. **St** 3-5 cm x 3-5 mm, smooth, buff-brown to dark brown, white pruinose at the apex. **Fl** cream. **Sm** mealy-rancid.

Common on fire sites.

Sa

Tephrocybe anthracophila

Tephrocybe palustris

C flattened convex, ⌀ 1.5-2.5 cm, translucent striate, honey-brown to ochrous brown, with dark centre. **G** broad, distant, cream to pale buff. **St** 5-7 cm x 3-4 mm, smooth, ochraceous brown, white pruinose at the apex. **Fl** cream. **Sm** somewhat mealy.

Not uncommon on living sphagnum in peat moors and bogs and on the edges of pools.

Pa

Flammulina

Flammulina velutipes

VELVET SHANK

C convex to plane, ⌀ 2-10 cm, smooth, slimy, yellow with orange-brown to red-brown centre. **G** pale yellow. **St** 3-5 cm x 3-4 mm, tough, velvety, dark brown, yellow at the apex. **Fl** yellowish. **Sm** pleasant. **Spo** white. Common on stumps, trunks, fallen branches of broad-leaved trees (alder, ash, poplar, elder) on rich soils. September to March. Sa (Pa) 🍴

Flammulina velutipes

Flammulina fennae

C convex to plane, ⌀ 2-8 cm, smooth, slimy, white to pale yellow or pale yellow-brown. **G** whitish yellow to pale yellow. **St** 3-5 cm x 3-4 mm, tough, velvety, dark brown, white-

Tephrocybe palustris

yellow at the apex. **Fl** pale yellowish. **Sm** pleasant. **Spo** white.

On (buried) wood or at the base of broad-leaved trees in woods, avenues, parks and undergrowth on rich, moi**St** soil. April to October.

R Sa (Pa)

Flammulina fennae

Hygrophorus and *Hygrocybe*

A group of usually brightly coloured agarics, often with slimy or viscid caps and with broad, waxy gills. **Spo** white to cream.

In Britain, 25 species of the genus *Hygrophorus* and 50 species of the genus *Hygrocybe (Camarophyllus)* occur.

Hygrophorus eburneus var. eburneus

IVORY WAX CAP

C hemispherical to flattened, ⌀ 3-9 cm, strongly slimy viscid to greasy, smooth, ivory-white, occasionally with pale yellow centre. **G** brown, white to light cream. **St** 4-12 cm x 5-13 mm, slimy-viscid when damp, white, clayey, yellowish at the apex. **Fl** white. **Sm** faint.

Near beech and *Quercus robur* in old avenues and woods on clayey and sandy soils thinly covered with litter.

VR RDL M

Hygrophorus eburneus var. eburneus

Hygrophorus agathosmus

C hemispherical to expanded, ⌀ 4-8 cm, slimy when damp; viscid when dry, smooth, buff-grey to brown-grey. **G** broad, whitish to cream or greyish. **St** 5-8 x 1-2 cm, dry, clayey-floccose, white, brownish in places. **Fl** whitish to pale olive grey. **Sm** of almonds.

Near spruce in coniferous woods on calcareous, loamy soil.

RDL M

Hygrophorus agathosmus

185

Hygrophorus persoonii (H. dichrous)

C hemispherical to convex, ∅ 7-12 cm, slimy, brown with dark centre and white margin. **G** thick, broad, distant, milky white with grey-green tinge. **St** 9-10 cm x 10-15 mm, mealy-floccose, white at the apex, with patches and bands of brown slime towards the tapering, rooting base. **Fl** white. **Sm** musty.

Near *Quercus robur* in broad-leaved woods on humous calcareous sand or river clay.

VR RDL M

Hygrophorus persoonii

Hygrophorus russula

C hemispherical, then expanded, ∅ 5-10 cm, slightly viscid, matt when dry, smooth to finely floccose-scaly, spotted or streaked wine red

Hygrophorus russula

on a white to pink background, with white margin. **G** white, with purple wine red blotches. **St** 4-8 cm x 15-22 mm, dry, purple-red fibrillose or with blotches on a white background. **Fl** white to pink. **Sm** pleasant, fruity. Near oak and beech in old woods and avenues.

RDL M

Hygrocybe virginea var. virginea (Camarophyllus niveus)

SNOWY WAX CAP

C top-shaped to flattened funnel-shaped, ∅ 2-5 cm, smooth, slimy-greasy, creamy white to yellow-white, occasionally with pink tinge when damp; matt, with translucent striate margin when dry. **G** broad, distant, creamy white, decurrent. **St** 3-7 cm x 3-7 mm, dry, creamy white. **Fl** watery creamy white to grey-white. **Sm** none.
Common in poor or lightly manured grassland, grassy spots in sand dunes and on roadsides.

Sa

Hygrocybe virginea var. *virginea*

Hygrocybe pratensis var. pratensis (Camarophyllus pratensis var. pratensis)

MEADOW WAX CAP

C convex to flattened, ∅ 2-6 cm, often with depressed centre, smooth, dry, apricot to brown-orange. **G** broad, decurrent, creamy orange. **St** 3-6 cm x 6-12 mm, smooth, dry, whitish cream to creamy orange. **Fl** creamy orange. **Sm** mushroomy. In old, poor grasslands. grassy roadsides and along dykes on poor sand or clay.

R RDL Sa

Hygrocybe pratensis var. *pratensis*

Hygrocybe russocoriacea (Camarophyllus russocoriaceus)

C hemispherical to flattened, ∅ 10-35 cm, smooth, shiny and viscid, white-yellow to pale yellow with faint olive tinge when damp; cream, with translucent striate margin when dry. **G** broad, decurrent, white to cream. **St** 3-6 cm x 3-7 mm, elastic, smooth, matt, whitish to creamy white, occasionally with pink tinge at the tapering base. **Fl** watery cream. **Sm** strong, of cedar or Russia leather. In poor grasslands, roadsides and on dykes on sand or clay.

R RDL Sa

Hygrocybe russocoriacea

Hygrocybe acutoconica var. *acutoconica*

C acutely conical to flattened with umbo, ∅ 2-6 cm, viscid striate, shiny when dry, yellow to yellow-orange. **G** yellow to yellow-orange, with yellow edge. **St** 3-10 cm x 3-8 mm, dry, orange-yellow to yellow. **Fl** orange-yellow to yellow. **Sm** faint.
Not uncommon in poor grasslands, roadsides and on grassy locations and along shell paths in sand dunes.

RDL Sa

Hygrocybe acutoconica var. *acutoconica*

Hygrocybe coccinea

C hemispherical to convex, ∅ 2-5 cm, shiny when damp; matt when dry, blood-red to cherry-red, paling ochrous yellow later. **G** broad, red-orange to yellow-orange. **St** 4-6 cm x 5-8 mm, fibrillose, cherry-red to orange-red. **Fl** watery red to orange. **Sm** none. In old,

Hygrocybe coccinea

poor, mossy grasslands, occasionally on road-sides or old lawns in churchyards.

R RDL Sa

Hygrocybe ceracea

C irregularly convex, occasionally with umbo, ∅ 2-4 cm, viscid to smooth, lemon-yellow to egg-yellow with orange tinge. **G** broad, distant, light yellow. **St** 3-4 cm x 2-4 mm, dry, lemon-yellow, with whitish base. **Fl** light yellow. **Sm** none.

Not uncommon in poor, mossy grassland, in grassy locations in sand dunes and on dykes and in roadsides.

RDL Sa

Hygrocybe ceracea

Hygrocybe conica var. conica f. pseudoconica

C obtusely conical, ∅ 4-7 cm, radially fibrillose, matt, viscid to dry, orange to red, occasionally with sulphur-yellow or green-yellow tinge, becoming black, with striate-appendiculate margin. **G** broad, nearly free, white to sulphur-yellow. **St** 3-9 cm x 5-12 mm, fibrillose striate, sulphur-yellow to orange-red or orange-yellow, staining black on being touched. **Fl** orange-yellow to yellow-white. **Sm** none. Fairly common in unmanured or sparsely manured grasslands, damp sand valleys and roadsides.

Sa

Hygrocybe conica var. *conica* f. *conica*

C acutely conical, ∅ 1-4 cm, orange to red, becoming black. **G** broad, white to sulphur-yellow. **St** 3-7 cm x 2-7 mm, fibrillose striate, sulphur-yellow or green-yellow to orange-yellow, staining black on being touched. **Fl** orange-yellow to yellow-white. **Sm** none. Fairly common in unmanured or sparsely manured grasslands, damp sand valleys and roadsides, also in broad-leaved woods.
Sa

Hygrocybe conica var. *conica* f. conica

Hygrocybe psittacina

PARROT WAX CAP

C hemispherical to convex, ∅ 2-4 cm, slimy-viscid, shiny, striate, yellow-green or green to green-orange, with whitish, yellowish or lilac spots. **G** broad, yellow-green to green or orange-

Hygrocybe conica var. *conica* f. *pseudoconica*

188

green. **St** 4-8 cm x 3-7 mm, slimy, green or green-yellow to orange-yellow, green at the apex and pallid at the base. **Fl** greenish or green-yellowish with orange tinge. **Sm** none. Not uncommon in close-grazed grasslands, roadsides, on dyke slopes and grassy spots in sand dunes, occasionally in broad-leaved woods on clay.

RDL Sa

Hygrocybe psittacina

Hygrocybe perplexa (H. sciophana)

C campanulate to convex, ⌀ 1-2 cm, slimy-viscid, shiny, brick-red to red-brown, paling ochre, with translucent striate margin. **G** distant, brick-red to pink-brown. **St** 4-5 cm x 2-3 mm, slimy, ochre to pale brick-red. **Fl** watery yellow. **Sm** faint.

In old, poor grasslands on dry, calcareous, loamy or clayey soil or on dune sand.

VR RDL Sa

Hygrocybe perplexa

Hygrocybe unguinosa

C hemispherical to convex, ⌀ 1-3 cm, slimy-viscid, translucent striate, ochraceous grey to grey-brown. **G** broad, grey-white. **St** 3-5 cm x 3-5 mm, flattened, slimy, light grey-brown, pallid at the apex. **Fl** watery grey-brown. **Sm** none.

In poor, old grasslands on sand, clay and peat.

VR RDL Sa

Hygrocybe unguinosa

Hygrocybe miniata var. miniata

C hemispherical to convex, ⌀ 1-2.5 cm, dry, finely scaly, scarlet to orange-red, occasionally with yellow margin. **G** broad, orange-red. **St** 2-4.5 cm x 2-5 mm, smooth, dry, matt, red to orange-red, with light orange-yellow to whitish base. **Fl** yellow to orange. **Sm** faint. Common on humous soil or litter in cropped grass in pastures, acid grasslands with very

Hygrocybe miniata var. *miniata*

poor soil and grassy areas on heaths, occasionally in peat bogs or broad-leaved and mixed woods on sandy or peaty soil.
Also *Mycena galopus* var. *galopus*.

Sa

Marasmius, Marasmiellus and Micromphale

A group of small agarics with thin, fleshy leathery tough or cartilagenous fruiting bodies, shrivelling up when dry or with age, reviving on wetting. **Spo** white to cream. In Britain, 40 species of the genera *Marasmius*, *Marasmiellus,* and *Micromphale* occur.

Marasmius oreades

FAIRY RING CHAMPIGNON

C convex to plane with broad umbo, ∅ 2-5 cm, reddish buff to flesh-cream. **G** distant, white to ochraceous cream. **St** 2-10 cm x 3-5 mm, stiff, tough, whitish to pale yellow. **Fl** whitish. **Sm** pleasant, of fresh sawduSt or almonds. Common on grass, grass roots and humus in grasslands, tangled growth, avenues and parks, occasionally on bare ground. Often in groups or fairy rings.

Sa (Pa) 🍽

Marasmius oreades

Marasmius alliaceus

C convex to broadly campanulate expanded, ∅ 1-4 cm, buff to pale brown or buff-brown, with grooved-striate margin. **G** whitish to pale yellow. **St** 5-20 cm x 1-3 mm, velvety, buff-brown at the apex, brown-black to black, with rooting base. **Fl** whitish to grey. **Sm** garlicky.

On (buried) beech branches in beech woods on calcareous soil.

Sa

Marasmius alliaceus

Marasmius rotula

C convex, with depressed centre, ∅ 0.5-1.5 cm, radially furrowed, whitish, occasionally with brown centre, with

Marasmius rotula

scalloped margin. **G** distant, whitish cream, attached to a collar or ring (collarium) free of the stem. **St** 2-7 cm x 1 mm, dark brown, white at the apex. **Fl** white to brown. **Sm** none.

Common on dead branches and twigs of broad-leaved trees in woods, parks and avenues.

Sa

Marasmius bulliardii

C convex, with depressed centre, ⌀ 2.5-6 mm, radially furrowed, matt, whitish cream to buff, with dark brown centre and undulate margin. **G** distant, whitish, attached to a collar free of the stem. **St** 2-4.5 cm x 0.2-0.5 mm, resembling horse hair, smooth, shiny, brown-black. **Sm** faint. Not uncommon on dead leaves of broad-leaved trees (beech, birch) in broad-leaved woods on calcareous or rich soil.

Sa ♀

Marasmius bulliardii

Marasmius androsaceus

HORSE-HAIR FUNGUS

C convex, with depressed centre, ⌀ 0.5-1 cm, membranous, radially furrowed, pale buff-pink, with red-brown centre. **G** distant, buff-pink. **St** 2-6 cm x 1 mm, resembling horse hair, tough, black. **Fl** whitish to dark brown. **Sm** none. Common on coarse litter of coniferous trees (fir) and heather in coniferous woods and mixed woods on sand and damp heath. In groups.

Sa ♀

Marasmiellus ramealis

C convex, with depressed centre, ⌀ 3-12 cm, membranous, matt, whitish to yellowish pink, often with darker centre. **G** distant, whitish pink. **St** 3-20 x 1 mm, scurfy to finely floccose, white-pink to yellowish, dark at the base. **Fl** white-pink. **Sm** faint. Common on branches, twigs and needles, occasionally on foliage or woody herbs, in broad-leaved and coniferous woodland.

Sa ♀

Marasmiellus ramealis

Marasmiellus vaillantii

C expanded to irregularly plane, with depressed centre, ⌀ 0.5-1.5 cm, wrinkled, matt, whitish, with pale yellow-brown to rusty

Marasmius androsaceus

brown centre. **G** distant, white to cream. **St** 1-3 cm x 1-2 mm, whitish yellowish with brown base. **Fl** cream. **Sm** faint, mushroomy. On grasses, herbaceous plants, foliage of broad-leaved trees, occasionally on branches and twigs, in open vegetation, marshes, tangled growth and woods.

Sa (Pa) ♀

Marasmiellus vaillantii

Micromphale foetidum

C hemispherical to irregularly expanded with depressed centre, Ø 15-35 mm, radially furrowed, darkly striate, smooth, dark red-brown to buff-brown. **G** broad, dingy light red-brown. **St** 2-5 cm x 2-4 mm, finely velvety, light red-brown at the apex and black-brown at the base. **Fl** membranous, cartilagenous, reddish brown. **Sm** disagreeable smell.

Micromphale foetidum

On branches and twigs of broad-leaved trees (hazel) in broad-leaved woods on dry, calcareous loam or clay.

R Sa

Micromphale perforans

C convex or expanded with depressed centre, Ø 8-17 mm, smooth, radially furrowed-striate, matt buff-brown or shiny flesh-brown. **G** membranous, thin, whitish. **St** 1-3 cm x 1 mm, hairy-felty, black-brown, more pallid to whitish at the apex. **Fl** whitish. **Sm** unpleasant, cabbagy or garlicky.

Fairly common on needles and needle litter (spruce) on sandy soil. In groups.

Sa ♀

Micromphale perforans

Crinipellis

Crinipellis scabellus (C. stipitaria)

C convex to expanded, with depressed centre, Ø 8-15 mm, dry, matt, whitish cream to buff, with radial, orange-brown to red-brown, fibrillose scales, centre dark red-brown to black-brown, denticulate at the margin. **G** broad, nearly free, whitish to cream. **St** 1-3 cm x 0.5-2 mm, tough, felty-hairy, dark red-brown to rusty brown. **Fl** cream. **Sm** faint, spicy. **Spo** white. Fairly common on grasses and grass debris in sand dunes, poor grasslands and open shrubberies, also on branches of broad-leaved trees and on clematis in broad-leaved woods on calcareous clay or loam.

Sa

Crinipellis scabellus

Myxomphalia

Crinipellis scabellus (C. stipitaria)

C convex funnel-shaped, with depressed centre, ⌀ 1-3 cm, smooth, striate, light to dark grey-brown. **G** decurrent, whitish to pale grey. **St** 2-4 cm x 2-4 mm, grey-brown. **Fl** white to greyish. **Sm** faint. **Spo** white.

Not uncommon on fire sites, also on chalky and mineral-rich soil in coniferous woods.

Sa

Myxomphalia maura

Baeospora

Baeospora myosura

C convex to nearly plane, ⌀ 1-3 cm, smooth, matt, pale brown to hazel, more pallid at the margin. **G** close, whitish. **St** 3-5 cm x 1-2 mm, cream to pale brown, elongated into a hairy root. **Fl** brownish. **Sm** musty. **Spo** white.

Fairly common on cones of coniferous trees, rarely on burnt wood of coniferous trees, in coniferous woods on sand.

Sa

Baeospora myosura

Omphalina and *Rickenella*

A group of small, usually funnel-shaped agarics growing on and among mosses, liverwort, grasses and on branches and wood. **Spo** white. In Britain, 30 species of the genera *Omphalina* (*Gerronema*, *Leptoglossum*) and *Rickenella* occur.

Omphalina postii (Gerronema postii)

C plane to depressed funnel-shaped, ⌀ 3-6 cm, smooth, with a lubricous gloss, orange-yellow to orange-brown, with an undulate, dentate margin. **G** deeply decurrent, white to cream. **St** 10-15 x 1 mm, orange-yellow. **Fl** orange-brown.

On Marchantia polymorpha on fire sites, in nurseries, greenhouses and along paths and ditches. Spring to autumn.

R Pa? ♀

Omphalina postii

Omphalina pyxidata

C depressed funnel-shaped, ∅ 1-2 cm, brown-red or flesh-brown to ochraceous brown, translucent striate. **G** slightly decurrent, narrow, close, pale ochraceous red-brown. **St** 2-3 cm x 3-4 mm, smooth, flesh-brown to ochraceous brown. **Fl** pallid. **Sm** faint.
Among mosses on sandy soil deficient in humus in sand dunes and in poor grassland and dune pastures, occasionally on old bonfire sites.

Sa

Omphalina pyxidata

Omphalina grossula
(Camarophyllus grossulus)

C convex to depressed funnel-shaped, ∅ 1-3 cm, smooth, matt, translucent striate, olive green to green-yellow, margin undulate. **G** thick, broad, decurrent, light yellow. **St** 1-3 cm x 1-3 mm, smooth, light yellow to green-yellow. **Fl** white. **Sm** none. On branches, bark and wood chips of coniferous trees.

VR RDL Sa

Omphalina grossula

Omphalina acerosa
(Leptoglossum acerosum)

C shell-shaped to funnel-shaped, ∅ 8-25 mm, white-felty with light and dark zones when dry, grey-brownish when damp, with an acute, pallid margin. **G** broad, grey to grey-brown. **St**

Omphalina acerosa

3-10 x 3-5 mm, rudimentary, eccentric, white-felty. **Fl** watery grey-brown. **Sm** none.

Among grass and mosses in damp, poor grassland.

R RDL Sa

Xeromphalina campanella

C convex funnel-shaped, umbilicate, ⌀ 5-25 mm, smooth, shiny, striate, orangey yellow-brown, with an acute margin. **G** sickle-shaped, decurrent, forked, cream to ochraceous brown. **St** 15-30 x 1-2 mm, cartilagenous, curved, orange-cream to red-brown, orange felt at the base. **Fl** watery brownish. **Sm** faint.

On decayed, mossy stumps of coniferous trees. Spring to summer.

Sa

Xeromphalina campanella

Rickenella fibula

C plane to convex funnel-shaped, umbilicate, ⌀ 4-10 cm, smooth, radially striate, yellow-orange to dark orange with dark centre and more pallid, striate-appendiculate margin. **G** broad, decurrent, creamy orange. **St** 3-5 cm x 1-2 mm, smooth, orange. **Fl** pale orange. **Sm** none.

Common among mosses in rich grassland and woodland. Summer to autumn.

Sa ♀

Rickenella swartzii (R. setipes)

C plane to convex funnel-shaped, umbilicate, ⌀ 4-10 mm, smooth, dark radially striate, centre grey-brown to dark purple-brown or black with violet tinge, with broad, undulate, pallid zone at the margin. **G** broad, white to light cream. **St** 3-5 cm x 1-2 mm, pale brown to purple-brown. **Fl** watery violet-brown. **Sm** none.

Common among mosses in rich grasslands and woods. Summer to autumn.

Sa ♀

Rickenella swartzii

Rickenella fibula

Mycena and Hemimycena

An extensive group of small, graceful, long-stemmed, thin-fleshed, saprotrophic agarics with convex or campanulate caps with a striate or translucent striate margin and pallid gills. **Spo** white.

In Britain, 100 species of the genus *Mycena* and 15 species of the genus *Hemimycena* occur.

Mycena galericulata

BONNET MYCENA

C conical to campanulate expanded, ∅ 2-6 cm, creamy brown or grey-brown to pink-brown, more pallid and finely furrowed-striate at the margin **G** broad, distant, adnate with a tooth, white to flesh-pink, the gills are often adnate and veined at the base. **St** 2-10 cm x 2-8 mm, hollow, tough, light grey-brown, with white-fibrillose base. **Fl** white. **Sm** mealy. Common on decaying wood and bark of (living) broad-leaved trees, occasionally of coniferous trees. Often tufted. Summer to autumn.

Mycena galericulata

Sa

Mycena polygramma

C convex, then expanded with umbo, ∅ 2-5 cm, dark grey to grey-brown, with striate-grooved margin. **G** whitish or pink to greyish. **St** 6-10 cm x 2-4 mm, longitudinally striate, silvery grey to grey-brown, with rooting base.

Fl whitish. **Sm** pleasant.

Common on stumps and branches and at the base of (living) broad-leaved trees (favouring oak), rarely on wood of coniferous trees.

Mycena polygramma

Sa

Mycena pura f. pura

C convex to expanded, ∅ 2-5 cm, finely striate, pink or lilac when damp; matt, pale pink or

Mycena pura f. pura

lilac when dry. **G** adnate, pink. **St** 5-10 cm x 4-10 mm, stiff, whitish pink, with white-felty base. **Fl** white. **Sm** of radish.

Common on leaf and needle litter of broad-leaved trees (oak, beech) and coniferous trees (spruce) in woods, tangled growth and grasslands.

Sa †

Mycena pura f. *lutea*

C convex to expanded, ∅ 2-5 cm, translucent striate, yellow when damp; matt, pale yellow when dry. **G** adnate, pale yellow. **St** 5-8 cm x 4-8 mm, stiff, pale violet, with white-felty base. **Fl** white. **Sm** of radish.

Not uncommon on leaf litter in woods and dune scrub.

Sa

Mycena pura f. *lutea*

Mycena haematopus

C conical to campanulate with umbo, ∅ 2-4 cm, striate, grey-brown to red-brown with dingy pink tinge when damp; matt, pale pink when dry, with dentate margin. **G** adnate, white to pale pink. **St** 4-10 cm x 2-3 mm, grey-pink to red-brown, exuding a blood-red milk when damaged. **Fl** blood-red. **Sm** none.

Common on dead wood and bark of (living) broad-leaved trees, occasionally on wood of coniferous trees. Usually in tufts or clusters. Summer to autumn.

Sa

Mycena haematopus

Mycena galopus var. *galopus*

C conical to campanulate, ∅ 1-2 cm, finely striate when damp, grey-brown with dark centre and whitish zone at the margin. **G** adnate, white to grey. **St** 5-10 cm x 2-3 mm, grey-brown, light at the apex and white-woolly at the base, exuding a white milk when damaged. **Fl** white. **Sm** faint.

Common on leaf litter and rotting wood in woods, heaths and poor grasslands (see photo of *Hygrocybe miniata* var. *miniata*). Summer to autumn.

Sa

Mycena galopus var. *galopus*

Mycena galopus var. *nigra* (*M. leucogala*)

C campanulate, ∅ 1-2 cm, grooved-striate, matt, brown-black to carbon black. **G** adnate, grey. **St** 5-10 cm x 2-3 mm, brown-black, exuding a white milk when damaged, with white-downy base. **Fl** grey. **Sm** faint. Common on leaf litter and rotting wood in woods, heaths and poor grasslands. Summer to autumn.

Sa

Mycena galopus var. *nigra*

Mycena galopus var. *candida* (*M. galopus* var. *alba*)

C conical to campanulate expanded, ⌀ 1-2 cm, finely striate when damp, white. **G** adnate, white. **St** 5-8 cm x 2-3 mm, exuding a white milk when damaged. **Fl** white. **Sm** faint.

Not uncommon on leaf litter and rotting wood in broad-leaved and coniferous woods.

Sa

Mycena galopus var. *candida*

Mycena inclinata

C conical to campanulate expanding with umbo, ⌀ 2-3 cm, finely striate, red-brown to chestnut, with scalloped margin. **G** adnate, whitish to pink. **St** 5-10 cm x 2-4 mm, whitish pruinose, pale brown to dark brown, with white-felty base. **Fl** whitish. **Sm** mealy.

Fairly common on stumps and lying oak trunks in broad-leaved woods. Tufted.

Sa

Mycena inclinata

Mycena arcangeliana (M. oortiana)

C broadly conical to convex, ⌀ 1-4 cm, striate, whitish yellow to grey-brown with olive green tinge. **G** close, adnexed, whitish to pale pink. **St** 2-4 cm x 1-2 mm, light grey to dark grey,

Mycena arcangeliana

with white-downy base. **Fl** pale yellow to grey. **Sm** mealy or of radish.

Common on branches and stumps of wood of broad-leaved trees, occasionally in large numbers on decaying thatched roofs. Tufted. Summer to autumn.

Sa

Mycena arcangeliana

Mycena cinerella

C hemispherical to expanded, ∅ 5-12 mm, smooth, translucent striate, ashen grey to light grey-brown. **G** broad, decurrent with a tooth, whitish grey. **St** 2-5 cm x 1 mm, smooth, pale grey-brown. **Fl** whitish grey. **Sm** mealy.

Common on needle and leaf litter in woods, poor grasslands and heaths.

Sa

Mycena cinerella

Mycena vitilis

C campanulate to expanded with umbo, ∅ 1-2 cm, matt, striate, white-fibrillose, cream to yellowish buff, with grey-brown centre and whitish margin. **G** white to light grey with white edge. **St** 4-11 cm x 1-3 mm, hollow, stiff, occasionally pruinose, whitish at the apex, grey to pink-brown. **Fl** whitish to watery grey. **Sm** none. Common on (buried) branches and pieces of decaying wood of broad-leaved trees in woods. Summer to autumn.

Sa

Mycena vitilis

Mycena acicula

C hemispherical, ∅ 2-10 mm, striate, orange to orange-red, with yellow margin. **G** pale yellow with whitish edge. **St** 2-4 cm x 1 mm, bright yellow. **Fl** pale orange. **Sm** none.

Common on branches, twigs and leaf litter of broad-leaved trees and shrubs.

Sa ♀

Mycena chlorantha

C conical to convex, ∅ 1-2 cm, striate, yellow to yellowish olive green. **G** yellowish green, with dark edge. **St** 4-6 cm x 1-3 mm, olive

Mycena acicula

grey-brown. **Fl** grey-green. **Sm** of iodine. Not uncommon on dead grass-stalks *(Ammophila arenaria)* and foliage in grassland and dune pastures.

Sa

Mycena chlorantha

Mycena adonis

C acutely conical to campanulate expanded, ⌀ 8-15 mm, smooth, matt, translucent striate, light bright red to coral-red, paling pink to whitish. **G** white with pink tinge. **St** 15-30 x 1-2 mm, watery white-grey. **Fl** watery pink to orange. **Sm** none.

On leaf litter in damp, poor grassland or hayland, sand valleys, peaty reed-lands, fields

(Molinia coerulea), living peat moors and dead wood in woods on calcareous soil.

R RDL Sa ♀

Mycena adonis

Mycena epipterygia var. lignicola

C campanulate to convex expanded, ⌀ 1-2 cm, with peelable, gelatinous cuticle, smooth, matt, shiny when damp, grooved-striate, olive yellow to olive brown, with whitish margin. **G** broad, adnate with a tooth, white to whitish yellow. **St** 3-5 cm x 1-2 mm, slimy-viscid, with gelatinous, peelable sheathing, light yellow-green. **Fl** olive grey to olive yellow. **Sm** of freshly mown grass. On wood of coniferous trees.

The variety *M. epipterygia* is common on litter among grass, foliage, needles and on decaying wood in broad-leaved and coniferous woods, heath and grassland.

Sa

Mycena epipterygia var. lignicola

Mycena sanguinolenta

Mycena sanguinolenta

C conical to campanulate, ∅ 1-2 cm, grooved-striate, pale brown to brownish red with dark centre. **G** adnate, white to flesh, with red-brown edge. **St** 4-6 cm x 1-2 mm, pale brown to brownish red, exuding a blood-red milk when damaged. **Fl** reddish. **Sm** faint.

Common on foliage, needle litter and decaying wood in coniferous and broad-leaved woods, heaths, peat bogs and grasslands. Summer to autumn.

Sa ♀

Mycena hiemalis

C conical or campanulate to expanded, ∅ 4-8 mm, smooth, matt, translucent striate, whitish to pale grey-brown with dark centre and pallid margin. **G** decurrent with a tooth, whitish. **St** 5-15 x 0.5-1 mm, curved, smooth, white pruinose, translucent, watery white-grey. **Fl** white. **Sm** none.
Not uncommon on dead wood and bark of broad-leaved trees.

RDL Sa ♀

Mycena rosella

C hemispherical to conical or campanulate, ∅ 5-15 mm, smooth, matt, furrowed-striate, deeply pink to orange-pink with dark centre and appendiculate margin. **G** slightly decurrent, pink. **St** 2-4 cm x 0.5-2 mm, hollow, smooth, pale brown with pink tinge. **Fl** watery

Mycena hiemalis

white. **Sm** faint. On slightly acid needle litter in coniferous woods (spruce).

Sa ⚲

Mycena rosella

Hemimycena candida

C convex to flattened funnel-shaped, occasionally umbilicate, ⌀ 5-15 mm, striate, white. **G** decurrent, white. **St** 2-5 cm x 0.5-1 mm, whitish grey. **Fl** white. **Sm** faint.

At the base of the stalk of comfrey *(Symphytum officinale)* in woods, roadsides and tangled growth on damp, fertile clay.

R Pa (Sa)

Hemimycena candida

Rimbachia

Rimbachia arachnoidea (Mniopetalum globisporum)

C irregularly ear- to shell-shaped, ⌀ 3-5 mm, white to cream. Lower surface smooth, white.

On *Mnium* on damp to wet soil.

Also *R. bryophila* (VR RDL) and *R. neckerae* (VR).

R RDL Pa ⚲

Rimbachia arachnoidea

Merismodes

Merismodes anomala (M. anomalus)

C cup- to saucer-shaped, ⌀ 0.2-0.5 mm. Inner surface smooth, cream to ochrous yellow. Outer surface hairy-felty, light brown, with

Merismodes anomala

brown hairs protruding over the cream margin.
On broad-leaved branches and trunks (saw cut) in broad-leaved and mixed woods.
In crowded colonies on a brown hyphal mat.

Also *M. confusa* (R).

R Sa ♀

Calyptella

A group of standing or hanging, cup-, bowl- or saucer-shaped Basidiomycetes without gills. **Spo** white. In Britain, X species of the genus *Calyptella* occur.

Calyptella capula

BRANDNETELKLOKJE

C hanging or standing, campanulate to funnel-shaped, 2-7 x 2-4 mm. Outer surface smooth, white to cream or yellowish, with appendiculate or scalloped margin. Inner surface smooth, whitish. **Fl** soft, tough.
Common on dead and living stalks of stinging nettles *(Urtica)*, occasionally on other herbaceous plants or on leaves and dead wood.

Sa (Pa?) ♀

Calyptella capula

Calyptella gibbosa

C hanging or standing, goblet- or bowl- to cup-shaped, 2-5 x 3-6 mm. Outer surface smooth, white to whitish grey. Inner surface smooth, white to whitish grey. **Fl** soft, tough.

On potato foliage and the stalks of stinging nettles, occasionally on dead wood.

VR Sa ♀

Calyptella gibbosa

Asterophora

Asterophora lycoperdoides

C globose, ∅ 5-15 mm, light brown, pruinose with chlamydospores. **G** thick, rudimentary or absent. **St** 5-10 x 2-5 mm, whitish, occasionally with lilac tinge. **Fl** grey-brown. **Spo** white. Common on fruiting bodies of *Russula* species *(Russula nigricans)*, occasionally on *Lactarius* species in broad-leaved woods and avenues on poor soil deficient in humus.

RDL Pa ♀

Asterophora lycoperdoides

Asterophora parasitica

C convex or campanulate to expanded, ∅ 5-15 mm, silky white-fibrillose, with grey-lilac tinge on a yellow-brown background. **G** thick, decurrent, pale, becoming brown. **St** 1-3 cm x 1-3 mm, often twisted, white with lilac-brown tinge. **Fl** brown. **Spo** white. On fruiting bodies of *Russula* species, occasionally of *Lactarius* species, in broad-leaved woods and avenues on poor soil deficient in humus.

Z RL Pa

Asterophora parasitica

Strobilurus

Strobilurus tenacellus

C convex to plane with umbo, ∅ 1-2.5 cm, smooth, matt, ochrous brown to dark grey-brown or red-brown, more pallid at the centre. **G** broad, nearly free, white to grey-white. **St** 3-

Strobilurus tenacellus

8 cm x 1.5-2 mm, tough, ochrous to red-brown, white at the apex and with a felty, rooting base. **Fl** white. **Sm** faint, pleasant. **Ta** bitter. **Spo** white.
On (buried) fir cones, rarely on spruce cones in coniferous and mixed woods on sand. March to June. Also *S. esculentus* and *S. stephanocystis*.

R Sa 🚫

Lactarius

An extensive group of agarics with firm, usually flattened funnel-shaped fruiting bodies, when damaged exuding a milk which may or may not discolour (see photograph of *Lactarius chrysorrheus*) and more or less decurrent gills. Mycorrhizal (see photograph of mycorrhiza, Chapter 1). **Spo** white, cream, creamy yellow or flesh-pink (see microphotograph of *Lactarius acris* spores in Chapter 1). In Britain, X species of the genus *Lactarius* occur.

Lactarius chrysorrheus

C convex funnel-shaped, ∅ 3-8 cm, concentrically zoned, pale salmon to pink-yellow, with dark, water spots. **G** close, decurrent, yellow-brown with pink tinge. **St** 3-8 x 1-2 cm, whitish to pale yellow-brown, with pink-tinged base. **Fl** whitish, milk abundant, white, rapidly becoming sulphur-yellow. **Ta** bitter, pungent. **Spo** pale cream. Fairly common near broad-leaved trees (oak) in broad-leaved woods and avenues on poor sandy and loamy soil.

RDL M

Lactarius chrysorrheus

Lactarius controversus

C convex to flattened saucer- or funnel-shaped, ∅ 8-20 cm, smooth, ivory to pale yellow, often with wine red blotches, with inrolled, downy margin. **G** close, narrow, decurrent, pale yellowish pink. **St** 3-7 x 2-4 cm, firm, ivory with vinaceous red spots, with tapering base. **Fl** white, milk white. **Ta** pungent. **Spo** pink-cream.
Not uncommon near poplar along roads and dykes on heavy soil and near white poplar and *Salix repens* in sand dunes. Occasionally remaining half-buried. Often in large groups.

M

Lactarius controversus

Lactarius deliciosus

Lactarius deliciosus

SAFFRON MILK-CAP

C convex to shallowly funnel-shaped, ∅ 3-10 cm, pale flesh to orange-brown, occasionally becoming greenish, with inrolled margin. **G** close, slightly decurrent, pale orange to yellow, becoming green when damaged. **St** 3-6 cm x 15-20 mm, pale yellow-brown or vinaceous to orange or pink, occasionally with depressed blotches becoming green. **Fl** pale yellow to faded grey-green, milk orange. **Ta** mild. **Spo** pale ochre.
Not uncommon near fir trees on poor sand.

RDL M 🍴

Lactarius semisanguifluus

C convex to flattened funnel-shaped, ∅ 5-10 cm, pruinose, pale to dingy orange, occasionally with wine red tinge, becoming an intense green at first, subsequently paling. **G** orange with pink tinge, staining wine red. **St** 5-7 x 1 cm, pale orange, becoming green. **Fl** orange, becoming vinaceous red, later becoming green, milk carrot-coloured to blood-red. **Ta** mild. **Spo** pale ochre. Near fir on moderately calcareous or rich sand or loam.

R RDL M 🍴

Lactarius semisanguifluus

Lactarius glyciosmus

COCONUT-SCENTED MILK-CAP

C irregularly convex to shallowly funnel-shaped, occasionally with papilla, ∅ 2-6 cm, pale grey-lilac to dull yellow-brown. **G** close, decurrent, pale yellowish or flesh to greyish lilac. **St** 2-6 x 0.5-1 cm, soft, brittle, pale grey-lilac or yellow-brown. **Fl** yellow-brown, milk white. **Ta** mild to pungent. **Sm** of coconut. **Spo** creamy white. Common near birch on poor sand or peat.

M

Lactarius glyciosmus

Lactarius helvus

C convex to shallowly funnel-shaped, ∅ 5-12 cm, matt, yellowish to reddish cinnamon, with dark spots and scales, with inrolled margin when young. **G** slightly decurrent, pale ochrous yellow to greyish ochre. **St** 5-12 x

1-3 cm, pruinose or finely downy, reddish ochre to cinnamon-brown or red-brown. **Fl** whitish, milk watery. **Ta** mild. **Sm** of lovage when dried. **Spo** whitish pink.

Fairly common near fir and Douglas spruce, occasionally near broad-leaved trees (birch, *Salix repens*) on acid, poor sand or loam.

M †

Lactarius helvus

Lactarius hepaticus

C convex to flattened funnel-shaped, ∅ 3-7 cm, dry, matt, lilver-coloured to greyish chestnut. **G** slightly decurrent, yellow-brown to pale ochre, with purple blush. **St** 3-7 cm x 4-8 mm, red-brown. **Fl** white, with pink-yellowish tinge, milk white, drying sulphur-yellow. **Ta** bitter, pungent. **Spo** cream.

Common near coniferous trees on acid, poor sand and loam.

M

Lactarius hepaticus

Lactarius lilacinus

C convex to depressed funnel-shaped, ∅ 5-7 cm, matt, pink-violet to flesh, with inrolled margin when young. **G** forked, flesh to ochre. **St** 5-6 x 1 cm, pruinose, flesh-ochre. **Fl** whitish pink to pale ochre, milk whitish. **Ta** mild. **Sm** of chicory when dried. **Spo** white.

Near alder on rich soil.

R RDL M

Lactarius lilacinus

Lactarius mitissimus

C convex to shallowly funnel-shaped, ∅ 3-6 cm, velvety, orange or bright orange-brown to apricot. **G** slightly decurrent, pale ochre. **St** 3-7 cm x 6-12 mm, orange-brown. **Fl** white, milk white. **Ta** mild. **Spo** creamy salmon.

Lactarius mitissimus

Not uncommon near coniferous trees (fir) and *Salix repens* on sand.

RDL M 🍴

Lactarius quietus

OAK MILK-CAP

C convex to shallowly or flattened funnel-shaped, ∅ 3-8 cm, dry, matt with concentric blotches, pale to greyish red-brown with cinnamon tinge. **G** slightly decurrent, brown-white to pale red-brown with lilac tinge. **St** 4-9 cm x 10-15 mm, matt, often grooved, pale greyish red-brown. **Fl** whitish brown-yellow, milk white to cream. **Ta** mild to bitter. **Sm** of train oil, of bugs. **Spo** cream. Common near oak in woods and avenues.
M 🚫

Lactarius quietus

Lactarius necator

C convex to shallowly funnel-shaped, ∅ 5-20 cm, viscid, dark olive green or olive brown to olive black, with inrolled margin when young. **G** narrow, close, adnate, cream to brown-yellow, staining sepia. **St** 4-8 x 1-3 cm, firm, slimy, dark olive green to olive brown, often with shallow pits. **Fl** white to brown, milk white. **Ta** burning hot. **Spo** creamy salmon.

Common near birch and coniferous trees, along paths and in logging areas on acid sandy and loamy soil.

M

Lactarius necator

Lactarius rufus

RUFOUS MILK-CAP

C convex to shallowly flattened funnel-shaped with umbo, ∅ 3-10 cm, dry, matt, red-brown or chestnut to deeply brick-red. **G** slightly decurrent, yellowish to pale red-brown. **St** 4-8 x 1-2 cm, pale red-brown. **Fl** white, milk white. **Ta** pungent and burning. **Spo** whitish cream. Common near coniferous trees, occasionally near birch on poor sandy soil.

M 🕭

Lactarius rufus

Lactarius torminosus

WOOLLY MILK-CAP

C convex to flattened funnel-shaped, ∅ 4-12 cm, pale salmon-yellow to pale pink-orange, with dark blotches and an inrolled, hairy-fibrillose margin. **G** slightly decurrent, pale flesh to salmon. **St** 4-8 x 1-2 cm, finely downy, pale flesh-orange. **Fl** white, milk white. **Ta** pungent, acrid. **Spo** yellowish cream. Fairly common near birch.

M

Lactarius torminosus

Lactarius mairei

C convex to plane or depressed funnel-shaped, ∅ 2-8 cm, zoned, light to dark cream, with upturned, dark cream to brown, hairy scales protruding over the margin. **G** thin, close, slightly decurrent, whitish to pale creamy ochre. **St** 2-6 cm x 5-15 mm, whitish to

Lactarius mairei

pale cream, with tapering base. **Fl** whitish, milk white. **Ta** burning hot. **Spo** pale cream. Near *Quercus robur* in old broad-leaved woods and avenues on rich and calcareous river clay.

VR RDL M

Lactarius vellereus

FLEECY MILK-CAP

C broadly funnel-shaped, ⌀ 10-25 cm, finely woolly, white to cream, with yellowish to pale reddish cinnamon blotches, with inrolled margin when young. **G** brittle, decurrent, pale ochre to cream. **St** 4-7 x 2-4 cm, firm, finely velvety, white to cream. **Fl** white, milk white. **Ta** mild. **Spo** white.
Near broad-leaved trees, favouring oak, in woods, roadsides and avenues.

R RDL M

Russula

An extensive group of agarics with compact, brittle fruiting bodies, usually with brightly coloured caps and with thick fleshy gills, regularly spaced and adnexed or nearly free (see photograph of gills in Chapter 1). Mycorrhizal. **Spo** white, cream, ochre, yellow.

In Britain, 120 species of the genus *Russula* occur. Certain species can only be identified with certainty using chemicals and a microscope.

Russula aeruginea

C globose to plane or depressed convex, ⌀ 4-9 cm, smooth or radially veined, pale grass-

Russula aeruginea

Lactarius vellereus

green with yellowish or brownish tinge, with dark grass-green centre and rusty brown spots. **G** nearly free, often forked, yellowish. **St** 4-8 x 1-2 cm, whitish. **Fl** white. **Ta** mild to pungent. **Spo** cream. Common near birch.

M

Russula undulata (R. atropurpurea)

BLACKISH-PURPLE RUSSULA

C convex to plane with depressed centre, ∅ 4-10 cm, deeply purple-red with black-purple centre. **G** close, adnexed, pale cream. **St** 3-6 x 1-2 cm, white. **Fl** white. **Ta** mild to pungent. **Sm** fruity (apple). **Spo** whitish. Common near broad-leaved trees (oak, beech) in avenues and woods.

M †

Russula undulata

Russula claroflava (R. flava)

YELLOW SWAMP RUSSULA

C convex to plane, ∅ 7-9 cm, viscid, shiny to matt, pale golden yellow to lemon-yellow. **G** close, forked, white to pale yellow. **St** 5-7 x 1-2 cm, white, later with grey veins. **Fl** white, becoming grey. **Ta** mild. **Spo** light ochre. Fairly common near birch.

M 🍴

Russula emetica f. longipes

EMETIC RUSSULA

C convex to plane, ∅ 3-10 cm, scarlet to cherry-red or blood-red. **G** free, cream to pale

straw-yellow. **St** 5-12 x 1-2 cm, white. **Fl** white. **Ta** very pungent. **Sm** fruity. **Spo** white. Common near broad-leaved and coniferous trees (fir) in marshy birch woods and coniferous woods on damp, acid soil.

M †

Russula emetica f. longipes

Russula amoenolens

C convex to plane with depressed centre, ∅ 3-6 cm, viscid, sepia to greyish sepia, with furrowed-grooved margin. **G** adnexed, cream to dingy whitish, edge becoming brown. **St** 3-6 x 1-2 cm, whitish. **Fl** white. **Ta** very pungent. **Sm** rancid. **Spo** pale cream.

Russula claroflava

Common near broad-leaved trees (oak, birch, lime) in avenues, parks and woods.

M

Russula amoenolens

Russula fragilis var. *fragilis*

FRAGILE RUSSULA

C convex to plane with depressed centre, ∅ 2-5 cm, colour highly variable: purple, violet, purple-red, olivaceous green, yellowish of combinations of all those, with a more pallid, furrowed-striate margin. **G** adnexed, white to pale cream, with serrate edge. **St** 3-6 cm x 5-15 mm, white. **Fl** white. **Ta** very pungent. **Sm** fruity. **Spo** whitish.
Common near broad-leaved and coniferous trees in avenues and woods.

M

Russula fragilis var. *fragilis*

Russula olivaceoviolascens (*R. atrorubens, R. laccata*)

C convex to irregularly plane, ∅ 7-9 cm, vinaceous reddish brown or dark violet-brown to reddish, with olivaceous brown or olivaceous ochre tinges. **G** close, white to cream. **St** 6-8 cm x 10-15 mm, whitish cream. **Fl** white. **Ta** pungent. **Sm** fruity. **Spo** cream.
Common near broad-leaved trees, favouring willow, alder, birch, poplar and oak. In this case 2 m above the ground on the stump of a pollarded willow in an osier bed.

M

Russula olivaceoviolascens

Russula mairei

BEECHWOOD SICKENER

C convex to plane, ∅ 3-6 cm, matt, red to pink-red. **G** adnexed, white with greenish

Russula mairei

tinge to cream. **St** 3-5 cm x 10-15 mm, white. **Fl** white. **Ta** pungent. **Sm** of coconut when young. Fairly common near beech in avenues and woods on sand and loamy sand.

M

Russula nigricans

BLACKENING RUSSULA

C convex to plane with depressed centre, ⌀ 5-20 cm, dry, matt, (below the surface) dingy white to brown, soon becoming black. **G** adnate, very thick, distant, brittle, straw-yellow to olivaceous, becoming grey-pink to black when damaged. **St** 3-8 x 1-4 cm, firm, white to dull brown and black. **Fl** white to grey and black. **Ta** mild. **Sm** fruity. **Spo** white. Common near broad-leaved trees.

M

Russula ochroleuca

COMMON YELLOW RUSSULA

C convex to plane with depressed centre, ⌀ 4-10 cm, matt, ochre to yellow, with smooth to grooved margin. **G** adnexed, cream. **St** 4-7 cm x 15-25 mm, white to watery grey. **Fl** white. **Ta** mild to pungent. **Spo** whitish to pale cream.

Common near broad-leaved and coniferous trees. Easily confused with *R. fellea*, which occurs mainly near beech and has a straw-yellow to honey-yellow cap and a pale yellow stem.

M

Russula ochroleuca

Russula paludosa

C convex to plane, ⌀ 8-10 cm, apple-pink or apple-red to orange-brown or pale orange. **G** close, partially forked, whitish to butter-yellow or ochre, with red edge. **St** 7-9 x 1.5-

Russula nigricans

2.5 cm, finely veined-grooved, white, occasionally with red hue, often grey at the base. **Fl** white. **Ta** mild, sweetish, gills pungent. **Spo** butter-yellow to light ochre.

Near coniferous trees (fir, spruce, larch) in old woodland.

R RDL M 🍴

Russula paludosa

Russula parazurea

C convex to plane, ⌀ 4-6 cm, blue pruinose, matt, blue-green to leaden greyish blue, occasionally with buff to pale brown centre. **G** close, forked, white to cream. **St** 3-5 cm x 10-15 mm, white, with swollen base. **Fl** white. **Ta** mild. **Sm** of cheese when old. **Spo** cream.

Common near broad-leaved trees (oak, beech, lime), occasionally near coniferous trees in avenues and woods on sandy soil.

M 🍴

Russula parazurea

Russula queletii

C convex to irregularly flattened, ⌀ 6-8 cm, matt, dark purple to blackish vinaceous red, more pallid at the margin. **G** close, white to creamy yellow. **St** 6-8 x 1.5-2 cm, carmine, white-downy, with swollen, pallid base. **Fl** whitish to watery grey. **Ta** burning hot. **Sm** fruity, of gooseberries. **Spo** creamy yellow.

Near spruce on calcareous soil.

R RDL M

Russula queletii

Russula rosea (R. rosacea)

C convex to plane with depressed centre, ⌀ 6-7 cm, dry, matt, pink-red to red. **G** partially forked, white to light yellow. **St** 5-6 cm x 10-15 mm, floccose, white, occasionally with pink nap. **Fl** white. **Ta** bitter. **Sm** of cedar wood. **Spo** whitish cream.
Near broad-leaved trees (oak, birch) on calcareous sand and clay.

VR RDL M

Russula rosea

Russula drimeia (R. sardonia)

C convex to depressed flattened, ∅ 7-9 cm, matt, red to vinaceous red-brown or dark purple-violet. **G** close, lemon-yellow to butter-yellow, shedding tears when young. **St** 6-8 x 1.5-2 cm, white-silvery velvety pruinose, light vinaceous red-brown to purple-violet. **Fl** white to pale yellow. **Sm** burning hot. **Sm** fruity. **Spo** cream to light ochre. Not uncommon near coniferous trees (fir) in coniferous woods on sandy soil.

M †

Russula drimeia

Volvariella

A small group of agarics with a universal veil remaining as a membranous volva at the base, and with free gills. **Spo** pink, pink-brown. In Britain, 10 species of the genus *Volvariella* occur.

Volvariella gloiocephala (var. speciosa)

C ovoid to convex or expanded, ∅ 6-14 cm, viscid when damp, faded white to pale grey-brown, occasionally with darker greyish to olivaceous brown, slightly raised centre. **G** whitish cream to yellowish dingy pink. **St** 9-22 cm x 7-15 mm, whitish, thickening at the base, which is enclosed in a sac-like, whitish or greyish volva. **Fl** white. **Sm** faint, of garden soil. Common on humus-rich soil, compost and wood chips in parks, gardens and tangled growth, on or along bridle paths, often on disturbed soil. Summer to autumn.

Sa ⓦ

Volvariella bombycina

C ovoid to campanulate, ∅ 7-19 cm, white, covered with long, fine, yellowish silky or hairy fibrils. **G** pale pink to pink-brown. **St** 7-19 cm x 7-20 mm, often curved, white, swollen at the base, which is enclosed in a large, membranous, slightly viscid, dingy brown tiger-striped volva. **Fl** white to yellowish. **Sm** of raw beans or radish. On decayed wood on

Volvariella bombycina

Volvariella gloiocephala var. *speciosa*

wounds on the trunk and in hollows or at the base of broad-leaved trees (maple, beech, poplar, horse chestnut) in old broad-leaved woods, avenues and parks. Has also been found on buried wood, waste paper and cardboard.

R RDL Sa 🦋

Volvariella surrecta

C hemispherical to expanded, ∅ 3-6 cm, ingrown radially silky fibrillose, with a dull shine, viscid, white to pale Isabella or flesh. **G** whitish cream to reddish brown. **St** 4-9 cm x 4-9 mm, white. **Fl** whitish to yellowish brown. **Sm** faint, sweetish.
On rotting fruiting bodies of *Clitocybe nebularis* in broad-leaved and coniferous woods.

R RDL Pa (Sa?)

Volvariella surrecta

Volvariella hypopithys

C campanulate to expanded, ∅ 2-7 cm, dry, shiny, whitish, with dentate margin. **G** white to pale pink. **St** 3-7 cm x 2-6 mm, downy, whitish to pale Isabella, the base enclosed in a white or faded ochraceous yellow, sac-like, 2- to 4-lobed volva. **Fl** drab white to pale yellow. **Sm** faint.

On humous soil in broad-leaved woods and parks or in grasslands on rich, calcareous sand or clay.

R Sa

Volvariella murinella

C hemispherical, ∅ 1-5 cm, radially hairy to fibrillose scaly, pale grey to grey, occasionally with a darker grey-brown centre. **G** whitish to flesh pink. **St** 1-7 cm x 1-5 mm, downy, whitish, the swollen base enclosed in a whitish to grey-brown, sac-like, 2- to 4-lobed volva. **Fl** white to light grey. **Sm** faint, of geranium (*Pelargonium*).
On the ground in broad-leaved woods, parks and grasslands on humous, rich loamy or clayey soil.

R RDL Sa

Volvariella murinella

Rhodocybe

A small group of agarics with fleshy fruiting bodies and adnate to decurrent gills. **Spo** pink.

Volvariella hypopithys

In Britain, 9 species of the genus *Rhodocybe* occur.

Rhodocybe gemina (R. truncata)

C convex to plane, ⌀ 8-12 cm, pruinose to smooth, pale reddish ochre, marbled yellow-brown or red-brown. **G** decurrent, pale reddish ochre. **St** 3-8 x 1-2 cm, whitish to pale reddish ochre. **Fl** pallid. **T** nutty. **Sm** mealy-sweetish.On humus in broad-leaved and coniferous woods and parks on rich and/or calcareous soil. Often in groups or fairy rings.

R RDL Sa ⊗

Macrocystidia

Macrocystidia cucumis

C hemispherical to convex, ⌀ 2-4 cm, velvety to smooth, red-brown to dark brown, with a sorrel-red to yellowish, translucent striate margin. **G** sinuate wit a tooth, whitish cream to flesh. **St** 4-6 cm x 4-5 mm, velvety, reddish brown to dark brown or black-brown. **Fl** cream to brownish. **Sm** of cod-liver oil. Not uncommon on humus and leaf litter in broad-leaved woods, parks, public gardens and roadsides on rich sand or clay (see microphotograph of cystides in Chapter 1).

Sa

Macrocystidia cucumis

Entoloma

A large group of agarics occurring mainly in grassland and shrubberies and exceptionally

Rhodocybe gemina

(with eccentric stem) on wood, with adnate, decurrent or nearly free gills discolouring pink with spores. **Spo** pink.

In Britain, about 175 species of the genus *Entoloma* occur.h Most species can only be identified with certainty by microscopic features.

Entoloma clypeatum var. clypeatum

C convex to plane with umbo, ∅ 3-10 cm, grey-brown, often with yellowish tinge and dark spots or radial striae. **G** pale grey to pink. **St** 3-5 cm x 8-15 mm, with white longitudinal fibrils, white with grey-brown tinge. **Fl** white. **Sm** mealy.

Not uncommon near hawthorn, blackthorn and fruit trees in woods, parks, hedges and shrubberies. Spring to early summer (see microphotograph of basidiomes in Chapter 1).

M (Pa) 🍴

Entoloma clypeatum var. clypeatum

Entoloma saundersii

C convex to irregularly expanded with umbo, ∅ 3-11 cm, matt, silvery fibrillose, whitish to pale grey-brown, with appendiculate or torn margin. **G** whitish cream to grey-pink. **St** 4-10 x 1-2 cm, fibrillose-striate, whitish to light grey. **Fl** whitish grey. **Sm** strongly mealy. Near elm on damp, heavy clay.

Often remaining half buried. Usually in groups. Winter to spring.

R Sa (M?)

Entoloma byssisedum

C shell- to fan-shaped, with short, lateral or eccentric stem, ∅ 3-11 cm, radially fibrillose, pale grey to brown. **G** distant, white to light grey. **St** 1-5 x 1 mm, velvety striate, pale grey-brown. **Ta** mealy, rancid. **Sm** mealy.

On dead vegetable matter (wood, rotting leaves) in damp spots in woods and shrubberies.

R Sa

Entoloma byssisedum

Entoloma euchroum

C hemispherical to convex, ∅ 2-2.5 cm, fibrillose-felty to scaly, blue-violet with light brown-grey centre. **G** adnate with a tooth, lilac to blue-grey, with dark edge. **St** 4-6 cm x 3-4 mm, hollow, longitudinally fibrillose

Entoloma saundersii

striate, lilac with silvery lower surface, more pallid at the apex and at the base. **Fl** grey. **Sm** none.

On dead wood and stumps of broad-leaved trees (alder) in marshy alder woodland and broad-leaved woods on damp soil.

R RDL Sa

Entoloma euchroum

Entoloma pleopodium (E. icterinum)

C campanulate to flattened convex, ⌀ 1-3 cm, smooth, translucent striate, pale yellow or dark yellow to olivaceous yellow or lemon-yellow, with more pallid marginal zone. **G** white or pale yellow to pink. **St** 2-7 cm x 2-4 mm, pale yellow or greyish brown to pink-brown. **Fl** pale yellowish olive colour. **Sm** strong, of burnt sugar, fruity. Not uncommon on humus in woods on rich soil, parks and gardens, often under stinging nettles.

Sa

Entoloma pleopodium

Entoloma conferendum var. *pusillum (E. xylophilum)*

C convex to flattened, ⌀ 10-15 mm, matt, striate, yellow-brown to reddish brown. **G** distant, white to pink. **St** 2-4 cm x 1 mm, pale yellow, silvery striate. **Fl** pale yellow-brown. **Sm** faint, mealy. On rotting broad-leaved stumps and dead root wildshoots (lime) in broad-leaved woods and parks on rich clayey soil.

VR Sa

Entoloma conferendum var. *pusillum*

Entoloma incanum

C convex to irregularly expanded, ⌀ 1-3 cm, translucent striate, yellow-greenish or yellow-brown to light olivaceous brown. **G** white-greenish to pale flesh. **St** 2-4 cm x 1-3 mm, yellow-green, white-felty at the base. **Fl** greenish. **Sm** strong, of mouse droppings. In

Entoloma incanum

unmanured, poor grasslands and roadsides on river clay and on chalk.

R RDL Sa

Entoloma sericeum var. sericeum

C convex to expanded, umbilicate or umbonate, ∅ 2-7 cm, dark sepia to reddish brown, more pallid at the margin when damp; smooth, shiny, ochraceous brown to grey-brown when dry. **G** pale grey-brown to dingy pink with red-brown tinge. **St** 2-7 cm x 2-6 mm, grey-brown to dark brown, silvery fibrillose. **Fl** watery whitish cream. **Sm** mealy.

Common in unmanured to moderately manured grasslands.

Sa

Entoloma sericeum var. *sericeum*

Entoloma chalybaeum (E. lazulinum)

C campanulate to convex, ∅ 2-4 cm, scaly-felty, radially fibrillose, indigo to blue-brown or violet-brown with black centre. **G** distant, grey-violet to grey-pink, with brownish edge. **St** 3-5 cm x 2-3 mm, bluish. **Fl** whitish. **Sm** none.
In poor grasslands and roadsides on sand, peat bog or chalk.

R RDL Sa

Pluteus

A small group of agarics usually growing on dead wood, free gills discolouring pink with spores. **Spo** pink. In Britain, 35 species of the genus *Pluteus* occur.

Pluteus cervinus (P. atricapillus)

C campanulate to flattened convex, ∅ 4-12 cm, sepia to dark brown. **G** white to grey-pink. **St** 7-10 x 1-2 cm, whitish, streaked with brown fibrils. **Fl** white. **Sm** of raw potatoes.

Common on trunks, branches, stumps and buried wood of broad-leaved trees, rarely on wood of coniferous trees (fir) or processed wood or bales of straw.
Summer to autumn.

Sa 🍴

Pluteus cervinus

Entoloma chalybaeum

Pluteus cinereofuscus

C convex to flattened, ∅ 3-4 cm, matt, grey or grey-brown to olivaceous brown or olivaceous grey, with light margin. **G** whitish to dingy pink. **St** 4-7 cm x 4-6 mm, fibrillose, whitish to light grey at the base. **Fl** grey. **Sm** faint.

Fairly common on humous soil in broad-leaved woods and parks on rich soil.

Sa

Pluteus cinereofuscus

Pluteus leoninus

C campanulate to convex expanded, ∅ 3-5 cm, matt, lemon yellow to bright golden yellow. **G** whitish cream to pink, occasionally with yellow edge. **St** 5-6 cm x 5-7 mm, whitish yellowish, felty-striate, with swollen base. **Fl** white. **Sm** none. On stumps and branches of broad-leaved trees (oak, alder, beech) in woods on mineral-rich soil.

R RDL Sa

Pluteus leoninus

Pluteus nanus

C campanulate to flattened convex with umbo, ∅ 2-6 cm, dark brown to dark greyish brown or greenish grey-brown. **G** whitish to pink-brown. **St** 3-7 cm x 2-8 mm, whitish to greyish brown. **Fl** grey. **Sm** faint. Fairly common on decaying wood of broad-leaved trees in woods on rich soil, also on humous soil and (as shown here, remaining relatively small) on marram grass (*Ammophila arenaria*).

Sa

Pluteus nanus

Pluteus romellii (P. lutescens)

C flattened convex, ∅ 2-5 cm, matt, dark yellow-brown to cinnamon, with yellowish margin. **G** dark yellow to yellowish pink. **St** 2-7 cm x 2-6 mm, bright lemon-yellow. **Fl** yellow. **Sm** none. Not uncommon on wood and on the ground among wood chips of broad-leaved trees in woods on damp soil.

Sa

Pluteus romellii

Pluteus salicinus

C convex to plane with umbo, ∅ 2-6 cm, matt, fibrillose, radially streaked with fibrils, bluish to greenish grey, with dark centre. **G** white to pink. **St** 3-6 cm x 8-12 mm, silky, whitish. **Fl** whitish greyish. **Sm** faint.

Common on branches, trunks and stumps of broad-leaved trees in broad-leaved woods and parks on damp soil. Spring to autumn.

Sa †

Pluteus salicinus

Pluteus thomsonii

C convex to expanded, ∅ 1.5-2.5 cm, velvety, matt, ashen grey or sepia to deeply dark brown, with veined centre. **G** close, whitish cream to pink. **St** 2-4 cm x 3-4 mm, light to dark grey, finely floccose, white pruinose. **Fl**

Pluteus thomsonii

white. **Sm** none. Not uncommon on branches, trunks and stumps of broad-leaved trees in woods.

Sa

Pluteus umbrosus

C convex to plane, ∅ 5-10 cm, matt, pale brown to brown, with radial, dark brown to brown-black veins. **G** white-yellowish to pink, with dark brown edge. **St** 6-8 cm x 8-10 mm, white, streaked with dark brown fibrils. **Fl** white. **Sm** of raw potatoes.

On stumps, trunks and branches of broad-leaved trees (poplar, beech) in broad-leaved woods on damp, fertile soil

R RDL Sa

Pluteus umbrosus

Cortinarius

An extensive group of agarics with fruiting bodies with a slimy-viscid or dry, matt cap, with a universal veil usually leaving remnants at the cap margin and at the base of the stem, and in the closed state with a partial veil or cortina that connects the cap margin to the stem and which after opening usually leaves a ring zone on the stem discolouring with the spores. Mycorrhizal. **Spo** yellow-brown, rusty brown, dark brown, black-brown, only in the case of the genus *Leucocortinarius* nearly white.

In Britain, more than 200 species of the genus *Cortinarius* occur. Most species can only be identified with certainty by specialists, using a microscope.

Cortinarius triumphans

C convex to flattened, ∅ 6-8 cm, viscid when damp; matt when dry, yellow-ochre or golden to lemon-yellowish or yellow-brown. **G** white or creamy buff to cinnamon, with white, serrate edge. **St** 6-8 x 1-2 cm, whitish, yellow to ochraceous yellow at the apex, with evanescent, woolly-fibrillose zones. **Fl** whitish. **Ta** mild. **Sm** none. **Spo** yellow-brown. Near birch in broad-leaved woods and avenues on rich soil.

VR RDL M 🛈

Cortinarius coerulescens
(C. caerulescens)

C convex to expanded, ∅ 6-10 cm, radially fibrillose, matt, grey-blue with violet tinge, ochraceous brown paling to pale ochre. **G** bluish to dark brown. **St** 8-10 x 2 cm, grey-blue, paling to whitish brown, with vague, rusty brown cortinal zone and with a rimmed, 3-4 cm wide, white-yellowish bulbous base. **Fl** pale blue to creamy ochre. **Sm** faint, mealy.

Cortinarius triumphans

Spo rusty brown. Near broad-leaved trees (oak, beech) in broad-leaved woods.

VR M

Cortinarius coerulescens

Cortinarius anomalus

C irregularly convex, ∅ 5-7 cm, silky-fibrillose, matt, grey-brown to yellow-brown with pale violet margin. **G** close, violet to violet-brown, with pallid edge. **St** 7-9 cm x 10-15 mm, violet, with ochraceous belts and the

base covered with violet mycelium. **Fl** pale violet. **Sm** none. **Spo** rusty brown.

Fairly common near broad-leaved trees (birch, beech, oak, willow) in broad-leaved woods, shrubberies and avenues on sand or loam deficient in humus.

M

Cortinarius anomalus

Cortinarius trivialis

C convex to expanded, ⌀ 4-11 cm, slimy, ochre to ochraceous brown. **G** pale clay-coloured to rusty brown. **St** 5-12 x 1-2 cm, slimy, white-yellowish, with brown cortinal zone and brownish belts of slimy velar remnants. **Fl** pale yellowish. **Ta** mild. **Spo** rusty brown.

Not uncommon near broad-leaved trees (poplar, willow, oak) in broad-leaved woods, shrubberies and avenues on damp, rich sand or clay.

M

Cortinarius trivialis

Cortinarius mucosus

C convex to plane, ⌀ 4-10 cm, viscid, yellow-brown to chestnut, often striate at the margin. **G** whitish to cinnamon. **St** 5-15 x 1-2 cm, silky white, with rusty brown cortinal zone. **Fl** whitish yellow-brown. **Ta** mild. **Spo** rusty brown. Near fir on dry sand deficient in humus.

VR RDL M 🛈

Cortinarius mucosus

Cortinarius delibutus

C convex to expanded, ⌀ 3-9 cm, viscid, yellow to yellow-brown with an ochraceous yellow centre. **G** violet to yellow-brown or cinnamon. **St** 5-10 cm x 7-15 mm, white-yellow to pale lilac, with a vague, rusty brown cortinal zone and with a white-downy, slightly

Cortinarius delibutus

swollen base. **Fl** whitish yellowish. **Ta** mild. **Sm** faint, of radish. **Spo** rusty brown.
Fairly common near broad-leaved trees in broad-leaved woods and avenues.

M ⊛

Cortinarius uraceus

C convex to expanded, with broad umbo, ⌀ 4-8 cm, dark brown to black-brown when damp; with a dull shine when dry, with ochre velar remnants and a pallid margin. **G** dark brown to red-brown. **St** 6-8 cm x 5-7 mm, dark brown, with whitish yellow, fibrillose zones and a white-felty base. **Fl** dark brown. **Sm** of garden soil. **Spo** rusty brown.
Near fir in coniferous and mixed woods.

R M

Cortinarius uraceus

Cortinarius paleaceus

C conical to expanded with umbo, ⌀ 2-3 cm, dark grey-brown when damp; pale brown to grey-brown when dry, with fine, fibrillose, whitish scales. **G** pallid to cinnamon. **St** 3-7 cm x 3-6 mm, brownish, with whitish scales below the white, woolly velar ring. **Fl** pallid. **Sm** of geranium (*Pelargonium*). **Spo** rusty brown. Fairly common near broad-leaved trees, occasionally near coniferous trees in woods, shrubberies, parks and avenues.

M

Cortinarius semisanguineus (Dermocybe semisanguinea)

C convex to expanded with umbo, ⌀ 6-8 cm, finely fibrillose, matt, ochraceous to olivaceous yellow-brown. **G** close, blood-red to dark red. **St** 7-8 cm x 6-7 mm, ochre to golden ochre. **Fl** ochre. **Ta** bitter. **Sm** faint. **Spo** rusty brown.
Near (young) coniferous trees on poor soil deficient in humus.

R RDL M †

Cortinarius semisanguineus

Cortinarius cinnabarinus (Dermocybe cinnabarina)

C convex to flattened with umbo, ⌀ 4-5 cm, radially striate, bright vermillion to yellowish orange-red. **G** distant, dark vermillion, with bright vermillion edge. **St** 5-6 cm x 4-6 mm,

Cortinarius paleaceus

dark vermillion. **Fl** buff-red. **Ta** of radish. **Sm** unpleasant. **Spo** rusty brown.

Near beech in broad-leaved woods.

VR RDL M †

Cortinarius cinnabarinus

Cortinarius uliginosus (Dermocybe uliginosa)

C convex to expanded with umbo, ⌀ 2-5 cm, finely fibrillose, bright yellow-orange to yellow-brown brick-red, more pallid at the margin. **G** lemon-yellow to ochraceous brown or yellow-brown. **St** 3-6 cm x 3-7 mm, pale yellowish brown-orange to orange-red, with rusty brown fibrils, a yellow cortina and a swollen base. **Fl** sulphur-yellow to yellow-brown. **Sm** of radish. **Spo** rusty brown. Fairly common near alder and willow on damp soils.

M

Cortinarius uliginosus

Rozites

Rozites caperatus

C conical or campanulate to expanded, ⌀ 8-10 cm, white pruinose, honey-yellow to pale ochraceous brown, with velar remnants at the torn cap margin when young. **G** cream to pale ochraceous brown, with appendiculate edge. **St** 7-9 cm x 10-15 mm, finely fibrillose whitish to fibrillose rusty brown, with a membranous, striate ring. **Fl** watery, cream. **Ta** mild. **Sm** faint, pleasant. **Spo** rusty yellow.
Near Scots pine, occasionally also near broad-leaved trees, in coniferous and mixed woods on poor, dry sandy soil.

VR RDL M 🍴

Rozites caperatus

Gymnopilus

A small group of golden yellow to orange-brown saprotrophic or parasytic agarics, growing on wood, or on the ground, on fire sites or on peat. **Spo** rusty brown.
In Britain, 9 species of the genus *Gymnopilus* occur.

Gymnopilus sapineus (G. penetrans)

C convex to plane, ⌀ 3-8 cm, smooth, golden yellow or orange-yellow to brown-yellow. **G** golden yellow, spotted brown. **St** 4-7 cm x 5-10 mm, brown with whitish scales, yellow at the apex and white-felty at the base. **Fl** yellow. **Ta** bitter. **Sm** strong, sweetish. Common on

branches and trunks of broad-leaved trees (oak, birch, beech) and coniferous trees in woods on poor sand or loam.

Sa

Gymnopilus junonius (G. spectabilis)

C convex to expanded, ⌀ 5-15 cm, golden yellow to orange-yellow, covered with adpressed, fibrillose, yellow-brown scales. **G** yellow to rusty brown. **St** 5-12 x 1-3 cm, fibrillose-scaly, chrome-yellow to ochrous

Gymnopilus junonius

yellow, with membranous, yellowish to rusty brown ring and swollen base. **Fl** pale yellow. **Ta** bitter. Common on wood of broad-leaved trees in woods, parks and avenues. Summer to autumn.

Sa (Pa) †

Pholiota

A group of slimy or dry, scaly, whitish or yellow to orange-brownish yellow agarics, often growing in clusters on wood or among sphagnum or on fire sites. **Spo** pale brown to rusty brown. In Britain, 30 species of the genus *Pholiota (Kuehneromyces)* occur.

Pholiota squarrosa

SHAGGY PHOLIOTA

C convex to expanded, ⌀ 5-15 cm, straw-yellow to golden yellow, with fine and coarse, upturned, red-brown scales, and inrolled margin. **G** close, pale yellow to cinnamon. **St** 5-15 cm x 10-25 mm, smooth, pale yellow at the apex, below the torn, membranous ring upturned, red-brown scales, red-brown or occasionally white-felty at the base. **Fl** tough, yellowish to red-brown. **Ta** of radish. **Sm** of straw. Common on broad-leaved trees, rarely on coniferous trees, in woods, parks and public gardens. Tufted.

Pa

Pholiota squarrosa

Pholiota flammans

C hemispherical to expanded, ∅ 3-7 cm, golden yellow to yellow-orange, with upturned, light yellow to sulphur-yellow scales and incurvate margin, overhung with velar remnants when young. **G** pale yellow to rusty brownish yellow. **St** 3-7 cm x 4-10 mm, bright yellow, below the yellow, woolly ring yellow to brown scales. **Fl** pale yellow to orange-yellow. **Ta** somewhat sour. **Sm** faint, fruity. Not uncommon on dead wood of coniferous trees in woods on sandy soil. Often in groups.

Sa

Pholiota flammans

Pholiota astragalina

C convex to expanded, ∅ 2-6 cm, slightly viscid, orange-yellow or saffron to apricot red. **G** pale orange with salmon tinge to cinnamon. **St** 5-8 cm x 4-9 mm, yellow-orange, the lower part, below the dark ring zone, brown felty-fibrillose, reddish brown at the base. **Fl** yellow to yellow-brown. **Ta** bitter.

Fairly common on stumps and dead wood of coniferous trees (fir, spruce) on sandy soil.

Sa

Pholiota astragalina

Pholiota populnea (P. destruens)

C convex to expanded with a hump, ∅ 6-20 cm, light creamy brown to greyish yellow, with large, woolly, white scales, with woolly velar remnants at the margin. **G** grey-whitish

Pholiota populnea

to dingy brown. **St** 6-10 x 2-3 cm, smooth, whitish to light creamy brown at the apex, with floccose, white scales below the membranous ring, and with a swollen base. **Fl** whitish. **Ta** bitter. **Sm** unpleasant.
Fairly common on living and dead wood of poplar, often on wounds and saw cuts.

Pa Sa

Pholiota lucifera

C convex to expanded, ⌀ 3-10 cm, viscid, bright yellow or golden yellow to orange-brown, with brown, fibrillose spots or scales. **G** close, light yellow to yellow-brown. **St** 4-8 cm x 5-14 mm, smooth, yellow at the apex, below the membranous ring yellow with brown scales. **Fl** yellow. **Ta** bitter.
On buried willow branches (at the flood-mark) and on mossy driftwood in damp spots along river banks.

VR Sa

Pholiota lucifera

Pholiota aurivella

C convex to expanded, ⌀ 5-15 cm, slimy-shiny, golden yellow with dark yellow-brown centre and adpressed, brown scales. **G** pale yellow to rusty brown. **St** 6-15 x 1-2 cm, usually curved, fibrillose, pale yellow to yellow-brown, scaly below the evanescent, floccose ring when young. **Fl** tough, pale yellow.

Fairly common on living trunks of broad-leaved trees, favouring beech, often at great height at wound areas on the trunk. Tufted.

Pa

Pholiota aurivella

Pholiota alnicola

C convex to plane, ⌀ 3-6 cm, smooth, viscid, bright lemon-yellow to olivaceous at the margin, which is often overhung with brown velar remnants. **G** pale yellow to cinnamon. **St** 4-12 cm x 5-11 mm, pale lemon-yellow at the apex, yellow, brown fibrillose below the zone with velar remnants, rusty brown at the base. **Fl** yellow to yellow-brown. **Ta** mild to bitter. **Sm** agreeably sweet. Fairly common on dead wood of broad-leaved trees, favouring alder and willow, in woods on sandy soil.

Sa

Pholiota alnicola

Pholiota gummosa

C hemispherical to flattened expanded, ⌀ 3-7 cm, whitish cream to yellow-greyish or greenish to dingy brown-yellow, with whitish to brown scales when young. **G** white-yellowish to brownish. **St** 4-6 cm x 3-7 mm, whitish cream, with yellowish brown fibrils and scales below the fibrillose ring zone, brown at the base. **Fl** yellowish to glassy greenish. Fairly common on dead wood of broad-leaved trees (buried in grassland) on clay or loam. Tufted.

Sa

Pholiota lenta

C hemispherical to plane, ⌀ 3-8 cm, slimy, with white scales when young, pale whitish cream or greyish ochre, with browner centre and more pallid at the margin. **G** close, whitish to loam-brown. **St** 3-6 cm x 6-12 mm, whitish, from the ring zone with whitish, fibrillose-floccose scales on a brown background. **Fl** whitish to creamy ochre. **Sm** of radish. Common on wood debris (hidden in humus) in broad-leaved (beech) and coniferous woods.

Sa

Pholiota lenta

Pholiota conissans
(P. graminis, P. lutaria)

C convex to plane, ⌀ 2-5 cm, slightly viscid, smooth, light ochre to lemon-yellow or yellow-greenish with ochrous brown to reddish brown centre. **G** close, grey-cream to cinnamon. **St** 2-7 cm x 2-4 mm, fibrillose-floccose, white to light yellow, with fibrillose ring zone and brown at the base. **Fl** whitish cream to yellow-brown. **Ta** mild.

Pholiota gummosa

Fairly common on dead wood of broad-leaved trees (willow) or on buried wood or roots of grasses (reed) in marshy spots.

Sa

Pholiota conissans

Pholiota highlandensis
(P. carbonaria)

C convex to plane, ∅ 2-5 cm, smooth, viscid-shiny, ochraceous brown to red-brown, with whitish scales and more pallid at the margin. **G** pale buff to cinnamon. **St** 2-5 cm x 3-7 mm, finely woolly-fibrillose, pale yellowish above the ring zone, whitish, reddish brown at the base. **Fl** pale yellow. **Ta** mild.
Fairly common on dead, burnt wood (coniferous trees, heather) on sites of fires.

Sa

Pholiota highlandensis

Pholiota oedipus
(Phaeogalera oedipus)

C hemispherical to slightly convex or plane, ∅ 1-4 cm, slimy, brown or light grey-yellowish with olivaceous green tinge to light brown or pale ochre, with striate margin when damp. **G** distant, whitish cream to loam-brown, with ciliate, white edge. **St** 2-6 cm x 2-6 mm, white, with fibrillose-floccose ring zone and white-felty base. **Fl** pale creamy ochre. **Ta** mild. **Sm** faint, mealy.
Not uncommon on wood debris and branches (poplar). Autumn to winter.

Sa

Pholiota oedipus

Pholiota mutabilis
(Kuehneromyces mutabilis)

C convex to expanded with umbo, ∅ 3-8 cm, smooth, cinnamon to orange-brown, drying bicoloured, with a pallid centre and a striate margin. **G** pallid to cinnamon. **St** 3-8 cm x 5-

Pholiota mutabilis

9 mm, smooth, yellowish at the apex and with whitish scales on a dark background below the membranous, brown ring, black-brown at the base. **Fl** white-brownish.Common on stumps of broad-leaved trees (oak, alder, birch, willow). Tufted. Summer to autumn.

Sa 🛡️

Hebeloma

A small group of whitish, pale ochraceous brown or pale cocoa-brown agarics, often with viscid caps, with sinuate, loam-coloured to cinnamon gills and pallid stems. Mycorrhizal. **Spo** grey-brown, cinnamon, rusty brown.
In Britain, 17 species of the genus *Hebeloma* occur.

Hebeloma crustuliniforme

POISON PIE

C hemispherical to convex, ⌀ 4-10 cm, viscid, whitish, with brown-yellow or pale ochraceous centre, with inrolled margin when young. **G** pale loam-coloured, with brown spots caused by droplets. **St** 4-7 x 1-2 cm, whitish floccose, cream. **Fl** white. **Ta** bitter. **Sm** of radish. Common near broad-leaved trees in broad-leaved woods, avenues and roadsides on clay or loam.

M †

Hebeloma crustuliniforme

Hebeloma mesophaeum

C hemispherical to flattened convex, ⌀ 2-5 cm, viscid, yellow-brown with reddish brown centre, with white velar remnants at the margin when young. **G** loam-coloured. **St** 4-7 cm x 4 mm, whitish at the apex, below the evanescent ring zone white-fibrillose on a dark background. **Fl** white to brownish. T bitter. **Sm** of radish. Common near broad-leaved trees (birch, oak, beech) and coniferous trees (fir, Norway spruce), often near young trees, in broad-leaved woods, avenues (lime, hazel) and shrubberies (*Salix repens*). Often in groups.

M 🛡️

Hebeloma mesophaeum

Hebeloma radicosum

C convex, ⌀ 6-9 cm, viscid, cream to pale yellowish brown. **G** pale to dark loam-coloured. **St** 5-8 cm x 10-15 mm, white at the apex, below the ring with fibrillose, brown scales, the base with a long tap root. **Fl** white. **Ta** sweet. **Sm** of almonds.
In broad-leaved woods on rich clay or loam, often rooting in mouse holes, mole holes, or wasps' nests.

R RDL M 🛡️

Hebeloma radicosum

Hebeloma anthracophilum

C hemispherical to convex, ⌀ 4-8 cm, slimy-viscid, pale buff-brown with dark brown centre and whitish margin. **G** buff-brown. **St** 4-5 cm x 5-7 mm, tough, with whitish zones on a yellowish background. **Fl** pallid, becoming brown. **Sm** faint, unpleasant.
On fire sites, burnt wood debris and animal droppings in broad-leaved and coniferous woods, public gardens, shrubberies, avenues and grasslands.

R Sa M

Hebeloma anthracophilum

Inocybe

An extensive group of usually small agarics with radially fibrillose or scaly, conical caps or expanded caps with a central umbo and appendiculate margin, some of them with a swollen bulbous base. Mycorrhizal. **Spo** pale grey-brown. In Britain, 120 species of the genus *Inocybe* occur. Most species can only be identified with certainty by microscopic features.

Inocybe asterospora

C campanulate to flattened expanded with obtuse umbo, ⌀ 3-7 cm, fibrillose splitting on lighter background, reddish to dark grey-brown. **G** whitish to olive brown. **St** 4-6 cm x 5-7 mm, slender, finely striate, red-brown to grey-brown, bulbous base distinctly marginate. **Fl** pallid to brown. **Sm** musty.
Not uncommon near broad-leaved trees, especially near oak, in woods and tree-lined roadsides on calcareous clay and sand.

M †

Inocybe asterospora

Inocybe corydalina

C campanulate to flattened expanded, ⌀ 3-7 cm, radially brown fibrillose, dingy white with olivaceous to blue-green centre and floccose margin. **G** pale loam-coloured with white edge. **St** 3-8 cm x 5-13 mm, white-greyish, with slightly swollen, occasionally blue-green base. **Fl** white to yellowish. **Ta** mild. **Sm** strong, of bread dough. Near broad-leaved trees (oak, beech) and young coniferous trees on clay and calcareous sand.

M 🚫

Inocybe corydalina

Inocybe geophylla var. *geophylla*

C conical to convex with umbo, ⌀ 1-3 cm, silky smooth, white, occasionally with a yellowish centre. **G** cream to loam-coloured. **St** 1-5 cm x 3-6 mm, silky fibrillose, white. **Fl** white. **Ta** mild. **Sm** earthy, of sperm. Common near broad-leaved trees, occasionally near coniferous trees in woods, parks and avenues on rich soil.

M †

Inocybe geophylla var. *geophylla*

Inocybe geophylla var. *lilacina*

C conical to convex with a yellowish umbo, ∅ 1-3 cm, silky smooth, lilac or violet on an ochrous brown background. **G** cream to loam-coloured. **St** 1-5 cm x 3-6 mm, silky fibrillose, lilac, ochrous yellow at the base. **Fl** white. **Ta** mild. **Sm** earthy, of sperm.
Fairly common near broad-leaved trees (or coniferous trees), in woods, parks and avenues on rich soil.

M †

Inocybe geophylla var. *lilacina*

Inocybe rimosa (I. fastigiata)

C conical to campanulate with umbo, ∅ 2-8 cm, radially fibrillose and splitting, straw-yellow to brown-yellow. **G** yellowish loam-coloured with white edge. **St** 3-7 cm x 4-12 mm, pale brown-yellow, white at the apex. **Fl** white. **Ta** mild to bitter. **Sm** faint, mealy. Fairly common near broad-leaved trees, occasionally near coniferous trees in avenues and parks or in woods and shrubberies on rich soil.

M †

Inocybe rimosa

Inocybe lacera

C convex with umbo, ∅ 1-3 cm, radially fibrillose, grey-brown to reddish brown. **G** white to loam-coloured with white edge. **St** 2-3 cm x 3-6 mm, fibrillose, brownish, pallid at the apex, somewhat bulbous swollen base. **Fl** white. **Ta** mild. **Sm** mealy.
Common near broad-leaved and coniferous trees in woods on acid, sand and peat deficient in humus, often along paths.

M †

Inocybe lacera

Inocybe squamata

C conical to expanded with umbo, ⌀ 3-8 cm, radially brown-fibrillose striate on a yellow to yellow-brown background, with brown scales at the centre, margin often splitting. **G** pale olive yellow to yellow-brown with light edge. **St** 5-7 cm x 6-9 mm, fibrillose, pale brown to yellowish brown. **Fl** pallid. **Sm** faint. Fairly common near poplar on clay.

M

Inocybe squamata

Inocybe vulpinella

Inocybe vulpinella (I. halophila)

C campanulate to convex with umbo, ⌀ 3-4 cm, red-brown scaly-fibrillose, with scaly, red-brown centre. **G** red-brown. **St** 3-5 cm x 4-6 mm, white, brown towards the base, with white, rimmed bulbous base. **Fl** pallid. **Sm** faint. Near willow, *Salix repens*, occasionally near poplar, on damp, calcareous sand.

R M

Bolbitius

Bolbitius vitellinus

C conical to campanulate, then flattened expanded, with deeply grooved margin, ⌀ 1-4 cm, viscid, translucent, chrome-yellow or egg-yellow, paling to grey-brown. **G** close, pale yellow to cinnamon-brown. **St** 3-8 cm x 2-4 mm, hollow, fragile, finely pruinose, whitish yellow, white-downy at the base. **Fl** thin, pallid. **Spo** rusty brown. Common on humus-rich soil, droppings, manure and compost heaps and rotting grass in gardens, roadsides, grasslands and the edges of woods on rich soil or manured areas. Summer to autumn.

Bolbitius vitellinus

In Britain, 6 species of the genus *Bolbitius* occur.

Sa

Conocybe

A group of fragile, often long-stemmed, Isabella, pale yellow or cream, or yellow-brown or reddish brown agarics with campanulate or conical to convex-expanded caps, some of them with a membranous ring. **Spo** yellow-brown to ochrous brown. In Britain, 45 species of the genus *Conocybe (Pholiotina)* occur. Most species can only be identified with certainty by microscopic features.

Conocybe tenera

C obtusely conical, ⌀ 1-4 cm, matt, ochraceous brown to cinnamon, drying yellow-brown. **G** adnate, close, whitish to cinnamon. **St** 5-10 cm x 4-7 mm, brittle, finely pruinose, whitish with pale ochrous brown tinge. **Fl** pale ochrous brown. **Sm** mushroomy. Common on the ground in grasslands, parks and roadsides, occasionally in broad-leaved woods, on moderately rich soil. Early summer to autumn.

Sa

Conocybe lactea

ISABELKLEURIG BREEKSTEELTJE

C conical to narrowly campanulate, ⌀ 1-2 cm, matt, whitish to yellowish cream. **G** cinnamon. **St** 3-10 cm x 1-2 mm, brittle, pruinose at the apex, white, with a rimmed bulbous base. Fairly common on humus-rich soil in parks, gardens and lawns.

Sa

Conocybe tenera

Conocybe lactea

Conocybe rickeniana

C campanulate to expanded, ∅ 1-3 cm, smooth, rusty brown to cinnamon striate on a yellow-brown background. **G** cinnamon. **St** 3-8 cm x 1-2 mm, whitish pruinose, red-brown, often with bulbous base.
Fairly common on humous soil in grasslands, parks, roadsides and broad-leaved woods on rich soil.

Sa

Conocybe rickeniana

Conocybe arrhenii (Pholiotina arrhenii)

C campanulate to expanded with umbo, ∅ 2-3 cm, matt, reddish brown to ochraceous yellow, striate at the margin. **G** loam-coloured to rusty brown. **St** 1-4 cm x 2-5 mm, pruinose-striate, whitish to silvery cream, with membranous ring which is striate on the upper surface. Not uncommon on the ground in broad-leaved woods, parks and avenues on humus-rich sand or clay. Summer to autumn.

Sa

Conocybe arrhenii

Conocybe aporos (Pholiotina aporos)

C hemispherical to expanded, ∅ 1-4 cm, matt, finely striate, yellowish to ochraceous brownish. **G** loam-coloured to dark ochraceous brown. **St** 2-6 cm x 2-4 mm, whitish-floccose, cream, with membranous ring which is striate on the upper surface. Not uncommon on the ground in broad-leaved woods, occasionally in parks on rich soil. Spring.

Sa

Conocybe aporos

Galerina

A group of small, fragile, honey-yellow or yellow-brown to red-brown agarics with campanulate to expanded caps, growing among and on mosses and on wood. **Spo** ochrous, rusty brown.

In Britain, 50 species of the genus *Galerina* occur. Most species can only be identified with certainty by microscopic features.

Galerina hypnorum

Galerina hypnorum

C campanulate to convex, ∅ 4-15 mm, smooth, translucent striate, dingy honey-yellow when damp; yellow-brown or ochraceous brown when dry. **G** ochrous brown. **St** 15-40 x 1-2 mm, pale yellowish ochre, pruinose at the apex and dark at the base.

Common among mosses on the ground and on mossy trunks and branches.

Sa

Galerina pumila

C campanulate, ∅ 5-15 mm, smooth, pale ochraceous yellow when dry, pale yellow to ochraceous yellow with a white margin and translucent striate when damp. **G** yellowish to rusty brown. **St** 2-5 cm x 1-3 mm, ochrous yellow, with white, silky fibrils and pallid, pruinose at the apex. Common on litter and humus, often among mosses, in poor grasslands, heaths and in grassy spots in sand dunes.

Sa

Galerina pumila

Galerina autumnalis

C campanulate or convex to expanded, ∅ 3-6 cm, viscid, ochraceous brown, with finely striate margin when damp; matt, yellow to ochrous yellow-brown when dry. **G** decurrent, light ochrous brown. **St** 3-9 cm x 3-8 mm, light ochrous yellow at the apex, brownish fibrillose below the ring, with yellow-brown zones, becoming increasingly dark brown towards the base, dark brown at the base. **Fl** yellowish to red-brown. **Ta** mild. **Sm** mushroomy. On branches and trunks,

Galerina autumnalis

especially on strongly decayed wood, usually of broad-leaved trees, on rich soil.

R Sa †

Alnicola

A groep of small, ochraceous yellowish brown, brown and dark brown agarics with a preference for damp habitats. **Spo** brown. Mycorrhizal, saprophytic.
In Britain, 20 species of the genus *Alnicola (Naucoria)* occur.

Alnicola escharoides (Naucoria escharoides)

C convex to flattened, ∅ 1-3 cm, ochraceous yellowish brown to pale brown. **G** ochraceous yellow to pale cinnamon-brown. **St** 4-5 cm x 3-4 mm, ochraceous brown, dark at the base. **Fl** yellow-brown. **Ta** bitter. **Sm** sweetish. Common near alder in marshy alder woods, in

Alnicola escharoides

broad-leaved woods with alder and in alder windbreaks.

M

Tubaria

A small group of agarics which digest wood, coarse litter and humus. Caps convex to expanded, some are downy at the base. **Spo** ochre.
In Britain, 5 species of the genus *Tubaria* occur.

Tubaria furfuracea

C convex to plane, ⌀ 2-4 cm, yellow-brown to dark yellow-brown, striate at the margin when damp; finely floccose, pale brown-yellow when dry, often with white velar remnants on and at the marginal zone. **G** distant, slightly decurrent, cinnamon. **St** 2-5 cm x 2-4 mm,cinnamon to pale brown-yellow, downy, white at the base. **Fl** brown-yellow. Common on wood chips, branches and twigs, occasionally on coarse litter and humus in broad-leaved woods, shrubberies, parks and gardens. Summer to autumn.

Sa

Tubaria furfuracea

Tubaria dispersa (T. autochtona)

C convex to plane, ⌀ 5-20 mm, finely velvety, creamy brown to ochraceous brownish yellow, striate at the margin when damp. **G** pale yellow to ochre. **St** 15-30 x 1-2 mm, whitish cream. **Fl** whitish. Common on coarse litter and humus of hawthorn in shrubberies, at the

Tubaria dispersa

edge of woods and in broad-leaved woods on calcareous, humus-rich sand.

Sa

Phaeolepiota

Phaeolepiota aurea

C hemispherical to convex or expanded, ⌀ 5-20 cm, finely mealy-granular, matt, ochraceous brown to golden yellow. **G** nearly free, loam-coloured to rusty brown. **St** 8-15 x 1-3 cm, smooth, light ochrous yellow at the apex, below the membranous, wide, brown ring mealy-granular, dark yellow-brown to pale ochraceous brown. **Fl** whitish to light yellow. **Ta** mild. **Sm** spicy, somewhat sour. **Spo** ochrous rusty brown. On rich clay or sandy soil in broad-leaved woods, parks, roadsides and tangled growth, often under stinging nettles.
R RDL Sa ⊕

Phaeolepiota aurea

Squamanita

A small group of agarics growing from a commun bulb, with a strong, sweetish smell. **Spo** light yellow.
In Britain, 2 or 3 species of the genus *Squamanita* occur.

Squamanita odorata

C campanulate to expanded, ∅ 7-35 mm, dry, with fibrillose, pallid and brown-black scales in concentric zones on a light grey-brown background, with an acute margin, overhung with velar remnants when young. **G** partially forked, dingy white to grey-brown, with appendiculate edge. **St** 1-3 cm x 2-5 mm, with grey-brown fibrils on a whitish background and upturned, dark grey-brown scales in belts above the rimmed, creamy yellow bulb. **Fl** whitish, becoming grey-brown. **Ta** mild. **Sm** strong, sweetish, of chocolates.
On sandy and loamy soil, after manuring, along the edge of paths and roads, occasionally in gardens, in wooded areas. Possibly parasitizing the mycelium of *Hebeloma* species.

VR RDL Sa (Pa?)

Squamanita odorata

Agaricus bernardii

Agaricus

A group of saprotrophic agarics with white or pink gills discolouring chocolate-brown with spores, a ring or belts around the stem and flesh usually becoming yellow, red or pink when damaged. **Spo** brown, dark brown.

In Britain, about 60 species of the genus *Agaricus* occur.

Agaricus bernardii
C hemispherical to irregularly flattened convex, ∅ 5-15 cm, whitish to light brown, cracking into rough, brownish scales and

becoming reddish when damaged. **G** pale grey or flesh-brown to dark brown. **St** 5-7 x 2-4 cm, whitish, with a single, thin, whitish ring and tapering, grey-brown at the base. **Fl** white, becoming reddish. **Ta** unpleasant. **Sm** fishy. On the ground on mud flats, brackish grasslands and sea embankments.

R Sa 🚫

Agaricus bisporus var. bisporus

C hemispherical to irregularly expanded, ∅ 5-13 cm, dingy brown to greyish brown, with radially, fibrillose, brown scales on a whitish background, whitish at the margin. **G** dingy pink to dark purple-brown. **St** 5-7 x 2-4 cm, white, floccose below the membranous, protruding ring. **Fl** white, reddening slightly. **Ta** mild, nutty. **Sm** somewhat sour, mushroomy.

Not uncommon on loose, humous soil and compost in parks, gardens and roadsides, occasionally in broad-leaved woods on rich soil. Summer to autumn.

The *albidus* variety is the form that is cultivated on compost mixed with horse dung or on artificial substrates.

sa 🍴

Agaricus bisporus var. *bisporus*

Agaricus silvaticus

C convex, ∅ 5-10 cm, with ochre to brown fibrils, cracking into adpressed scales on a lighter background. **G** pale reddish to dark brown. **St** 5-10 cm x 10-15 mm, whitish, occasionally with brownish, fibrillose scales below the dingy brown ring. **Fl** white, becoming red to brownish. **Ta** mild. **Sm** pleasant, spicy. Fairly common on humus soil

Agaricus silvaticus

in broad-leaved and coniferous woods on rich soil. Summer to autumn.

Sa 🍴

Agaricus subperonatus

C hemispherical to convex expanded, ∅ 7-10 cm, dingy cream to pale grey, with flattened, fibrillose, brown scales, margin overhung with velar remnants. **G** dingy red-brown to chocolate-brown. **St** 8-10 cm x 15-20 mm, whitish to pale brown, below the thin, whitish and pale brown ring a ring-like belt and a tapering base. **Fl** whitish, reddening strongly. **Ta** mild. **Sm** disagreeably sweetish to fruity.

On the ground and on compoSt in parks, young scrub and roadsides on recently disturbed, rich soil (clay).

R Sa 🚫

Agaricus subperonatus

Agaricus vaporarius

C globose to flattened convex, ∅ 10-15 cm, dingy brown, cracking into large scales on a whitish background. **G** pale pink to chocolate-brown. **St** 6-12 x 3-5 cm, whitish, with fibrillose, brown scales when young, with a thick, pendulous, white ring and a tapering base. **Fl** white, reddening slightly. **Ta** nutty. **Sm** somewhat sour, mushroomy.

On the ground and on compoSt in parks, young scrub, roadsides and in churchyards on rich soil. Often pushing up through the soil in trooping, deep-rooting groups.

R Sa 🍴

Agaricus vaporarius

Agaricus arvensis

HORSE MUSHROOM

C hemispherical to expanded, ∅ 8-20 cm, creamy white, becoming yellow with age or when damaged. **G** free, white or pink to chocolate-brown. **St** 8-10 x 2-3 cm, creamy white, yellowing, with a white, double ring, the lower one splitting open into a star shape, and a club-shaped swollen base. **Fl** white. **Ta** mushroomy. **Sm** of aniseed. Common on the ground in pastures, roadsides, parks, public gardens or recently planted woodland on humus soil.

Sa 🍴

Agaricus xanthoderma

YELLOW STAINER

C hemispherical to convex or expanded, ∅ 5-15 cm, strongly discolouring chrome-yellow

Agaricus arvensis

on bruising. **G** white or pink to grey-brown. **St** 5-15 x 1-2 cm, white, with a white ring and a swollen base. **Fl** white, becoming chrome-yellow at the base. **Ta** unpleasant. **Sm** of phenol. Not uncommon on the ground in (young) broad-leaved woods, parks and public gardens on rich, calcareous soil.

Sa †

Agaricus xanthoderma

Agaricus praeclaresquamosus (A. placomyces var. meleagris)

C hemispherical to expanded, ∅ 5-9 cm, with grey-brown scales on a whitish background, yellowing on bruising. **G** pink to black-brown. **St** 6-9 cm x 10-12 mm, whitish, with scales, below the membranous ring whitish to pale brown, bulbous base, yellowing on bruising. **Fl** white, becoming yellow. **Ta** strong, unpleasant. **Sm** strong, unpleasant. On humus

Agaricus praeclaresquamosus

soil in dune scrub and broad-leaved woods on humous, rich and calcareous soil. Summer to autumn.

R Sa †

Agaricus geesterani

C hemispherical to convex, ∅ 8-20 cm, pale vinaceous red, with vinaceous red scales on a lighter background. **G** whitish to dark brown. **St** 5-12 x 3-4 cm, floccose, creamy white to pink-cream, with vinaceous brown ring zones. **Fl** firm, rapidly yellowing on bruising and subsequently becoming brown-red. **Ta** mild. **Sm** on cutting ar first strongly soapy, then faint, pleasant, nutty.

On the ground in parks, young scrub and roadsides on rich, humus or clayey soil.

VR RDL Sa

Agaricus geesterani

Agrocybe

A group of saprophytic agarics growing in grasslands and on humus, coarse litter or wood, with white, cream to ochrous brown or (dark) reddish brown caps. **Spo** tobacco, dark brown.

In Britain, 12 species of the genus *Agrocybe* occur.

Agrocybe cylindracea (A. aegerita)

C convex to flattened expanded, ∅ 4-10 cm, matt, whitish or creamy yellow, with darker to hazel centre. **G** cream to dark brown. **St** 5-10 x 1-2 cm, finely scaly, cream to pale brown, ring browning with spores. **Fl** whitish. **Ta** mild, nutty or of radish. **Sm** pleasant, of radish or fruity.

On trunks and stumps of (pollarded) poplar, occasionally on willow, in avenues and broad-leaved windbreaks on rich soil. Summer to autumn.

R Sa ⑪

Agrocybe cylindracea

Agrocybe praecox

Agrocybe praecox

C convex, ⌀ 3-6 cm, matt, creamy ochre to pale ochrous brown, drying whitish. **G** adnate, pale pink-brown to dark brown. **St** 4-6 cm x 4-8 mm, cream to creamy yellow, with a ring. **Fl** white to cream. **Ta** mealy. **Sm** mealy. Common on the ground and on wood chips in gardens, parks, public gardens and roadsides on rich soil. Spring.

Sa 🍴

Agrocybe dura

C convex to pale, ⌀ 3-7 cm, matt, cracking, ivory to creamy yellowish, with velar remnants at the margin. **G** adnate, pale brown to grey-brown. **St** 5-8 cm x 3-7 mm, whitish to pale yellowish, with floccose ring. **Fl** whitish. **Ta** faint, bitter. **Sm** mushroomy.

Not uncommon on litter or wood chips or in grassy roadsides in city parks, public gardens, broad-leaved woods and grasslands on rich, often slightly disturbed soil. Spring to summer.

Sa 🍴

Agrocybe dura

Agrocybe pediades
(A. semiorbicularis)

C hemispherical to convex, ⌀ 15-35 mm, viscid, velvety matt when dry, light yellow or ochraceous yellow to orange-yellow or brown-yellow, with acute margin overhung with velar remnants when young. **G** creamy buff to rusty brown, with white ciliate edge. **St** 3-7 cm x 2-5 mm, white pruinose, pale yellow to orange-yellow. **Fl** whitish to ochrous yellow. **Ta** mild. **Sm** mealy. Fairly common on the ground in city parks, public gardens, lawns, roadsides and grasslands on rich soil. Summer.

Sa 🚫

Agrocybe pediades

Agrocybe putaminum

C hemispherical or convex to irregularly flattened, ⌀ 2-7 cm, velvety, matt, cream or bright yellow-brown to ochraceous brown. **G** close, whitish pale yellow to pale brown. **St** 2-8 cm x 4-8 mm, fibrillose, pale brown to pale yellow, dark brown at the base. **Fl** whitish to pale brown. **Ta** mealy. **Sm** mealy. On wood chips in osier beds, town parks and public gardens.

VR Sa

Agrocybe putaminum

Psilocybe

A group of agarics highly variable in colour (green, orange-red, red, yellow, ochraceous yellow, yellow-brown, orange-brown, red-brown), with conical to convex caps, occasionally with umbo. **Spo** brown, purple-brown, purple-black.

In Britain, about 50 species of the genus *Psilocybe (Hypholoma, Stropharia, Melanotus)* occur.

Psilocybe fascicularis (Hypholoma fascicularis)

C convex, ⌀ 2-7 cm, bright sulphur-yellow, with orange-brown centre, margin often with pale yellow to brown velar remnants. **G** lemon-yellowish green to dingy grey-green. **St** 4-10 cm x 5-10 mm, curved, sulphur-yellow, with a faint ring zone becoming purple-brown with spores, brown at the base. **Fl** sulphur-yellow. **Ta** very bitter. **Sm** mushroomy. Common on dead wood of coniferous and broad-leaved trees in woods and public gardens. In clusters or groups. Spring to autumn.

Sa †

Psilocybe fascicularis

Psilocybe sublateritia

Psilocybe sublateritia (Hypholoma sublateritium)

C convex, ⌀ 3-10 cm, brick-red, with whitish to ochre marginal zone with fibrillose velar remnants. **G** cream or pale yellow to olivaceous brown. **St** 5-12 cm x 5-12 mm, pale yellow, below the cortinal zone ochraceous brown. **Fl** pale yellowish. **Ta** bitter. **Sm** mushroomy. Common on trunks, stumps and thick branches of broad-leaved trees (oak, birch, beech) in broad-leaved woods. In groups.

Sa

Psilocybe capnoides (Hypholoma capnoides)

C convex with umbo, ∅ 2-6 cm, pale ochre with yellow-brown centre, with light yellow marginal zone. **G** cream to grey-lilac or olive black. **St** 4-7 cm x 3-9 mm, ochrous brownish yellow, with whitish cortinal zone and dark brown base. **Fl** yellowish. **Ta** sweetish. **Sm** faint. Common on dead wood of coniferous trees. Summer to autumn.

Sa 🍄

Psilocybe capnoides

Psilocybe elongata (Hypholoma elongatipes)

C convex to flattened, ∅ 1-2 cm, matt when dry, lubricous when damp, striate, pale orange-brown, with acute, pale yellow to green-yellow margin. **G** whitish or grey-buff to violet-brown. **St** 3-6 cm x 1 mm, elastic, hollow, matt, longitudinally whitish-fibrillose, light yellow at the apex and orange-brown at

Psilocybe elongata

the base. **Fl** pale yellow to orange-yellow. **Ta** mild. **Sm** musty. Fairly common among sphagnum and other mosses or on coarse litter on peat moors, along pools and in wet heaths and poor grasslands. Summer to autumn.

Sa 🍄

Psilocybe aeruginosa (Stropharia aeruginosa)

C campanulate to convex with broad umbo, ∅ 2-8 cm, slimy, blue-green to deep green, paling yellow-green to yellowish, with white scales and with white velar remnants at the margin. **G** whitish pink to lilac-brown with white edge. **St** 4-8 cm x 4-10 mm, finely felty at the apex, pale blue-green, below the fibrillose-membranous ring with upturned, fibrillose, white scales on a coarsely felty, blue or blue-green background, becoming greenish yellow. **Fl** blue-white. **Ta** mild. **Sm** faint, somewhat sour. Common on strongly decayed wood, coarse litter or on the ground in coniferous and broad-leaved woods on acid, sandy soil. Summer to autumn.

Sa

Psilocybe aeruginosa

Psilocybe caerulea (Stropharia cyanea)

C hemispherical to flattened expanded, ∅ 3-6 cm, slightly slimy-viscid, blue-green or yellow-green to pale yellow or pale ochre, often with yellowish blotches, with evanescent, whitish scales at the margin. **G** light reddish brown to dark brown. **St** 4-7 cm x 4-10 mm, finely felty at the apex, whitish to pale blue, below the imperfect ring with upturned, whitish scales on a blue or blue-green background, becoming yellowish, white-felty at the base. **Fl** white to blue-green. **Ta** mild. **Sm** faint, somewhat sour. Common on coarse litter and wood chips, among leaves and grass debris in woods, parks, gardens and public gardens. Summer to autumn.

Sa 🚫

Psilocybe caerulea

Psilocybe aurantiaca (Stropharia aurantiaca)

C convex, ∅ 2-7 cm, orange-red with yellowish or dark red blotches, often with white velar remnants at the margin. **G** cream to olivaceous brown. **St** 2-8 cm x 4-10 mm, ochre to orange-red, pallid at the apex and rudimentary ring. **Fl** cream to yellowish orange. **Ta** mild. **Sm** faint.

Not uncommon on wood debris, especially wood chips, in woods, parks and public gardens. Summer to autumn.

Sa

Psilocybe aurantiaca

Psilocybe coronilla (Stropharia coronilla)

C convex, ∅ 2-5 cm, viscid, light yellow to ochraceous yellow. **G** pale grey-brown to purple-brown. **St** 4-6 cm x 5-8 mm, white at the apex, matt, white to yellowish brown below the membranous ring, striate on its upper surface, **Fl** whitish. **Ta** mild. **Sm** faint. Fairly common on bare soil and grass debris in poor grasslands and among marram grass *(Ammophila arenaria)*.

Sa 🚫

Psilocybe coronilla

Psilocybe semiglobata (Stropharia semiglobata)

C hemispherical to convex, occasionally with umbo, ∅ 1-4 cm, slimy-viscid, yellow to yellow-brown. **G** pale grey to purple-black. **St** 5-10 cm x 3-5 mm, viscid, cream to pale yellow, below the evanescent ring fine, light brown scales. **Fl** cream. **Ta** mild. **Sm** none. Common on manure and strongly manured spots in grasslands on sandy soil.

Sa 🚫

Psilocybe semiglobata

Psilocybe squamosa
(Stropharia squamosa)

C hemispherical to convex, ∅ 2-5 cm, slimy-viscid, ochraceous brown to date-brown, with concentric, whitish to grey-brown scales when dry. **G** light grey-brown to grey-black. **St** 6-11 cm x 4-9 mm, whitish to light brown at the apex, below the pendulous, membranous ring white-felty-scaly on a light brown background. **Fl** creamy yellow. **Ta** mild. **Sm** faint. Not uncommon on wood chips, coarse litter or buried wood debris in broad-leaved woods, parks and public gardens on rich clay and dry sandy soil.

Sa 🚫

Psilocybe squamosa

Psilocybe semilanceata

LIBERTY CAP

C conical with acute umbo, ∅ 5-15 mm, 6-13 mm high, viscid, olive brown to grey-brown, straw-yellow to ochre when dry, with

Psilocybe semilanceata

inrolled margin when young. **G** pale brown-grey to purple-brown. **St** 5-9 cm x 1-2 mm, whitish to cream, occasionally tinged blue-green at the base. **Fl** grey-brown to buff. **Ta** mild. **Sm** of radish. Fairly common on the ground and on grass debris in fairly poor to manured grasslands.

Sa †

Psilocybe coprophila

C hemispherical to campanulate, ∅ 10-25 mm, viscid, shiny, yellowish brown to pale reddish brown. **G** close, whitish grey to lilac-brown. **St** 2-4 cm x 1-2 mm, white-floccose, pale brown, white pruinose at the apex. **Fl** pale brown. **Ta** mild. **Sm** faint, pleasant. Not uncommon on horse and sheep dung and rabbit and hare droppings in poor to moderately rich grasslands and heaths. Summer to autumn.

Sa 🚫

Psilocybe coprophila

Psilocybe montana

Psilocybe montana

C hemispherical, Ø 4-12 mm, striate, dark brown when damp; matt, ochraceous to buff when dry, with velar remnants at the margin when young. **G** cream to dark purple-brown. **St** 15-20 x 1 mm, longitudinally white-fibrillose, grey-ochre. **Fl** whitish to grey-brown. **Ta** mild. **Sm** faint, spicy.

Fairly common among mosses in sand drifts, poor (dune) pastures and heaths on dry, sandy soil. Often in groups. Summer to autumn.

Sa †

Psilocybe muscorum

C hemispherical to convex with umbo, Ø 5-14 mm, viscid, shiny, dark striate, red-brown when damp; matt, ochrous buff to pale buff-brown when dry. **G** dingy cream to dark brown. **St** 15-25 x 1-2 mm, longitudinally

Psilocybe muscorum

Psilocybe caricicola

white-fibrillose, grey-brown. **Fl** light grey-brown. **Ta** mild. **Sm** faint. Not uncommon among mosses and grass in sand drifts, poor grasslands and gardens on dry, poor sandy soil. In groups. Spring to autumn.

Can be distinguished with certainty from *P. montana* and a few other small *Psilocybe* species only by microscopic features.

Sa

Psilocybe caricicola
(Melanotus caricicola)

C roundish to shell- or kidney-shaped, Ø 5-10 mm, stem eccentric or lateral, finely felty, brownish translucent striate, brown-ochre to flesh. **G** light ochre to flesh-red. **St** 1-3 x 0,5 mm, light brown to rusty brown, white-felty at the base. **Fl** light ochre.

On dead leaves of *Glyceria maxima* in shore vegetation. Also *P. philipsii* (R).

VR Sa ♀

Psathyrella and Lacrymaria

A large group of usually fragile, long-stemmed saprophytic agarics, with caps that often show a marked change in colour on becoming damp or dry. With velar remnants at the margin when young. **Spo** purple-black to black (but see photograph of sterile *Psathyrella* in chapter 1).

In Britain, about 100 species of the genera *Psathyrella* and *Lacrymaria* occur.

Most species can only be identified with certainty by microscopic features of young specimens.

Psathyrella candolleana

C campanulate to flattened expanded, Ø 2-6 cm, pale ochraceous brown when damp; white when dry, margin overhung with white velar remnants. **G** light grey-violet to chocolate-brown. **St** 4-8 cm x 4-8 mm, hollow, brittle, floccose, white. **Fl** white.

Common on or near dead branches, stumps, trunks and buried wood of broad-leaved trees in broad-leaved woods, parks, avenues, shrubberies, osier beds, grasslands and gardens. From one single cap a small but complete

Psathyrella candolleana

fruiting body has grown, with the stem pointing upwards. In groups or clusters. Spring to autumn.

Sa

Psathyrella piluliformis (P. hydrophila)

C convex to plane **G** 2-6 cm pale yellow-brown or ochraceous brown to chestnut, often with dark centre, margin overhung with white velar remnants when young. **G** grey-buff to chocolate-brown, with whitish edge. **St** 3-7 cm x 3-8 mm, white, yellow-brown at the base. **Fl** watery brown. **Ta** bitter. **Sm** faint.

Common on or near dead trunks, stumps and buried wood of broad-leaved trees (oak, beech) in broad-leaved woods, parks and avenues on sandy soil. In clusters. Summer to autumn.

Sa

Psathyrella piluliformis

Psathyrella marcescibilis

C conical to campanulate, ∅ 2-4 cm, grey-brown when damp; light grey-brown to creamy white when dry, margin with white velar remnants. **G** whitish grey to dark purple-brown. **St** 3-6 cm x 2-3 mm, hollow, fragile, creamy white, white-floccose at the base. **Fl** whitish. **Ta** mild. **Sm** none. Not uncommon on humous soil or wood chips in parks, public gardens, windbreaks and roadsides. Summer to autumn.

Sa

Psathyrella marcescibilis

Psathyrella conopilus

C conical to campanulate, ∅ 2-4 cm, smooth, shiny, translucent striate, red-brown, with ochraceous tinge at the centre when damp; dingy buff to grey-buff when dry. **G** light brown to dark purple-brown. **St** 9-14 cm x 3-4 mm, hollow, fragile, silky, whitish buff, pruinose at the apex. **Fl** cream. **Ta** mild. **Sm** none.

Common on pieces of wood and wood chips, occasionally on humous soil, in parks, public gardens, roadsides and woods. Often in groups. Summer to autumn.

Sa

Psathyrella conopilus

Psathyrella prona f. prona

C conical to campanulate, ∅ 1-2 cm, dark grey-brown when damp; matt, ochraceous yellow-brown to greyish brown, striate when dry, with faintly appendiculate margin, overhung

Psathyrella prona f. *prona*

with velar remnants when young. **G** whitish to dark purple-brown, with red edge. **St** 3-7 cm x 2-3 mm, white-fibrillose, white to cream, with light brown, swollen bulbous base. **Fl** whitish grey-brown. **Ta** mild. **Sm** faint, unpleasant. Common on the ground and on wood chips in broad-leaved woods, parks, gardens, roadsides, tangled growth and grasslands on rich clay and humous sand. Summer to autumn.

Sa 🖊

Psathyrella multipedata

C hemispherical to conical or campanulate, ∅ 10-25 mm, smooth, matt, striate, ochraceous brown to grey-brown when damp; whitish grey to light ochraceous brown or buff-brown when dry. **G** light grey-brown to dark violet-brown. **St** 3-10 cm x 2-4 mm, hollow, fragile, whitish, tufted, white-felty at the base. **Fl** orange-brown to buff-brown. **Ta** mild. **Sm** none. Not uncommon on the ground in parks, avenues and broad-leaved woods, often on overgrown sites, on rich clay and loam.

Sa 🖊

Psathyrella multipedata

Psathyrella ammophila

C convex to expanded, ∅ 3-5 cm, fibrillose, matt, ochraceous brown to dingy grey-brown. **G** dark brown. **St** 5-8 cm x 3-5 mm, whitish to yellowish brown, deeply rooting in sand. **Fl** whitish brown. Not uncommon on buried, dead parts of marram grass *(Ammophila arenaria)* below the surface of the sand along the sea coast.

Sa

Psathyrella ammophila

Psathyrella bipellis

C campanulate to convex, occasionally with umbo, ∅ 2-4 cm, matt, red-brown or purple-brown to chestnut, paling grey-pink to grey-buff. **G** grey-pink to brownish. **St** 4-6 cm x 3-5 mm, elastic, longitudinally light brown fibrillose on a flesh background, grey-brown at the base. **Fl** pink-grey to watery brown. **Ta** mild. **Sm** fruity. On humous soil, occasionally on wood chips, in parks, gardens and broad-leaved woods on rich, humus soil. Summer to autumn.

R RDL Sa 🚫

Psathyrella bipellis

Psathyrella caput-medusae

C convex to flattened convex, ∅ 4-6 cm, fibrillose-woolly, white, cracking into dark brown, hairy scales on a red-brown background, with margin overhung with woolly-floccose velar remnants **G** light to dark brown, with ciliate, white edge. **St** 6-8 cm x 10-15 mm, silky, whitish, with falling woolly-fibrillose scales below the fibrillose-woolly ring. **Fl** whitish. **Sm** none.
On stumps and buried wood of coniferous trees in woods on poor, acid sandy soil. Tufted.

VR RDL Sa

Psathyrella caput-medusae

Psathyrella obtusata

C campanulate to expanded, ∅ 2-4 cm, matt, translucent striate, deeply dark red-brown when damp; reddish to black-brown when dry, acute margin with white velar remnants.

Psathyrella obtusata

G light brown to dark purple-brown. **St** 4-7 cm x 3-6 mm, pruinose, whitish. **Fl** light brown. **Ta** mild. **Sm** faint, spicy. On humus soil in broad-leaved and mixed woods, parks and avenues on rich soil. Summer to autumn. Occasionally in clusters or groups.

R Sa

Psathyrella artemisiae (P. squamosa)

C hemispherical to flattened campanulate, ∅ 15-35 mm, with white, woolly velar remnants on an ochraceous brown background, margin overhung with velar remnants. **G** cream to dark red-brown. **St** 3-5 cm x 2-4 mm, white fibrillose-floccose on a light brown background, occasionally with evanescent, floccose ring when young. **Fl** cream to brownish. **Ta** mild. **Sm** none. Common on dead branches and wood debris of broad-leaved and coniferous trees, or on the ground, in woods, occasionally in avenues and on heaths, on poor, acid soil.

Sa

Psathyrella artemisiae

Psathyrella spadicea

Psathyrella spadicea

C convex to irregularly flattened, ∅ 2-6 cm, smooth, matt, dark buff-brown to ochraceous brown or reddish brown when damp; light ochraceous brown to buff-brown when dry. **G** light brown to red-brown. **St** 4-6 cm x 5-10 mm, splitting longitudinally into fibrils, often fasciate at the base. **Fl** dingy white to grey-brown. **Ta** mild. **Sm** mushroomy.

Not uncommon on wood of broad-leaved trees, usually on or at the base of broad-leaved trees (elm, horse chestnut) in woods, parks and avenues on (moderately) rich soil. Late autumn. In clusters or groups.

Sa

Lacrymaria lacrymabunda

Lacrymaria lacrymabunda (Psathyrella velutina)

WEEPING WIDOW

C convex to expanded with broad umbo, ∅ 2-10 cm, brown-ochre to orange-brown, with woolly fibrils and cream velar remnants at the margin. **G** close, dark purple-brown to black, blotched, shedding tears in damp weather, with whitish edge. **St** 5-10 cm x 5-10 mm, pruinose at the apex, whitish, with fibrillose, rusty brown scales on a light yellow background below the woolly-fibrillose ring zone, which becomes black with spores, white-felty at the base. **Fl** orange-brown to olive brown. **Ta** unpleasant. **Sm** faint. Common on humous, disturbed soil in parks, gardens, grassy roadsides and broad-leaved woods, often along paths and car parks. Occasionally in groups. Late spring to autumn.

Sa

Coprinus

A group of saprotrophic, usually short-lived, often fragile agarics with ovoid to conical caps and deliquescing edges, dripping black inky liquid. **Spo** brown-black, black.
In Britain, about 100 species of the genus *Coprinus* occur. A large number of smaller species can only be identified with certainty by microscopic features of specimens collected when young.

Coprinus comatus

SHAGGY INK CAP

C ovoid to campanulate, ⌀ 2-5 cm, 5-15 cm high, white, with light yellow-brown, smooth centre and large, fibrillose, white to yellow-brown scales and torn, deliquescent margin. **G** white or pink to black. **St** 10-20 x 1-3 cm, white to cream, with a movable, narrow, white ring. **Fl** white. **Ta** mild. **Sm** faint, pleasant. Common on recently dug, rich soil on dykes, in fields, lawns, pastures, roadsides, parks and on the edge of woods. Often in groups. Summer to autumn.

Sa

Coprinus atramentarius

COMMON INK CAP

C campanulate to expanded, ⌀ 3-10 cm, 3-8 cm high, smooth, matt, radially striate-wrinkled, buffish ochre to light grey, with a light ochrous brown centre and an acute, cracking margin. **G** close, white to black. **St** 4-15 cm x 8-15 mm, smooth, whitish, with swollen ring zone at the base. **Fl** whitish. **Ta**

Coprinus atramentarius

Coprinus comatus

mild. **Sm** faint. Common on (buried) broad-leaved wood, roots and stumps. Often in clusters. Summer to autumn.

Sa †

Coprinus picaceus

Coprinus picaceus

MAGPIE FUNGUS

C ovoid or conical to expanded, ∅ 4-8 cm, 4-6 cm high, shiny, radially wrinkled-striate, date-brown to dark brown, covered in concentric zones with fibrillose, whitish scales becoming pale brown, wrinkled-striate at the margin. **G** white or grey-pink to black. **St** 12-15 x 10-15 mm, white-fibrillose, white, bulbous base with belt-like zones. **Fl** watery grey-brown. **Ta** unpleasant. **Sm** of phenol. On humus soil in old broad-leaved woods and avenues on fertile clay or on loamy soil. Summer to autumn.

R RDL Sa ⌀

Coprinus flocculosus

C ovoid to campanulate, ∅ 15-45 mm, 10-25 mm high, radially striate, creamy ochre to pale ochraceous brown, covered with fibrillose-floccose, white veil, cracking into concentric, flattened scaly zones. **G** whitish grey to black. **St** 5-11 cm x 3-7 mm, smooth, white, becoming brown on being touched, the lower part white-floccose. **Fl** whitish. **Ta** mild. **Sm** none.
On humous soil or on wood and bark chips in broad-leaved woods, parks and sand dunes on rich soil. Spring to summer.

R Sa ⌀

Coprinus flocculosus

Coprinus domesticus

C ovoid to campanulate, ∅ 2-4 cm, 1-3 cm high, cream with light ochraceous brown centre, with fibrillose, brown scales when young, later with granular, whitish scales and striate-furrowed margin. **G** white to purplish brown-black. **St** 3-8 cm x 2-9 mm, downy, white, yellowish at the base. **Fl** whitish. **Ta** mild. **Sm** faint. Usually growing from an orange-brown to rusty brown hyphal mat or ozonium (see photograph of ozonium in Chapter 1). Fairly common on dead branches, stumps and trunks of broad-leaved trees (poplar, alder, maple) on rich soil. Spring to autumn.

Sa ⌀

Coprinus domesticus

Coprinus micaceus

GLISTENING INK CAP

C ovoid to campanulate, ∅ 1-3 cm, 10-25 mm high, radially striate-furrowed, ochre or honey-yellowish brown to grey-black, covered with granular white to brown veil, with torn margin. **G** white to lilac-grey or black. **St** 3-10 cm x 2-5 mm, fragile, mealy white pruinose, base becoming yellowish. **Fl** olive brown. **Ta** mild. **Sm** none.

Coprinus micaceus

Common on dead stumps, trunks and thick branches of broad-leaved trees in broad-leaved woods, parks and roadsides on rich soil. In clusters or groups.
Spring to autumn.

Sa ⚭

Coprinus plicatilis

C ovoid to expanded with depressed centre, ∅ 1-3 cm, 8-13 mm high, deeply radially furrowed, matt, light brown to white-grey, with orange-brown centre. **G** whitish to grey-black. **St** 4-6 cm x 1-2 mm, fragile, matt, white, with bulbous base. **Fl** grey-buff. **Ta** mild. **Sm** none.
Common on humous soil, often among grass on rich soil. Summer to autumn.

Also *C. leiocephalus*, which can only be distinguished with certainty from *C. plicatilis* by microscopic features.

Sa

Coprinus plicatilis

Coprinus lagopus

C ovoid to campanulate expanded, ∅ 2-4 cm, 1-3 cm high, radially striate-furrowed, light grey to mouse-grey, with brownish centre, covered with floccose, whitish veil, margin torn. **G** white to grey-black. **St** 7-13 cm x 3-5 mm, hollow, fragile, floccose or smooth, white. **Fl** greyish. **Ta** mild. **Sm** none.
Common on the ground and on wood chips in woods, public gardens, parks and roadsides on rich soil. Often in groups. Summer to autumn.

Can be confused with the larger *C. lagopides*, which grows on fire sites and along paths covered with wood chips, and can only be distinguished with certainty by microscopic features.
The photograph also shows a young specimen of *Tubaria furfuracea*.

Sa

Coprinus lagopus

Coprinus niveus

C conical to campanulate expanded, ∅ 2-4 cm, 2-3 cm high, mealy-floccose, white to whitish grey, with cracking margin. **G** white to black. **St** 4-9 cm x 3-7 mm, mealy-floccose, white. **Fl** greyish. **Ta** mild. **Sm** none.

Coprinus niveus

Not uncommon on old (horse) manure in poor, little-grazed grasslands, woods and heaths and on dunghills.

Sa 🐝

Coprinus auricomus

C ovoid or campanulate to expanded, ∅ 15-45 mm, 10-25 mm high, shiny, wrinkled-striate, chestnut or rusty brown to grey-brown, with smooth, dark brown centre and fine, upturned hairs, margin appendiculate. **G** whitish to brown-black. **St** 5-11 cm x 2-4 mm, hollow, fragile, smooth, whitish yellowish. **Fl** grey-brown. **Ta** mild. **Sm** faint.
Not uncommon on (buried) wood debris on wood-chip paths or among grass in lawns. Summer to autumn.

Sa ♀

Coprinus angulatus

C conical to campanulate, ∅ 5-30 mm, 5-20 mm high, smooth, striate-furrowed, grey-buff to ochrous brown or light chestnut. **G** cream to black. **St** 15-50 x 1-3 mm, hollow,

Coprinus auricomus

fragile, matt, whitish fibrillose, pale cream. **Fl** brownish. **Ta** mild. **Sm** none. On sites of fires. Summer to autumn.

R Sa

Coprinus congregatus

C conical, ∅ 8-12 mm, 5-20 mm high, ochrous brown to greyish, with yellow-brown centre. **G** cream or reddish brown to black. **St** 2-8 cm

Coprinus angulatus

x 1-4 mm, whitish, with white-felty base. **Fl** brownish. **Sm** faint, pleasant. On manure rich in straw in flowerbeds and on dunghills rich in straw. In clusters.

R Sa

Coprinus congregatus

Coprinus disseminatus

FAIRIES' BONNETS

C campanulate, ∅ 5-12 mm, striate-furrowed, cream to mouse-grey with ochre centre, covered with fine, white, hairy-woolly veil when young. **G** whitish to brown-black. **St** 3-5 cm x 1 mm, fragile, translucent white, occasionally light yellow at the base. **Fl** grey-white. **Ta** mild. **Sm** none. Common on wood, especially on dead stumps and trunks of broad-leaved trees, occasionally on the bark of living trees and on buried wood, in broad-leaved woods, parks and gardens on damp, fertile soil. Spring to autumn.
Sa ♀

Coprinus disseminatus

Coprinus semitalis

C ovoid to campanulate, ∅ 1-2 cm, 5-20 mm high, covered with floccose-granular, whitish to pale grey veil, blackening from the torn, upturned, striate margin. **G** white to black. **St** 5-7 cm x 2-4 mm, hollow, fragile, white pruinose on a light grey background. **Fl** whitish. **Ta** mild. **Sm** none. On the ground in poor, grazed grassland and in parks on sandy or clayey soil. Summer to autumn (see microphotograph of perispores in Chapter 1).

VR Sa

Coprinus semitalis

Coprinus erythrocephalus

C ovoid to campanulate, ∅ 1-2 cm, light grey-brown, covered with an orange-red to coral-red veil. **G** pallid to brown-black. **St** 2-7 cm x 2-3 mm, whitish, with orange-red to coral-red scales.
On the ground, especially with buried wood debris, or on wood chips, in parks and broad-leaved woods on rich soil. Occasionally in large numbers. Summer to autumn.

R Sa

Coprinus erythrocephalus

Leucocoprinus

A small group of fragile agarics, moSt of which are only found indoors, in flowerpots or greenhouses. **Spo** white, pink-cream.

In Britain, about 8 species of the genus *Leucocoprinus* occur.

Leucocoprinus birnbaumii

C campanulate to expanded, ∅ 2-4 cm, matt, finely scaly, sulphur-yellow to golden yellow, with striate, acute margin. **G** pale yellow to sulphur-yellow. **St** 5-7 cm x 5-8 mm, smooth at the apex, pale yellow, below the limp, evanescent ring finely yellow-floccose or pruinose, sulphur-yellow, with swollen base. **Fl** yellowish. **Ta** mild. **Sm** unpleasant. Fairly common on humus-rich or composted soil in flowerpots and flower boxes, only in greenhouses or in buildings.
Can only be distinguished with certainty from *L. denudatus* (R) by microscopic features.

Sa

Leucocoprinus birnbaumii

Leucocoprinus lilacinogranulosus

C conical or campanulate to expanded with obtuse umbo, ∅ 2-4 cm, matt, with fibrillose, pink to lilac scales on a whitish to cream background, centre lilac-brown, striate at the margin. **G** white. **St** 4-6 cm x 3-4 mm, white at the apex, white-floccose below the membranous ring, becoming brown when damaged, with swollen base. **Fl** white. **Ta** mild. **Sm** faint, of garlic. On very humus-rich

Leucocoprinus lilacinogranulosus

or composted soil in flower boxes in buildings or greenhouses.

R Sa

Leucocoprinus brebissonii

C globose or ovoid to expanded, ∅ 15-30 mm, matt, with granular-fibrillose, dark brown to black scales on a white background, centre smooth, black-brown, floccose at the margin. **G** white. **St** 3-5 cm x 2-3 mm, fragile, white pruinose, with membranous, pendulous, white ring. **Fl** white. **Ta** mild. **Sm** none. Fairly common on very humus-rich soil or soil covered with coarse litter, especially in broad-leaved woods. Summer to autumn.
Sa

Leucocoprinus brebissonii

Panaeolus

A group of grey-brown or brown to brown-black agarics typically growing on dung, with campanulate caps and gills staining black due to uneven maturation of the spores. **Spo** black or purple-black. In Britain, 12 *Panaeolus* species occur.

Panaeolus fimiputris (Anellaria semiovata)

C ovoid to hemispherical or campanulate, ⌀ 1-3 cm, 1-3 cm high, smooth, viscid when damp; shiny when dry, cream to ochraceous brown or brown, with dark centre, with cracked patches, with pallid overhanging margin. **G** grey to black. **St** 4-15 cm x 2-8 mm, smooth, white pruinose, whitish, with evanescent, membranous, white ring and ochraceous brown base. **Fl** white. **Ta** mild. **Sm** mushroomy. Fairly common on horse and cow dung rich in straw in sparsely manured grassland and heathland on sandy soil. Summer to autumn.

RDL Sa

Panaeolus foenisecii

Panaeolus foenisecii (Panaeolina foenisecii)

C hemispherical or conical to expanded-campanulate, ⌀ 1-3 cm, smooth, matt, dark tobacco-brown or reddish brown when damp; creamy buff with dark centre when dry. **G** light grey-brown to dark brown, mottled black. **St** 4-7 cm x 1-3 mm, smooth, silky, creamy white, with reddish hue. **Fl** dingy

Panaeolus fimiputris

cream to dark brown. **Ta** mild. **Sm** pleasant, spicy.

Common in parks, public gardens, on lawns, in gardens and manured grassland on humus-rich sandy soil. Summer to autumn.

Sa †

Panaeolus ater

C hemispherical to convex, Ø 15-30 mm, smooth, shiny, dark red-brown or black-brown to black when damp; becoming pallid when dry. **G** dingy brown to black-brown. **St** 3-5 cm x 2-3 mm, apex white pruinose, white-fibrillose on red-brown background. **Fl** dingy brown. **Ta** mild. **Sm** none. Not uncommon on humous soil in unmanured or sparsely manured grassland on sandy soil. Summer to autumn.

Sa †

Panaeolus ater

Panaeolus fimicola

Panaeolus fimicola (P. olivaceus)

C conical to campanulate with umbo, Ø 10-25 mm, matt, dark brown to red-brown when damp; whitish grey, fibrillose to dingy ochraceous buff with brownish centre when dry, acute margin with velar remnants forming delicate teeth. **G** grey-buff to brown-black. **St** 5-10 cm x 1-3 mm, smooth, matt, whitish pruinose, whitish, dark brown base with a hint of vinaceous red. **Fl** buff to grey-brown. **Ta** peppery, spicy. **Sm** spicy.

Common on the ground near or on dung in grassland, public gardens, lawns and road-sides on sandy soil. Summer to autumn.

Sa †

Panaeolus sphinctrinus

C ovoid to campanulate with papilla, Ø 1-4 cm, smooth, matt, light to dark brown-grey when damp; drying whitish greyish, margin with velar remnants forming fine white teeth. **G** grey to black. **St** 6-14 cm x 1-3 mm, white pruinose, light grey-brown to dark brown, with white-felty base. **Fl** cream. **Ta** mild. **Sm** faint, mushroomy.

Common on old cow, horse and sheep dung in grassland, parks, roadsides and along bridle paths. Summer to autumn.

Sa †

Panaeolus sphinctrinus

Pleurotus

A group of shell- to fan-shaped agarics, stem absent or lateral, usually growing on wood. **Spo** white, pale grey-lilac.
In Britain, 8 species of the genus *Pleurotus* occur.

Pleurotus ostreatus

OYSTER MUSHROOM

C tongue- or shell-shaped to fan-shaped, stem absent, 4-20 x 6-20 cm, matt, creamy buff or grey-lilac to violet-brown or steel-blue to lilac-black. **G** white to cream. **Fl** white to grey-white. **Ta** mild. **Sm** mushroomy-fishy. Common on living and dead trunks, stumps and branches of broad-leaved trees (poplar, beech, willow, birch), rarely on those of coniferous trees, in woods, parks, avenues and wooded banks. Autumn to winter.

Sa (Pa)

Pleurotus dryinus

C flattened bracket-like, with stem, ∅ 4-15 cm, matt, fibrillose-felty, white or cream to light or dark grey-brown, occasionally becoming

Pleurotus ostreatus

yellowish, margin appendiculate with evanescent velum. **G** white or cream to yellowish, mottled brown, decurrent. **St** 2-6 x 1-4 cm, eccentric, fibrillose-felty, white to cream, occasionally with evanescent ring zone. **Fl** whitish. **Ta** mild, nutty. **Sm** faint. Not uncommon on wounds on living trunks and on dead trunks and stumps of broad-leaved trees (beech, oak, poplar) in broad-leaved woods, parks and avenues.

Pa (Sa)

Pleurotus dryinus

Pleurotus pulmonarius

C tongue- or spatula-shaped to shell-shaped, stem short, ∅ 7-8 cm, smooth, mat; shiny when damp, white or cream to dingy yellow. **G** decurrent, whitish. **St** 1 cm long, eccentric, whitish. **Fl** flexible, whitish **Ta** mild. **Sm** faint, mealy or of aniseed. On living and dead trunks, stumps, and branches of broad-leaved trees (beech, willow) in woods and parks on rich soil, particularly in osier beds. Summer to autumn.

R Sa (Pa)

Pleurotus pulmonarius

Pleurotus eryngii

C shell- or funnel-shaped to convex, with stem, ∅ 5-10 cm, matt, finely fibrillose-felty, dingy white or creamy ochre to grey-brown, incurvate at the margin. **G** white to yellow or orange-yellow. **St** 2-4 cm x 15-25 mm,

Pleurotus eryngii

eccentric, whitish to yellowish ochre. **Fl** whitish. **Ta** mild, pleasant. **Sm** faint.
On roots of *Eryngium campestre* in grasslands on mineral-rich clay or sandy soil, often on dykes.

R RDL Pa ⑭

Hohenbuehelia

A small group of tongue-, shell- or fan-shaped agarics, stem absent or short; some of them with a nematode-catching mycelium. **Spo** white, light cream.
n Britain, 7 species of the genus *Hohenbuehelia* occur.

Hohenbuehelia mastrucata

C shell- to fan-shaped, stem absent or short, ∅ 1-5 cm, greyish brown to dingy white, whitish to creamy fibrillose. **G** cream to yellowish cream, occasionally with brownish edge. **St** absent, or 3 x 3-5 mm, white-felty. **Fl** whitish. **Ta** mealy. **Sm** faint, mealy. On dead trunks and branches of broad-leaved trees (mountain ash, oak, beech, birch) in broad-leaved woods.

R RDL Sa

Hohenbuehelia mastrucata

Hohenbuehelia culmicola

C spatula- to shell-shaped, with short stem, ∅ 10-25 mm, felty, matt, grey-white to dark or black-brown. **G** whitish grey to creamy pale ochre, occasionally with brown to grey-black edge. **St** 2-10 cm x 2-6 mm, eccentric, white-

Hohenbuehelia culmicola

felty, grey-white to dark brown. **Fl** white. **Ta** mealy. **Sm** faint, mealy. On the base of the upright stems of marram grass *(Ammophila arenaria)* in outer coastal sand dunes.

VR RDL Sa (Pa)

Rhodotus

Rhodotus palmatus

C fan-shaped to convex, with stem, ∅ 4-15 cm, salmon-pink to flesh, often with wrinkled, veined centre. **G** pallid flesh-pink, occasionally with yellowish blotches. **St** 2-4 cm x 6-17 mm, eccentric, whitish, mottled pink, with a pink-brown to yellow-brown base. **Fl** gelatinous, salmon to pink. **Ta** bitter. **Sm** strong, pleasant, fruity. **Spo** white. On dead standing and lying trunks of broad-leaved trees (elm).

R RDL Sa

Rhodotus palmatus

Lentinellus

The genus *Lentinellus* is now classified as belonging to the Aphyllophorales.

Lentinellus cochleatus

C Semi-funnel-shaped to shell-shaped, umbilicate, ∅ 3-6 cm, undulate, smooth, matt, yellowish brown to brown-red, with incurvate, acute margin. **G** whitish to brownish, deeply decurrent, with appendiculate edge. **St** 3-10 cm x 3-8 mm, tough, longitudinally furrowed, yellowish to red-brown with dark grey-brown to red-brown base. **Fl** whitish to grey-brown. **Ta** mild. **Sm** strong, of aniseed. **Spo** whitish cream.

Not uncommon on broad-leaved trees (beech, oak) in broad-leaved woods on dry sand or loam. Often tufted.
Also *L. omphalodes* (VR).

Sa 🐌

Lentinellus cochleatus

Panellus

A small group of shell-shaped agarics with stems absent or rudimentary. **Spo** whitish.
In Britain, 4 species of the genus *Panellus* occur.

Panellus mitis

C shell- to kidney-shaped, stem absent or short, ∅ 5-30 mm, matt, white to yellowish or pink-brown. **G** partially forked, white to grey-pink or pink-ochre, with separable, gelatinous edge. **St** 2-7 x 2-5 mm, fibrillose-floccose, whitish, occasionally with pink tinge. **Fl**

Panellus mitis

tough, elastic, 2-layered, watery grey-white to olive brown. **Ta** mild. **Sm** mushroomy.
Fairly common on branches and twigs of coniferous trees on dry, poor sand. Autumn to winter.

Sa

Panellus serotinus

C kidney-shaped, lateral stem, ∅ 3-7 cm, matt, viscid when damp, ochre to olivaceous green. **G** pale yellow to orange-yellow, becoming pale. **St** 10-25 x 8-15 mm, yellow or yellowish,

with minute brown scales. **Fl** white, with a gelatinous layer. **Ta** faint. **Sm** faint, sweetish. Common on dead trunks and stumps of broad-leaved trees (alder, birch, beech, oak) in woods. Autumn to winter.

Sa ⊕

Panellus stipticus

C fan- to kidney-shaped, lateral stem, ∅ 2-4 cm, with minute scales, matt, pale ochraceous brown to cinnamon. **G** viscid, pale

Panellus serotinus

Panellus stipticus

cinnamon. **St** 5-20 x 2-5 mm, pale ochraceous brown. **Fl** whitish to cream. **Ta** pungent. **Sm** fruity. Common on stumps, trunks and branches of broad-leaved trees, favouring oak, in woods. Spring to winter.

Sa 🪱

Lentinus and Lentinula

A small group of saprotrophic agarics with tough flesh and an eccentric or lateral stem, growing on wood. **Spo** white.

In Britain, 4 species of the genera *Lentinus* and *Lentinula* occur.

Lentinus lepideus

C convex to depressed flattened, ∅ 5-10 cm, matt, cream to light brown, with minute to large pale brown scales. **G** decurrent, white to yellowish, edge appendiculate-serrate. **St** 3-6 x 1-2 cm, whitish cream, scaly below the woolly-fibrillose velar zone, with brown to brown-black base. **Fl** tough, whitish. **Ta** mild. **Sm** sweetish.
Not uncommon on processed wood of coniferous trees in buildings and in parks and gardens, particularly on sleepers, occasionally on dead or living trunks and stumps of coniferous trees. Summer to autumn.

Sa 🪱

Lentinus lepideus

Lentinus tigrinus

C funnel-shaped to depressed convex, ∅ 4-10 cm, creamy to yellowish white, with fibrillose, brown-black scales and acute, torn margin. **G** decurrent, cream to yellowish, with serrulate edge. **St** 3-5 cm x 4-8 mm, creamy white, with grey-brown scales at the rooting base. **Fl** whitish yellowish. **Ta** mild. **Sm** pleasant, fruity.

Fairly common on trunks, stumps and branches of broad-leaved trees (willow, ash, beech) in osier beds on wet, rich clay and ash coppice on sandy soil. Spring to autumn.

Sa 🪱

Lentinus tigrinus

Lentinula edodes (Lentinus edodes)

SHIITAKE

C convex to expanded, ∅ 8-20 cm, felty-fibrillose, grey-brown to red-brown, with inrolled margin with whitish velar scales. **G** whitish or cream to greyish flesh-brown, staining rusty brown, with serrated edge. **St** 3-5 cm x 10-13 mm, brown, with large fibrillose-woolly scales and a fibrillose ring zone, with tapering base. **Fl** corky, white. **Ta** spicy. **Sm**

Lentinula edodes

aromatic. Cultivated in buildings and in the open, also in gardens, on dead trunks of broad-leaved trees (oak).
Imported from East-Asia. Found growing in the wild once so far.

Sa ⊕

Resupinatus

Resupinatus applicatus (R. trichotis)

C shell- to fan-shaped, stem absent, ⌀ 2-12 mm, hairy-fibrillose in the black-brown centre, grey-brown, with whitish, mealy marginal zone. **G** pale grey or dark grey to black, with white edge. **Fl** greyish. **Ta** mild to bitter. **Sm** none. **Spo** white.
Fairly common on dead wood debris, branches and twigs, occasionally on woody parts of perennial herbs, in woods and shrubberies.

Sa ♀

Resupinatus applicatus

Crepidotus

A small group of shell- to kidney-shaped, white or creamy yellow agarics, stem absent. **Spo** white-cream, yellow-brown, pink-brown, tobacco-brown.
In Britain, about 10 species of the genus *Crepidotus* occur.
Some of them can only be distinguished by microscopic features.

Crepidotus variabilis

C kidney- to shell-shaped, ⌀ 5-30 mm, felty, white to creamy yellow. **G** distant, white to flesh-brown. **Fl** white.
Common on branches, occasionally on stalks of herbaceous plants or on leaf litter in broad-leaved woods on poor soil. Autumn to early winter.

Sa

Crepidotus variabilis

Crepidotus epibryus (Pleurotellus herbarum)

C kidney-shaped, ⌀ 5-15 mm, silky, whitish cream. **G** whitish to cream. **Fl** whitish.

Not uncommon on mosses, grasses, leaves and branches in broad-leaved woods, shrubberies, parks and mossy, poor grasslands.

Sa ♀

Crepidotus epibryus

Chroogomphus and Gomphidius

A small group of agarics resembling antique, hand-forged hobnails or rivets, with thick, decurrent distant gills and a slimy or cobweblike velum, which leaves a ring zone on the stem. Mycorrhizal parasites. **Spo** brown-black, black.

In Britain, 5 species of the genera *Chroogomphus* and *Gomphidius* occur.

Chroogomphus rutilus

C convex with umbo, ⌀ 4-8 cm, smooth, viscid, shiny, brick-red to copper-red, with vinaceous tinge. **G** olivaceous ochre to dingy purple. **St** 5-12 cm x 5-15 mm, orangey ochre, vinaceous at the apex, with ring-shaped velar remnants and tapering base with dingy ochraceous to pink mycelium. **Fl** orangey ochre. **Ta** mild, nutty. **Sm** none.

Not uncommon near two-needled pines in coniferous woods on dry sandy soil with little litter and in coastal sand dunes. Possibly also as a parasite on the mycelium of *Suillus* and *Rhizopogon* species.

RDL M (Pa) 🍴

Chroogomphus rutilus

Gomphidius glutinosus

C convex to flattened funnel-shaped, ⌀ 5-12 cm, slimy, greyish violet-brown. **G** pale to grey-brown. **St** 3-10 x 1-2 cm, slimy, whitish, whitish to light grey-brown below the slimy, blackening ring zone, lemon-yellow at the base. **Fl** whitish, with vinaceous or lemon-yellow tinge. **Ta** none. **Sm** none.

Near coniferous trees in coniferous woods on poor, slightly acid sandy soil with little needle litter. Possibly also as a parasite on the mycelium of *Suillus* and *Rhizopogon* species.

VR RDL M (Pa?) 🍴

Gomphidius glutinosus

Gomphidius roseus

Gomphidius roseus

C convex to flattened funnel-shaped, ⌀ 3-6 cm, viscid, pink-red to coral-red or brick-red. **G** greyish to mouse-grey. **St** 3-6 cm x 10-15 mm, whitish, with pink to vinaceous or brownish tinges, a white, slimy ring zone, coloured black by spores, and a tapering base. **Fl** dingy white with pink tinge. **Ta** none. **Sm** none.
Not uncommon near fir, partially parasitic on mycelium of *Suilus bovinus*, in coniferous woods on dry, poor sandy soil with little litter.

RDL M Pa

Cantharellula

Cantharellula umbonata

C funnel-shaped, occasionally with umbo, ⌀ 2-4 cm, matt, grey or mouse-grey to grey-brown, pallid and reflexed at the margin. **G** forked, decurrent, distant, white to creamy

Cantharellula umbonata

white, staining red when damaged. **St** 3-5 cm x 5-6 mm, elastic, hollow, felty-fibrillose, grey to grey-brown, with white-felty base. **Fl** whitish to watery grey. **Sm** none. **Spo** white. On mosses (*Polytrichum commune*) in broad-leaved and coniferous woods and heathland on poor sandy soil.

VR RDL Pa

Hygrophoropsis

Hygrophoropsis aurantiaca

FALSE CHANTERELLE
C convex to shallowly funnel-shaped, ⌀ 2-8 cm, finely downy, matt, orange-yellow, more pallid and inrolled at the margin. **G** forked, decurrent, orange. **St** 3-5 cm x 5-10 mm, often curved, orange-yellow. **Fl** tough, yellowish to orange. **Ta** mushroomy. **Sm** mushroomy. **Spo** white. Common on wood, needles and leaves in coniferous and mixed woods on poor soil. Also *H. fuscosquamula* (VR) and *H. macrospora = pallida* (R RDL).

Sa

Hygrophoropsis aurantiaca

Paxillus

A small group of brown, funnel-shaped or shell- to fan-shaped agarics, related to Boletes, with gills that peel easily from the cap and inrolled at the margin. Saprotrophic or mycorrhizal. **Spo** ochrous brown, rusty brown.

In Britain, 4 *Paxillus* species occur.

Paxillus involutus

BROWN ROLL-RIM

C convex to plane or depressed funnel-shaped, ∅ 5-12 cm, felty, matt, viscid when damp, ochrous brown with olive tinge to rusty brown or grey-brown, with inrolled, slightly furrowed margin. **G** close, decurrent, pale ochrous yellow to olive yellow or loam-brown, staining brown on bruising. **St** 4-8 cm x 8-12 mm, central or slightly eccentric, yellowish pruinose when young, olive brown to rusty brown, staining brown on bruising. **Fl** tough, yellowish white, bruising red-brown. **Ta** sour. **Sm** mushroomy. Common near broad-leaved and coniferous trees, occasionally on decayed wood. Summer to autumn.
M (Sa) †

Paxillus involutus

Paxillus filamentosus
(P. rubicundulus)

C convex to plane or depressed funnel-shaped, ∅ 5-7 cm, matt, slightly viscid when damp, brown-yellow to reddish brown, cracking, with pale brown cracks, with

Paxillus filamentosus

inrolled margin when young. **G** close, decurrent, partially forked, yellowish to ochraceous brown, staining rusty brown on bruising. **St** 5-6 x 1 cm, fibrillose, reddish brown, staining dark on bruising, with tapering base. **Fl** ochre, becoming red-brown. **Ta** somewhat sour. **Sm** faint. Near elms in broad-leaved woods and windbreaks on damp, rich soil.

R RDL M 🥀

Paxillus atrotomentosus

C shell-shaped, ∅ 10-15 cm, velvety-felty, with patches cracking into scales, ochraceous brown to olivaceous brown or red-brown, with inrolled margin. **G** close, veined near the stem, decurrent, cream to pale ochre, staining brown on bruising. **St** 3-6 x 2-4 cm, eccentric, velvety, black-brown. **Fl** yellowish. **Ta** bitter. **Sm** somewhat sour. Not uncommon on stumps and buried wood of coniferous trees in coniferous woods on poor sand.

Sa 🥀

Paxillus atrotomentosus

Paxillus panuoides var. panuoides

C shell- to fan-shaped, stem short or absent, ∅ 4-7 cm, felty, granular-scaly, matt, cream to olivaceous yellow or brown-yellow, with thin, inrolled margin. **G** close, interconnected at the base, whitish ochre to olivaceous yellow or pale cinnamon. **St** absent of very short, eccentric, olivaceous yellow to brown-yellow. **Fl** whitish yellowish **Ta** mild. **Sm** none. On dead trunks, stumps and thick branches of coniferous trees (fir) in coniferous woods on

Paxillus panuoides var. *panuoides*

poor sandy soil, occasionally on processed wood of coniferous trees outside the woods or near buildings.

R Sa

Boletaceae

An extensive group of fleshy Basidiomycetes with easily separable tubes under the cap and a central stem. Usually mycorrhizal. In Britain, about 90 boletus species occur,

including the genera *Boletus (Xerocomus)*, *Tylopilus*, *Gyrodon*, *Gyroporus*, *Boletinus*, *Leccinum*, *Chalciporus* and *Suillus*.

Boletus edulis

CEP

C hemispherical to convex, ⌀ 8-20 cm, matt, pale brown to chestnut. **Tu** white to greyish yellow. **Po** circular, whitish. **St** 3-23 x 3-7 cm, obese, whitish to creamy yellow, upper portion covered with white net. **Fl** white. **Ta** nutty. **Sm** pleasant. **Spo** olive brown.

Common near broad-leaved trees (oak, beech) and coniferous trees, particularly in avenues, roadsides and wood edges on sandy or loamy soil. Summer to autumn.

M

Boletus erythropus var. *erythropus*

C hemispherical to convex, ⌀ 8-20 cm, velvety, matt, brown to olivaceous, towards the margin yellowish ochre. **Tu** lemon-yellow to greenish, dark blue when damaged. **Po** small, circular, orange-red to rusty brown, yellow

Boletus edulis

Boletus erythropus var. *erythropus*

towards the margin, bruising dark blue to black. **St** 4-12 x 2-5 cm, yellowish, with red dots and red apex. **Fl** yellow, dark blue on bruising. **Ta** faint. **Sm** none. **Spo** olive. Fairly common near oak and beech, rare near coniferous trees, mainly in roadsides with poor soil and avenues lined with old trees on dry, acid soils. Summer to autumn.

M ⑨

Boletus luridus var. luridus

C hemispherical to convex, ∅ 6-14 cm, matt, yellowish grey-brown to olivaceous, with rusty brown tinges, bruising dark brown to blue-black. **Tu** yellowish green, turning blue when damaged. **Po** small, orange-red to yellow, becoming dark blue on bruising. **St** 8-14 x 1-3 cm, yellowish, with an orange-red net, bruising blue. **Fl** lemon-yellow, green-blue to

Boletus luridus var. *luridus*

dark blue on bruising. **Ta** none. **Sm** faint. **Spo** olive brown. Not uncommon near broad-leaved trees (oak, beech, lime), particularly in avenues and roadsides with old trees, occasionally in parks and woodland. Summer to autumn.

RDL M †

Boletus radicans var. radicans

C hemispherical to convex, ∅ 8-16 cm, matt, dingy white to light loam-brown, with ochraceous tinges, scaly cracks, grey margin. **Tu** lemon-yellow, blue when damaged. **Po** small, circular, lemon-yellow, bruising blue. **St** 5-8 cm x 3-4 mm, lemon-yellow at the apex, covered with a straw-coloured net, with a rooting, dark ochre base with red-brown blotches. **Fl** yellow, becoming white, or becoming pale blue at first, and becoming paler with age. **Ta** bitter. **Sm** spicy. **Spo** olivaceous brown.
Near oak and beech in avenues with poor soils and roadsides with old trees on calcareous river clay or humus, loamy sand. Summer to autumn.

R RDL M ⌀

Boletus radicans var. *radicans*

Boletus badius (Xerocomus badius)

BAY BOLETUS

C hemispherical to convex, ∅ 4-14 cm, downy to smooth and shiny, ochrous brown to chestnut or dark reddish black-brown. **Tu** creamy yellow to lemon-yellow, blue-green when damaged. **Po** large, creamy yellow to lemon-yellow, blue-green on bruising. **St** 4-12 x 1-4 cm, downy, light ochraceous brown to red-brown. **Fl** white to lemon-yellow, bluing slightly. **Ta** mushroomy. **Sm** mushroomy. **Spo** olive brown.

Common near broad-leaved trees (oak, beech) and coniferous trees (fir, spruce, larch) in woods on poor, acid, sandy or loamy soil, often in thick litter. Summer to autumn.

M ⊕

Boletus badius

Boletus chrysenteron

Boletus chrysenteron (Xerocomus chrysenteron)

RED-CRACKED BOLETUS

C hemispherical to convex, ⌀ 4-11 cm, matt, cracking into red and yellow fissures, dingy brown to olivaceous brown, occasionally with pink-red tinge. **Tu** sulphur-yellow or lemon-yellow to greenish. **Po** large, angular, sulphur-yellow to lemon-yellow, becoming green-blue on bruising. **St** 4-8 cm x 10-15 mm, lemon-yellow at the apex, with reddish central part becoming red to red-brown towards base. **Fl** cream to lemon-yellow, bluing slightly. **Ta** faint. **Sm** faint. **Spo** olivaceous brown. Common near broad-leaved trees (beech, oak), rare near coniferous trees, in broad-leaved and mixed woodland, along avenues and in roadsides with old trees on humus-rich soil. Summer to autumn.

M 🔗

Boletus parasiticus (Xerocomus parasiticus)

C hemispherical to convex, ⌀ 2-5 cm, matt, straw-yellow with olive tinge to reddish brown. **Tu** lemon-yellow to ochre. **Po** lemon-

Boletus parasiticus

yellow, becoming rusty brown. **St** 3-4 x 1cm, often curved, straw-colour to reddish brown. **Fl** pale lemon-yellow. **Ta** none. **Sm** faint. **Spo** olive brown. Fairly common, parasitic on Common Earth-ball *(Scleroderma citrinum)* in broad-leaved and mixed woods.

Pa 🍴

Boletus rubellus (Xerocomus rubellus)

C hemispherical to convex, ∅ 3-6 cm, matt, scarlet to vinaceous red, with pallid margin. **Tu** lemon-yellow to greenish. **Po** large, angular, lemon-yellow, becoming blue on bruising. **St** 4-7 cm x 10-15 mm, lemon-yellow or chrome-yellow at the apex, red, with rusty brown base. **Fl** yellowish brown to wine red, bluing slightly. **Ta** none. **Sm** faint. **Spo** olive brown. Fairly common among grass near broad-leaved trees.

M 🍴

Boletus rubellus

Boletus subtomentosus (Xerocomus subtomentosus)

C convex, ∅ 4-8 cm, velvety, matt, olivaceous grey-yellow to pale brown. **Tu** bright yellow to greenish or brownish yellow. **Po** wide, irregularly angular, occasionally dentate, bright yellow (see photograph of pores and tubes in Chapter 1). **St** 6-9 cm x 15-20 mm, finely granular, longitudinally red-brown fibrillose on pale yellow background. **Fl** whitish yellow. **Ta** mild. **Sm** fruity. **Spo** ochrous to olivae brown. Fairly common near broad-leaved trees (oak, beech) in broad-leaved and mixed woods and planted roadsides on poor, sandy soil deficient in humus.

RDL M 🍴

Boletus subtomentosus

Tylopilus felleus

BITTER BOLETE

C hemispherical to convex, ∅ 6-12 cm, matt, creamy brown or yellow-brown to dark

Tylopilus felleus

brown. **Tu** light salmon to coral-pink. **Po** salmon to coral-pink, becoming brown on bruising. **St** 7-10 x 2-3 cm, creamy ochre, with a dark brown net and swollen base. **Fl** white to cream. **Ta** bitter. **Sm** unpleasant. **Spo** grey-pink to wine red.

Near broad-leaved trees (oak, beech, birch), occasionally near coniferous trees, in broad-leaved and mixed woods, or along roads and avenues with old trees on poor, acid sandy and loamy soil.

R RDL M

Gyrodon lividus

C convex, ⌀ 4-10 cm, viscid, matt, straw-colour to pale yellow-brown, with rusty brown tinge. **Tu** bright sulphur-yellow, becoming green-blue to brownish. **Po** large, angular, bright sulphur-yellow, becoming dark blue-grey on bruising. **St** 3-7 x 1-2 cm, pale yellow-brown, with vinaceous or brown tinge. **Fl** whitish to rusty brown, becoming bluish. **Ta** none. **Sm** faint. **Spo** olive brown. Near alder in broad-leaved woods and on wood edges or damp, rich loam or sand, occasionally in groups.

R RDL M

Gyrodon lividus

Gyroporus cyanescens

C convex, ⌀ 6-12 cm, felty, matt, pale creamy ochre or dingy white to dun, becoming blue or brown when damaged, with shaggy, torn margin. **Tu** white to pale yellow, with a hint of green-yellow. **Po** white to pale yellow, bruising blue. **St** obese, 5-10 x 2-4 mm, often cracking into ring-like zones, light creamy

ochre to dun. **Fl** white, becoming blue-green when damaged. **Ta** none. **Sm** faint. **Spo** pale straw-colour. Near broad-leaved trees (beech, oak), occasionally near fir, in young or mature woods on poor, acid, dry sandy soil with little litter.

Summer to autumn.

R RDL M

Gyroporus cyanescens

Boletinus cavipes

C convex with umbo to irregularly expanded, ⌀ 3-8 cm, downy-felty scaly, ochrous brown or orange-brown to rusty brown or dark brown, whitish velar remnants at the margin. **Tu** short, yellowish to olive. **Po** wide, angular, yellowish to olivaceous. **St** 4-8 x 1-2 cm, hollow, lemon-yellow at the apex with faint net, yellow-brown below the floccose, white ring, with brownish fibrils. **Fl** whitish

Boletinus cavipes

yellowish. **Ta** pleasant. **Sm** pleasant. **Spo** olivaceous brown. Near larch in medium-old to old coniferous and mixed woods on acid, poor sandy or loamy soils.

R RDL M

Leccinum scabrum

BROWN BIRCH BOLETUS

C hemispherical to convex, ∅ 5-15 cm, matt, brown to grey-brown. **Tu** white to dingy ochre. **Po** small, white to dingy white, ochrous on bruising. **St** 7-20 x2-3 cm, creamy white to grey, covered with brown-black scales. **Fl** white to pink, becoming blue-green in the base. **Ta** pleasant. **Sm** pleasant. **Spo** yellowish brown. Common near birch in broad-leaved and mixed woods in coastal sand dunes and on poor, acid soil, often in pathsides and roadsides. Summer to autumn.

M 🍴

Leccinum scabrum

Leccinum versipelle *(L. testaceoscabrum)*

ORANGE BIRCH BOLETE

C hemispherical to convex, ∅ 8-20 cm, yellowish orange-brown. **Tu** white to yellowish brown, wine red on bruising. **Po** small,

Leccinum versipelle

grey to ochre, wine red on bruising. **St** 10-18 x 2-3 cm, whitish grey, covered with woolly, brown-black scales. **Fl** white to dark vinaceous, blue-green to black in stem base. **Ta** pleasant. **Sm** pleasant. **Spo** dark ochraceous brown.

Near birch in broad-leaved and mixed woods and in avenues on poor, dry, sandy or loamy soil. Summer to autumn.

R RDL M 🍴

Leccinum rufum (L. aurantiacum)

C hemispherical to convex, ∅ 8-16 cm, matt, orange or apricot to reddish brown. **Tu** white, vinaceous on bruising. **Po** small, white or cream, wine red on bruising. **St** 8-14 x 2-4 cm, whitish cream, covered with white scales, which become rusty brown. **Fl** cream, becoming wine red, greyish in stem base. **Ta** pleasant. **Sm** pleasant. **Spo** ochraceous brown. Near poplar in woodland and avenues on moderately rich sandy and loamy soil.

R RDL M 🍴

Leccinum rufum

Chalciporus piperatus

C hemispherical, ∅ 3-7 cm, ochraceous to reddish brown. **Tu** slightly decurrent, cinnamon to rusty brown. **Po** angular, reddish brown. **St** 1-4 cm x 5-20 mm, slender, yellow-brown, with tapering, lemon-yellow base. **Fl** reddish brown, lemon-yellow in stem base. **Ta** pungent. **Sm** faint. **Spo** dark cinnamon-brown. Fairly common near broad-leaved trees (birch, beech, oak), occasionally near coniferous trees, in roadsides with poor soil

Chalciporus piperatus

and avenues, occasionally in broad-leaved or mixed woods, on poor sandy and loamy soil.

M 🞂

Suillus bovinus

C convex, ∅ 3-10 cm, viscid, loam-coloured with cinnamon-brown or ochraceous brown tinges, with pallid margin. **Tu** light olive yellow. **Po** large, angular, light olive brown-yellow to ochre. **St** 4-6 cm x 5-8 mm, ochraceous yellow-brown to loam-coloured ochre, with pink mycelium at the base. **Fl** whitish yellow to grey-pink or rusty brown. **Ta** pleasant, sweetish. **Sm** fruity. **Spo** olive brown.

Fairly common near fir in coniferous and mixed woods on poor soil with little litter, or near self-seeded fir on heathland (see also under *Gomphidius roseus*).

M 🍴

Suillus bovinus

Suillus granulatus

C convex, ∅ 3-9 cm, viscid, shiny, rusty brown to yellowish. **Tu** pale yellow to yellow-brown. **Po** small, pale yellow to yellow-brown, with pale milky droplets. **St** lemon-yellow, with white, or pale yellow granules exuding watery liquid at the apex, vinaceous to brown-red tinge at the base. **Fl** lemon-yellow. **Ta** faint, pleasant. **Sm** faint, pleasant. **Spo** ochrous yellow-brown. Not uncommon near fir in young fir forests on dry sandy soil with little litter.

RDL M

Suillus granulatus

Suillus luteus

SLIPPERY JACK

C hemispherical to convex, ∅ 5-10 cm, slimy and viscid, shiny, chestnut to sepia-brown. **Tu** straw-yellow to lemon-yellow. **Po** circular, straw-yellow to lemon-yellow, becoming reddish brown. **St** 5-10 x 2-3 cm, pale straw-colour with dark dots, with a large, membranous, white to cream ring becoming brown-black, white at the base, becoming vinaceous brown. **Fl** white. **Ta** faint. **Sm** faint. **Spo** clay-brown to ochrous brown. Near coniferous trees in young coniferous woods and near wild shoots on dry sandy soil with little litter.

R M

Suillus grevillei

LARCH BOLETE

C hemispherical to convex, ∅ 3-10 cm, viscid, shiny, yellow to chrome yellow orange-brown. **Tu** pale yellow. **Po** small, angular, lemon-yellow, becoming rusty brown on bruising. **St** 5-7 cm x 15-20 mm, yellow at the apex, occasionally covered with coarse net, floccose below white ring, with cinnamon tinge. **Fl** pale yellow to lemon-yellow. **Ta** faint. **Sm** faint. **Spo** ochrous brown to yellowish brown. Near

Suillus luteus

Suillus grevillei

larch in coniferous and mixed woods on humous, poor sand and loam, particularly along paths and on the edge of woods. R RDL M 🍴

Suillus variegatus

Suillus variegatus

C convex, ⌀ 6-13 cm, ochre to yellowish or olivaceous brown, with small flattened, adpressed brown scales. **Tu** dark yellow-brown. **Po** angular, ochrous olive brown to cinnamon-brown. **St** 5-9 cm x 15-20 mm, ochre, with reddish brown base. **Fl** lemon-yellow to bright yellow. **Ta** faint. **Sm** mushroomy. **Spo** dark yellow-brown.

Not uncommon near fir in fir and mixed woods on poor, dry sandy soil with little litter, occasionally near self-seede fir on heathland.

R RDL M 🍴

Bibliography

Allegro, J.M., *De heilige paddestoel en het kruis*, De Haan, Bussum, the Netherlands, 1971.

Arnolds, E., Kuyper, Th.W. & Noordeloos, M.E., *Overzicht van de paddestoelen in Nederland*, Nederlandse Mycologische Vereniging, Wijster, the Netherlands, 1995.

Bas, C., et al., *Flora Agaricina Neerlandica*, vol. 1-2-3, Balkema, Rotterdam, the Netherlands, 1988, 1990, 1995.

Bon, M., *Pareys Buch der Pilze*, Parey, Hamburg, Germany, 1988.

Breitenbach, J. & Kränzlin, F., *Pilze der Schweiz*, vol. 1-2-3-4, Verlag Mykologia, Lucerne, Switzerland, 1981, 1986, 1991, 1995.

Courtecuisse, R. & Duhem, B., *Guide des champignons de France et d'Europe*, Delachaux & Niestlé, Lausanne, Switzerland.

Dähncke, R.M., *1200 Pilze*, AT Verlag, Aarau, Switzerland, 1993.

Dennis, R.W.G., *British Ascomycetes*, Cramer, Vaduz, Liechtenstein, 1981.

Ellis, M.B. & Ellis, J.P., *Microfungi on land plants*, Croom Helm, London, U.K., 1985.

Ellis, M.B. & Ellis, J.P., *Microfungi on miscellaneous substrates*, Croom Helm, U.K., London, 1988.

Enderle, M. & Laux, H.E., *Pilze auf Holz*, Keller, Stuttgart, Germany, 1980.

Gombrich, E.H., *Eeuwige schoonheid*, De Haan, Bussum, the Netherlands, 1977.

Hohmeyer, H., *'Ein Schlüssel zu den Europäischen Arten der Gattung Peziza L.'*, Zeitschrift für Mykologie 51 (1), pp. 161-180, 1986.

Jahn, H., *Mitteleuropäische Porlinge*, Bibliotheca Mycologica, vol. 29, Cramer, Vaduz, Liechtenstein, 1976.

Jahn, H., *Pilze an Bäumen*, 2nd printing, Patzer Verlag, Berlin-Hanover, Germany, 1979.

Jalink, L.M., 'De aardsterren van Nederland en België', *Coolia 38*, supplement, 1995.

Jülich, W., *Die Nichtblätterpilze, Gallertpilze und Bauchpilze*, Kleine Kryptogamenflora, vol. 11b/1, Fischer Verlag, Stuttgart, Germany, 1984.

Keizer, G.J., 'Enkele interessante inoperculate Ascomyceten van de werkweek in De Peel 1987', *Coolia* 31(2), pp. 33-38, 1988.

Keizer, G.J., 'De vogelveerzwam op een ongewoon substraat', *Coolia* 32(2), p. 30, 1989.

Keizer, G.J., 'Russula op ooghoogte', Coolia 32(2), pp. 30-31, 1989.

Keizer, G.J., 'Een waarneming over *Entoloma conferendum* var. *pussilum*', *Coolia* 32(2), p. 31, 1989.

Keizer, G.J., 'De paddestoelen van de duinen van Voorne', *Natura* 87/2, pp. 44-48, March 1990.

Keizer, G.J., 'Twee opvallende zeldzame ascomyceten: *Catinella olivacea en Jafneadelphus amethystinus*', Coolia 33(3), pp. 58-62, 1990.

Keizer, G.J., 'De vogelveerzwam', *Natura* 1000, 89/8, p. 192, October 1992.

Keizer, G.J., *'Agrocybe putanium'*, Coolia 36(1), p. 29, 1993.

Keizer, G.J., 'Honderd jaar mycophilatelie', *Philatelie* 11, pp. 864-867, November 1994.

Keizer, G.J., 'Nogmaals de muur(beker)zwam', *Coolia* 38(1), p. 43, 1995.

Keizer, G.J., 'Ecologie en verspreiding van *Pholiota lucifera* in Nederland', *Coolia* 38(3), pp. 116-118, 1995.

Keizer, G.J., 'Tonderzwammen in een Belgisch parkbos', *Coolia* 38(4), p. 195, 1995.

Keizer, G.J., 'De beurszwammen van Nederland', *Natura* 92/5, pp. 111-112, 1995.

Keizer, G.J., 'De spijkerzwammen van Nederland', *Natura* 92/7, p. 154, September 1995.

Kuyper, Th.W. & Kaag, K., 'Paddestoelen, ecologie en onderzoeksmogelijkheden', *Natura* 1000, 89/8, pp. 179-182, October 1992.

Kuyper, Th.W., 'De betekenis van paddestoelen voor het functioneren van oecosystemen', Paddestoelen en natuurbeheer. Wetenschappelijke Mededeling K.N.N.V., No. 212, pp. 17-25, 1994.

Lange, M., *Elseviers Paddestoelengids*, Elsevier, Amsterdam, the Netherlands, 1974.

Lemaire, T., *Godenspijs of duivelsbrood*, Ambo, Baarn, the Netherlands, 1995.

Maas Geesteranus, R.A., 'De fungi van Nederland I Geoglossaceae-aardtongen', Wetenschappelijke Mededeling K.N.N.V., No. 52, 1964.

Maas Geesteranus, R.A., 'De fungi van Nederland 2a. Pezizales-deel 1 en 2b. Pezizales-deel 2', Wetenschappelijke Mededeling K.N.N.V., Nos. 69 and 80, 1967, 1969.

Maas Geesteranus, R.A., 'Gasteromyceten in Nederland', *Coolia* 15(3), pp. 50-92, 1971.

Maas Geesteranus, R.A., 'De Clavarioide fungi', Wetenschappelijke Mededeling K.N.N.V., No. 113, 1980.

Moreau, C., *Larousse paddestoelenencyclopedie*, Heideland-Orbis/Kosmos, Hasselt, Belgium, 1980.

Moser, M., *Ascomyceten*, Kleine Kryptogamenflora, vol. IIa, Fischer Verlag, Stuttgart, Germany, 1963.

Moser, M., *Die Röhrlinge und Blätterpilze*, Kleine Kryptogamenflora, vol. IIb/2, Fischer Verlag, Stuttgart, Germany, 1978.

Nannenga-Bremekamp, N.E., 'De Nederlandse myxomyceten', K.N.N.V. publication, No. 18, 1974.

Nauta, M.M., *Revisie van de in Nederland voorkomende soorten van het geslacht Agrocybe (leemhoeden)*, Rijksherbarium, Leiden, the Netherlands, 1987.

Nauta, M.M. & Vellinga, E.C., *Atlas van Nederlandse paddestoelen*, Balkema, Rotterdam, the Netherlands, 1995.

Noordeloos, M.E., *Caputcolleges Mycologie*, Rijksherbarium, Leiden, the Netherlands, 1995-1996.

Phillips, R., *Paddestoelen en schimmels van West-Europa*, Spectrum, Utrecht-Antwerp, the Netherlands/Belgium, 1981.

Ryman, S. & Holmåsen, I., *Pilze*, Thalacker Verlag, Brunswick, Germany, 1992.

Ryvarden, L. & Gilbertson, R.L., European Polypores, vol. 1-2, Fungiflora A/S, Oslo, Norway, 1993, 1994.

Schultes, R.E. & Hofmann, A., *Over de planten der goden*, Spectrum, Utrecht/Antwerp, the Netherlands/Belgium, 1983.

Tjallingii-Beukers, D., 'Het geslacht *Pholiota* (bundelzwammen)', Wetenschappelijke Mededeling K.N.N.V., No. 185, 1987.

Vries, G.A. de, 'De fungi van Nederland 3. *Hypogaea*', Wetenschappelijke Mededeling K.N.N.V., No. 88, 1971.

Willard, T., *Reishi Mushroom*, Sylvan Press, Washington DC, U.S.A., 1990.

Zeitlmayer, L., *Thieme's Paddestoelenboek*, Thieme & Cie, Zutphen, the Netherlands, 1977.

Acknowledgements

We would like to thank the following members of the Dutch Mycological Society for permission to use their slides:

R. Chrispijn: *Hericium clathroides; Volvariella surrecta*

G.T.H. Dings: *Mitrula paludosa*

G. Fransen-Batenburg: *Peziza proteana* f. *sparassoides; Rhodotus palmatus*

L.M. Jalink & M.M. Nauta: *Sarcodon imbricatus; Disciseda bovista; Phallus hadriani; Inocybe geophylla* var. *lilacina*

J.M. Ketelaar: *Inocybe corydalina; Inocybe vulpinella; Lactarius deliciosus*

R. Knol: *Cordyceps ophioglossoides; Microglossum viride; Sarcodon scabrosus; Conocybe lactea; Conocybe tenera; Inocybe rimosa; Leucoagaricus leucothites; Leucocoprinus birnbaumii; Mycena pura* var. *pura; Paxillus atrotomentosus*

With special thanks to Machiel Noordeloos for permission to attend his fascinating lectures on the various aspects of the fungal kingdom.

Address of the secretarial office of the Dutch Mycological Society:
Biologisch Station Wijster, Kampsweg 27, 9418 PD Wijster, the Netherlands.

Index